AERODYNAMIC CAPTURE

OF PARTICLES

AERODYNAMIC CAPTURE
OF PARTICLES

PROCEEDINGS OF A CONFERENCE HELD AT B.C.U.R.A.
LEATHERHEAD, SURREY, 1960

Edited by

E. G. RICHARDSON
King's College, Newcastle upon Tyne

SYMPOSIUM PUBLICATIONS DIVISION

PERGAMON PRESS

OXFORD · LONDON · NEW YORK · PARIS

1960

PERGAMON PRESS LTD.
Headington Hill Hall, Oxford
4 & 5 Fitzroy Square, London, W.1

PERGAMON PRESS INC.
122 East 55th Street, New York 22, N.Y.
P.O. Box 47715, Los Angeles, California

PERGAMON PRESS S.A.R.L.
24 Rue des Écoles, Paris Vᵉ

PERGAMON PRESS G.m.b.H.
Kaiserstrasse 75, Frankfurt am Main

Library of Congress Card No. 60–14947

Printed in Great Britain by Page Bros. (Norwich), Ltd.

67/   1044

FOREWORD

THIS book contains the papers presented at a symposium, held in the lecture room of the British Coal Utilisation Research Association, Leatherhead.

The Proceedings were opened by Dr. W. Idris Jones, Director General of Research, National Coal Board. After each group of papers, organised in three sessions, there was a discussion which follows in the text. At the conclusion Mr. W. H. Walton, on behalf of the visitors, thanked B.C.U.R.A. for the hospitality of their laboratories (which were inspected by the participants after the formal sessions were completed) and Mr. B. B. Morgan for acting as local secretary.

E. G. RICHARDSON

CONTENTS

CONTENTS

THIRD SESSION: CAPTURE OF PARTICLES BY RAINDROPS

FIRST SESSION:
THEORETICAL AND FUNDAMENTAL ASPECTS

INTRODUCTION AND HISTORICAL SURVEY

by E. G. Richardson
King's College, Newcastle upon Tyne

In spite of the fact that the coagulation of particles carried in a stream of gas or liquid either among themselves or of their impact on a solid body placed therein occur in many industrial operations and also in nature, it seems that no general discussion of the process has yet been held among those who are concerned in the varied applications. It therefore seemed opportune to a few of us to hold a small symposium devoted to this subject.

We shall not here specifically discuss the sizing of the particles. That aspect was well covered by a larger symposium, held under the auspices of the Institute of Physics at Nottingham in 1954, to which reference may be made, nor shall we discuss how the suspension originates. The discussion starts from the point where dispersion in the stream has already taken place.

The wide scope of the applications of this study can be seen by looking through the list of titles offered at this symposium. In "pure" meteorology one studies cloud formation and collision of raindrops, in applied meteorology the wash-out by rain of particulate matter, whether this be the product of industrial air pollution or of an atomic explosion. A number of cognate problems arise in the laying of mine dusts by water sprays. Then we have the impact of water drops or ice crystals on large moving surfaces such as aircraft wings or turbine blades; when both the obstacle and particles are on a smaller scale we have the action of the gas-mask filter (one of the earliest applications).

The coagulation of particles carried by a stream of air or water is, of course, of great interest and involves many applications where solid or liquid particles have to be transported from place to place, e.g. in the industrial process of fluidization.

In all cases the physical state of the particles may have a large effect, e.g. whether or not they are electrified or wettable. We have papers discussing these "surface effects".

Although the surfaces of solid bodies set in a stream conveying small solid or liquid particles have been in use as a means of collecting or sampling the particles for some time, the dynamics of the process by which the collection takes place; the question of whether the total impinging sample gives a true weight (in the statistical sense) of the aerosol and whether the particles will stay attached to the body on which they are caught has been studied only over the past thirty years.

This problem has been treated from two main aspects.

1. Small particles are supposed to be carried by a stream which eventually impinges on a much larger obstacle in the form of a sphere, cylinder or plate;

2. The particles are either all of one size or cover a small range of size and collide as they are carried along by the fluid, either due to the differential effect of gravity or other "external" force—in the latter case—or due to turbulence in either case.

It appears that Albrecht[1] was, in 1925 and 1931 the first to study the problem of the transport and deposit of particles from a stream. He was concerned at first with

3

the collection of water drops and ice crystals suspended in a stream of air by the surface of a hygrometer.

He considered (Fig. 1) a particle shot with a velocity whose components are u and v into a uniform stream having velocity components U and V. He was then able to write

$$dc(U-u)=m\dot{u}$$
$$dc(V-v)=m\dot{v} \tag{1}$$

m being the mass and d the diameter of the particle (σ specific gravity in relation to fluid) and c the Stokes constant ($=3\pi\eta$, η being the viscosity of the fluid).

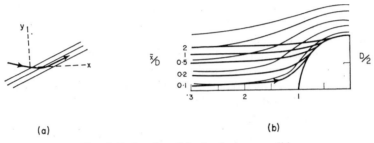

(a)   (b)

Fig. 1. Paths of particles impinging on solid.

The particle attains the velocity of the stream exponentially and the trajectory of a particle having initial velocity given by components u_0 and v_0 is described by the equations

$$x=Ut+\frac{\pi\sigma d^2}{6c}\left(u_0-U\right)\left[1-\exp\left(-\frac{6ct}{\pi\sigma d^2}\right)\right] \tag{2}$$

$$y=Vt+\frac{\pi\sigma d^2}{6c}\left(v_0-V\right)\left[1-\exp\left(-\frac{6ct}{\pi\sigma d^2}\right)\right]$$

A useful parameter for describing the track s was introduced by Albrecht in the form mU_0/c, U_0 being the velocity far upstream of a collector. He then proceeded to calculate the trajectory step by step for a particle carried by an initially uniform stream which then impinges on a cylinder of diameter D, using prescribed values of $\bar{x}/D$. (Fig. 1b), where $\bar{x}$ has the value of the constant $\pi\sigma d^2/6c$ appearing in Equation (2)*.

It was he who introduced what is now called the collection efficiency E as the ratio of the projected area of the obstacle to the area of stream from which particles impinge on the obstacle. To every $\bar{x}/D$ there corresponds a certain proportionate collection. As this Albrecht parameter increases the efficiency passes along an S-shaped curve. It is assumed in this "ideal" case that

1. The particles have infinitesimal size.
2. The initial flow is non-turbulent.
3. The aerosol is Newtonian in flow, i.e. the particles do not distort the velocity gradient in flow in which they find themselves.
4. The particles do not collide with each other.

* Usually written nowadays $P=\dfrac{\sigma d^2 U}{9D\eta}$ and called particle parameter. Cf. Appendix.

5. The particles do not interact with each other or with the obstacle through gravitational or electrostatic forces.

6. The resistance of a particle is given by Stokes law.

He proceeded to apply these ideas to particulate filters, showing that the efficiency increases with the velocity, density and size of particle but diminishes with the width of the fibres constituting the filter.

Langmuir[2] and his collaborators, Davies[3,4] and his co-workers have modified the theory to deal with changes in Reynolds number of the flow, and consequently of the resistance law, and to finite particle size respectively. The limits of collection efficiency are found with potential flow, and viscous flow (i.e. high and low Reynolds numbers) respectively. (Fig. 2.) The results of Gregory,[5] who used lycopodium spores ($r=15\mu$) and of Ranz and Wong[6] who used lycoperdon ($r=1\mu$) fall within the two S curves. In this theory it is assumed that the collected particle is small in size compared to that of the collector.

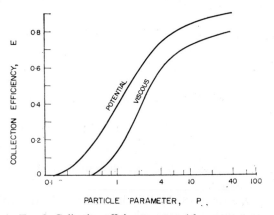

FIG. 2. Collection efficiency vs. particle parameter.

All these workers assumed that collection necessarily followed on impact, but we know that some particles will bounce on collision. The effect of wettability (if the collector is a liquid drop) or of electric charges is discussed in some papers in this symposium.

When the impinging particle becomes comparable in size with the one it is likely to hit, it is impossible to treat the flow as undisturbed by the former. Under these circumstances the problem of collision becomes tedious and difficult to treat mathematically. We can, however, ignore the disturbances to the flow of both contestants and treat the collision as a straightforward crossing of two paths.

Such collisions can occur:

1. On the macroscopic scale due to the difference of resistance of particles of different sizes or densities in an external field of force.

2. On the microscopic scale due to Brownian motion (molecular diffusion) even if all are of the same size.

3. Due to turbulent diffusion, even if all are of the same size.

(From the first aspect collisions cannot occur between microscopic particles, all of the same size, in laminar flow.)

Coagulation of a polydisperse system settling under gravity has been treated, on the basis that a hit ensures coalescence, by a number of meteorologists interested in the fall of raindrops and by rheologists concerned with the disappearance of emulsions (in the absence of a surface-wetting agent). If in such cases there is at the same time a disrupting mechanism at work, if for example, the emulsion is being sheared, the system tends to reach a uniform size distribution.

It is established that, in still air, under suitable conditions the rate of coagulation of an aerosol is determined by the Schmolukowski[7] law of increase in particulate volume (n^{-1}) viz.

$$\frac{1}{n} - \frac{1}{n_0} = kt \tag{3}$$

n_0 being the initial number concentration and n that after time t; k being the coagulation constant. The formula is usually regarded as satisfactory in the sense that a plot of n^{-1} against t is a straight line, though there are practical difficulties in determining the origin of the time scale and k is abnormally large for a dense aerosol in the initial stages of its life.

Most theories which have envisaged the suspension as being subject to turbulent processes of collision, have supposed that the turbulence is engendered by a shear, due to the velocity gradient in a boundary layer, as when a low cloud is carried by the wind over the ground or a river carrying silt flows over its bed. Schmolukowski himself adopted this point of view when he added a term to his coagulation formula to allow for shearing effects.

$$-\frac{\dot{n}}{n} = k'd^3 \left| \frac{\partial U}{\partial x} \right| \tag{4}$$

Further, $\partial U/\partial x$ can be expressed as u'/λ according to Taylor[8] where u' is the intensity and λ the scale of turbulence.

A formula of this type was used by Wigand and Frankenberger[9] for collisions of raindrops in clouds in a turbulent atmosphere, assuming a velocity gradient of order unity.

As an example, it may be said that, depending on the velocity gradient, Brownian motion may become inconsiderable in a cloud of particles of 0·1 to 0·5 micron submitted to turbulence. The weakness of this treatment lies in the assumption of a constant velocity gradient over the expanse of the suspension.

The modified Schmolukowski theory makes the additional collision term depend on the shearing of the flow by a boundary. Another aspect of turbulence is the diffusion of the eddies which in their motion carry the particles with them. On this view particles which lie entirely within an eddy are likely to be brought into contact only on the microscopic scale, that of Brownian motion, but on a macroscopic scale eddy diffusion can cause coagulation even of a monodisperse suspension.

In meteorology, some of these ideas find application to the action of falling water drops in depositing a cloud of suspended particles to the ground by collision. The suspended particles may be an industrial fog, a cloud of mine dust or a cloud of radioactive particles such as follow the setting off of an atomic explosion or the recent leakage from the atomic reactor at Windscale.

If all the coagulation took place in still air, by the action of Brownian motion alone, the effect would fall off rapidly with particle diameter, but when the atmosphere is turbulent, as it is in fact in the troposphere, the coagulation constant is nearly the same for all particles below 1 micron. When both coagulation processes operate, the latter limits the life-time (in the sense of time till deposition) of the larger particles. By making a number of other assumptions Greenfield[10] has constructed a graph (reproduced in Fig. 3) showing the expectation of life for particles scavenged by an artificial rainfall consisting of uniform drops of 20 microns diameter.

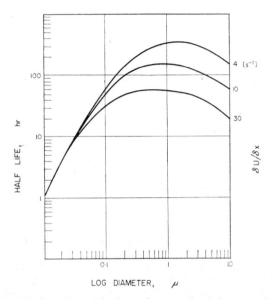

FIG. 3. Life-time of particles in a mist, $20\,\mu$ dia. (*after Greenfield*).

The total mass washed out can be calculated using the expressions for the collection efficiency of spheres if the concentration and size of the droplets is known and the depth and extent of the region (cloud) occupied by the watery collectors. The size-frequency and concentration of droplets for average rainfall (Best[11]) and fog (Mahrous[12]) is known.

REFERENCES

1. ALBRECHT, F. *Phys. Z.*, **32**, 48 (1931).
2. LANGMUIR, I. *J. Met.*, **5**, 175 (1948).
3. DAVIES, C. N. and AYLWARD, M. *Proc. Phys. Soc.*, **B64**, 889 (1951).
4. DAVIES, C. N. and PEETZ, C. V. *Proc. Roy. Soc.*, **A234**, 269 (1956).
5. GREGORY, P. H. *Ann. Appl. Biol.*, **38**, 357 (1951).
6. RANZ, W. E. and WONG, J. B. *Industr. Engng. Chem.*, **44**, 1371 (1952).
7. SCHMOLUKOWSKI, M. *Z. Phys. Chem.*, **92**, 129 (1917).
8. TAYLOR. G. I. *Proc. Roy. Soc.*, **A151**, 421 (1935).
9. WIGAND, A. and FRANKENBERGER, E. *Phys. Z.*, **31**, 204 (1930).
10. GREENFIELD, S. M. *J. Met.*, **14**, 115 (1957).
11. BEST, A. C. *Q.J. Roy. Met. Soc.*, **77**, 418 (1950).
12. MAHROUS, M. A. *Q. J. Roy. Met. Soc.*, **80**, 99 (1954).

DUST DEPOSITION FROM A TURBULENT AIRSTREAM

by P. R. OWEN
Department of the Mechanics of Fluids,
University of Manchester

Summary—Given an isothermal, turbulent flow of dust-laden fluid past a smooth surface, which might be the floor or the roof or a side wall of a duct, the problem here considered is to explain the mechanism by which dust is transported from the stream and deposited on the surface, as well as to derive a quantitative estimate of the rate of deposition.

The analysis is subject to two restrictions on the flow: (a) it is slow enough to ensure that particles once deposited on the surface are not subsequently swept away, and (b), that its dust content comprises particles of 10^{-1} micron diameter and greater which are not susceptible to any appreciable diffusion due to Brownian motion.

Throughout the greater part of the turbulent flow the transport can be described in terms of an eddy diffusivity, in the usual way. A reconsideration of the distribution of eddy viscosity near a plane surface, including the viscous sub-layer, is given in Section 1.1, since it is argued that in the absence of any diffusivity inherent in the system of particles, estimates of the eddy diffusivity are required to be more accurate than those which suffice for the analysis of heat transfer or the transfer of molecular matter. Very close to the surface, where both the turbulent fluctuations and eddy viscosity vanish, an alternative means of transport is needed—a problem which becomes obvious in the case of deposition from below on to a roof, where gravity opposes the upward flight of a particle—and after rejecting mechanisms involving aerodynamic forces due to particle spin and shear in the fluid as much too feeble, it is concluded that the final stage in the approach to the surface is achieved by a particle under the impetus afforded to it by turbulence some distance from the surface. Based on this idea, expressions are worked out for the rate of deposition on to roof-like and floor-like horizontal surfaces and on to vertical surfaces, which involve one disposable constant, predictable in order of magnitude and related to the distance from the surface at which the "free-flight" phase of the particle's trajectory commences. A comparison made in Section 5 with experiments by Dawes and Slack[23] on coal-dust deposition from an airstream permits the constant to be evaluated and shows that the theory gives acceptable predictions of the deposition rate.

Finally, brief consideration is given to the effect of a temperature difference between the surface and the fluid on the deposition rate and is shown to be negligibly small for the order of temperature difference which might arise by accident in practice.

(1) INTRODUCTION

THE flow of a dust-laden fluid over a smooth surface is a feature of many industrial processes and it is often useful and sometimes essential to be able to predict the rate at which particles are deposited from the stream on to the surface. A typical situation of this kind is encountered in coal-mining where dust from the coal-face, carried in suspension around the mine by the ventilating current, is gradually deposited on the floor, roof and walls of various subterranean passages thereby contributing to a potential explosion hazard.

Our object is to explain the physical mechanism of deposition and for this purpose we shall consider a two-dimensional, isothermal flow, uniform in velocity and concentration except near a surface where there is a turbulent boundary layer. The analysis can equally well be applied to the turbulent flow through a channel provided that the velocity at the centre of the channel is identified with the velocity, U_1, at the edge of the boundary layer.

The restriction to turbulent flow hardly needs comment: unless the flow were turbulent none but the minutest particles—those capable of participating in a diffusive Brownian motion—could be transported across the flow other than by gravitational force and some extremely weak forces arising from spin of the particles and fluid shear. We exclude such a possibility from the discussion as trivial, except outside the boundary layer where, the velocity and concentration being constant, the particles are freely accessible to gravitational pull and as a result possess a constant downward velocity equal to their terminal velocity. A more important restriction to be placed on the theory is that it applies solely to the process of deposition and that once a particle has struck the surface it will remain there. In order to meet this restriction we require (a) that a particle does not rebound on striking the surface, so that impact by itself is a sufficient condition for deposition and (b) that the fluid moves so slowly as to be ineffective in dislodging particles from the surface. The work of Jordan[1] suggests that under the action of cohesive force (a) is satisfied for *perfectly* spherical particles of diameter d (cm) and density $1 \cdot 5$ g/cm³ provided that on impact the normal component of velocity does not exceed $0(10/d)$ cm/sec. Since it will emerge that on account of turbulence the impact velocity is $0(u_\tau)$, where u_τ is the friction velocity that even particles as large as 100μ $(10^{-2}$ cm) in diameter will adhere to the surface if u_τ is less than $0(10)$ m/sec. Condition (b) is less satisfactorily determined, (u_τ is defined as $(\tau_0/\rho)^{\frac{1}{2}}$, where τ_0 is the skin friction and ρ the fluid density), it appears except when gravity opposes the dislocation of a particle from the surface; here, Shields,[2] Bagnold,[3] Chepil[4] and others have shown that a particle is undisturbed from

its position on the surface if $u_\tau{}^2 a < \dfrac{\rho' - \rho}{\rho} \, gd$, where a is a constant and $(\rho' - \rho)$ is the

apparent density of the particulate material in a fluid of density ρ. Using Shields' value of about $0 \cdot 10$ for a and setting $(\rho' - \rho)/\rho \approx 10^3$, a value appropriate to carbonaceous or silicaceous materials in air, we have $u_\tau < 300 d^{\frac{1}{2}}$ cm/sec. Thus, the maximum values of u_τ which may be considered for the purpose of the theory are roughly 3 cm/sec for 1μ particles, 9 cm/sec for 10μ particles and 30 cm/sec for 100μ particles.* When the surface is vertical, such as a side-wall of a duct, or is horizontal and roof-like (deposition on to it from below), gravity no longer impeding the movement of a particle, the limitation on u_τ is likely to be more severe, but no quantitative information in these circumstances is available. In any case, it is clear that the limitation on fluid speed imposed by (b) amply secures condition (a).

Given the concentration of particles in the main stream, the velocity of the main stream and the thickness of the boundary layer, or any other quantity such as u_τ suitably defining the boundary layer characteristics, the problem of calculating the rate of mass transport from the stream to the surface falls into two distinct parts. In the outer region of the layer, assuming the dust concentration to be small enough for it to have a negligible effect on density, the rate of transport can be estimated by assuming an eddy diffusivity proportional to the eddy viscosity. This view of mass transport as being brought about principally by a gradient diffusion (modified in a straightforward way to include the gravitational force on a particle) has abundant support in the literature on sedimentation, for instance, Hurst,[5] Richardson,[6] Hunter

---

* The estimates of u_τ for the smaller particles are almost certainly conservative because as the diameter decreases cohesive forces, which were not too obtrusive in the experiments of Shields and others, increase in importance and tend to resist particle movement.

B

Rouse[7] and Vanoni,[8] although on theoretical grounds it is known to ignore certain features of boundary layer turbulence especially near the outer edge of the layer where the action of large eddies is to introduce a convective type of transport as described by Townsend.[9] Granted the use of an eddy viscosity, then close to the surface a more accurate estimate of its magnitude is needed than that accepted for example in the study of heat transfer, Squire,[10] or of evaporation, Owen and Ormerod.[11] The reason is that in the present study eddy diffusivity is the *only* agent, apart from gravity, available for transferring material from one place to another (we again exclude Brownian diffusion which is significant only for particle diameters less than $10^{-1} \mu$). Estimates of the eddy diffusivity near the surface will be presented in Section 2.1, but at this stage it is worth drawing particular attention to the fact that it is the absence of a diffusive mechanism inherent in the system of particles which distinguishes the present problem so sharply from the problem of transport of molecular properties like heat and momentum. Thus, the concept of a viscous sub-layer adjacent to the surface is not relevant here, except insofar as it represents the region in which the turbulence and eddy diffusivity are evanescent; we cannot adopt the usual argument that in the neighbourhood of the surface the enfeebled transport by turbulence is replaced by some other, more powerful, method of transport—for this is none. It is really this microscopic problem of accounting for the final stage of the particle's motion, from the time it is freed from the diffusive action of turbulence until it strikes the surface, that requires special consideration and constitutes the second stage in the analysis. We shall show that it can be answered extremely simply by supposing that the last bit of the particle's trajectory is a kind of "free-flight" under the action of gravity and viscous resistance, the initial momentum being acquired by the particle from turbulent fluctuations in the viscous sub-layer. It appears from the analysis, after the value of a disposable constant has been settled by a comparison with experiment, that the distance over which the particle travels in free-flight is of the same order of magnitude as, but rather less than, the thickness of the viscous sub-layer.

Were we solely concerned with the question of deposition on to a horizontal surface from above, the need for a special treatment very close to the surface might have been overlooked, but it is the problem of accounting for deposition from below on to a roof-like surface which draws attention to this crucial matter, for in this latter case, accepting that the eddy diffusivity vanishes as the surface is approached and noting that gravity opposes the upward motion of particles, there is no way of explaining how the particles can ever reach the surface (that they do is an observed fact) unless some projecting action is operative. It may be recalled that we have supposed isothermal conditions which exclude the possibility of the flow of particles down temperature gradients, a phenomenon which will be discussed briefly in Section 5; the assistance to deposition from electrostatic forces on particles containing stray electric charge can also be excluded, in the absence of any deliberately imposed field, since Pereles[12] showed that, except within a particle diameter or so from an equipotential wall, such forces are negligibly small for the charge densities found in practice, a few electrons per (micron)^2 of surface.

Finally, it may be remarked that although from time to time appeal is made in the literature on dust transport to forces arising from particle spin (Magnus force) and shear in the fluid—undoubtedly relevant to certain laminar flows, such as the arterial flow of blood and the associated motion of corpuscles—it is easily demonstrated that they are much too small to have any serious effect on the particles of roughly 10^{-1} micron diameter and upwards considered in this paper.

(2) TURBULENT DIFFUSION IN THE REGION AWAY FROM THE SURFACE

Imagine a smooth, plane surface, $y=0$, to be swept by a dust-laden airstream. Outside the boundary layer the stream is assumed uniform with respect to both velocity, U_1, and (dilute) dust concentration ψ_1; inside, it is characterized by the velocity distribution $U(y)$ and concentration $\psi(y)$, where the concentration is defined as the number of particles in unit volume. Suppose that the dust particles are so small that under all conditions the Reynolds number of their motion relative to the fluid is less than unity, in which case their resistance is given by Stokes' law. Further, suppose that the particles are so small compared with the scale of the turbulent energy-containing eddies that their agitated motion consists of a series of quasi-equilibrium states in which their vertical velocity relative to the local fluid is v_0, the terminal velocity in still fluid. For this condition to hold, the time-scale, t_d, for a particle to adjust itself to the velocity in a new environment must be small compared with the time, t_τ, taken for the environment to change. It is easily shown that t_d is $0\left(10^{-1}\dfrac{\rho' - \rho}{\rho}\dfrac{d^2}{\nu}\right)$, where d is the diameter of the particle, ρ' its density and ρ, ν are respectively the density and kinematic viscosity of the fluid. The smallest value of t_τ for the turbulence is $0(\nu/u_\tau^2)$, appropriate to the eddies close to the surface. Hence, for dust particles in air, for which ρ'/ρ is $0(10^3)$, $t_d < t_\tau$ provided that $u_\tau d/\nu < 0(10^{-1})$. It is worth emphasizing that this argument is meant to apply only to those parts of the boundary layer in which turbulent diffusion is an effective form of particle transport. In Section 3, where we shall discuss the state of affairs *very* close to the surface, the idea of a quasi-equilibrium between the particle and the turbulent eddies will be abandoned; instead, we shall argue that the particle *fails* to adjust its motion to the turbulent velocity, the relevant condition here being that the time of flight should not be large compared with t_τ.

Continuity of mass requires

$$\frac{\partial \Psi}{\partial t} + \frac{\partial}{\partial x_i}(v_i\,\Psi) = 0,$$

where v_i is the absolute velocity of a dust particle and Ψ the concentration at any instant of time, t. If Ψ is so small that its effect on fluid density may be neglected,

$$\frac{\partial v_i}{\partial x_i} = 0,$$

since the fluid velocity differs from v_i by the constant terminal velocity, v_0, reckoned as positive when it is directed towards the surface. Hence, resolving v_i and Ψ into mean and fluctuating components, namely $v_i = V_i + v_i'$, $\Psi = \psi + \psi'$, it follows that on the average

$$\frac{\partial \psi}{\partial t} + \frac{\partial}{\partial x_i}(V_i\psi + \overline{v_i'\,\psi'}) = 0 \qquad (1)$$

For a two-dimensional flow, (1) reduces to

$$\frac{\partial \psi}{\partial t} + \frac{U \partial \psi}{\partial x} + \left(V - v_0\right)\frac{\partial \psi}{\partial y} = -\frac{\partial}{\partial y}\,\overline{(v'\,\psi')} \tag{2}$$

(2) may be simplified by supposing the mean flow to be steady so that $\partial \psi / \partial t = 0$, and by introducing the approximation, commonly made in the analysis of turbulent boundary layer flows at large Reynolds numbers, that at any given value of x the growth of the boundary layer may be ignored. Accordingly, we set $V = \partial \psi / \partial x = 0$ and obtain

$$v_0 \frac{\partial \psi}{\partial y} = \frac{\partial}{\partial y}\,\overline{(v'\,\psi')} \tag{3}$$

as the transport equation.

(3) can be integrated with respect to y to give

$$v_0 \psi - \overline{v'\,\psi'} = N, \tag{4}$$

where N is the number of particles transported on the average across unit area perpendicular to the y-direction in unit time. We note that it is constant across the boundary layer, because it has been agreed to neglect convection and diffusion in the x-direction, and is therefore equal to the rate of deposition on to the surface.

In order to solve (4), assume that the Reynolds transport, $\overline{v'\psi'}$ is given by

$$\overline{v'\,\psi'} = -D_M\,\frac{\partial \psi}{\partial y}, \tag{5}$$

where D_M is an eddy diffusivity related to the eddy viscosity, ν_T, by

$$D_M = \sigma \nu_T \tag{6}$$

Experiments connected with problems in meteorology, Rider,[13] Pasquill,[14] oceanography, Proudman,[15] and heat transfer, Reichardt,[16] suggest that σ may lie between 1·2 and 1·5 provided that density gradients are negligible. Recently Turner* at the Mechanics of Fluids Laboratory, Manchester, determined σ as a function of density

gradient—or, more precisely Richardson number, $R_i = -g\dfrac{d\rho}{dy}\Big/\left(\dfrac{dU}{dy}\right)^2$—and

found that, at zero Richardson number, $\sigma \approx 1\cdot4$, a value we shall subsequently adopt in our calculations. However, the assumption of zero Richardson number in the dust–fluid mixture requires further examination since σ depends rather critically on R_i, falling from 1·4 to 0·6, for example, as R_i increases from zero to about 0·2. Such an examination can of course only be made *a posteriori* and the following Table, compiled from the results of Sections 4 and 5, shows the maximum permissible concentration in the main stream—for the particular case of dust of density 1·4 g/cm³ in air—for which the local Richardson number in the boundary layer nowhere exceeds $\pm 10^{-2}$. For a Richardson number as small as this, σ cannot depart appreciably from its value of 1·4 at $R_i = 0$.

* Private communication

TABLE 1

d (microns)	0·5	1	2	4	8
Floor deposition $u_\tau = 11$ cm/sec (ψ_1) max.	$2\cdot5 \times 10^8$	$3\cdot6 \times 10^7$	$3\cdot8 \times 10^6$	$4\cdot8 \times 10^5$	$2\cdot4 \times 10^4$
$u_\tau = 3\cdot5$ cm/sec	$8\cdot6 \times 10^6$	$9\cdot2 \times 10^5$	$4\cdot8 \times 10^4$	$2\cdot3 \times 10^3$	$2\cdot2 \times 10^6$
Roof deposition $u_\tau = 11$ cm/sec (ψ_1) max.	$2\cdot7 \times 10^8$	$3\cdot3 \times 10^7$	$3\cdot9 \times 10^6$	$6\cdot5 \times 10^5$	$1\cdot2 \times 10^5$
$u_\tau = 3\cdot5$ cm/sec	$9\cdot1 \times 10^6$	$1\cdot1 \times 10^6$	$1\cdot5 \times 10^5$	$9\cdot1 \times 10^4$	—

On the understanding that $\sigma = 1\cdot4$, (4), (5) and (6) may be written

$$v_0\psi + \sigma\nu_T \frac{d\psi}{dy} = N, \qquad (7)$$

where v_0 can be found from Stokes' law for the drag of a sphere,

$$v_0 = \frac{1}{18} \frac{(\rho' - \rho)}{\rho} \frac{g}{\nu} \left(\frac{d}{s}\right)^2, \qquad (8)$$

account being taken of departures from sphericity by introducing a "shape factor", s; d is the particle diameter as determined, say, microscopically. Again, the assumption of very small concentration implies that the kinematic viscosity, ν, is indistinguishable from its value in the pure fluid.

Since (7) is linear in ψ, and ψ is assumed to be very small so that interference between neighbouring particles can be ignored, it may be applied to each separate band of the spectrum of particle diameters composing the dust cloud.

(2.1) *The Distribution of Eddy Viscosity in a Boundary Layer*

Calculations of the transport of molecular properties across a turbulent boundary layer are usually based on estimates of the eddy viscosity near the surface which can be quite coarse, since in this region of the flow the contribution to the transport from molecular diffusion is comparable with or greater than that from the turbulence. In contrast, the present investigation demands a more refined estimate of the eddy diffusivity owing to the absence of an intrinsic diffusivity from an assemblage of dust particles.

We begin by discarding the usual approximation of zero eddy diffusivity within the viscous sub-layer, $0 \leqslant y \leqslant 5 \, \nu/u_\tau$. Instead, we note from the equation of continuity for the *turbulent* velocity fluctuations,

$$\frac{\partial u'}{\partial x} + \frac{\partial v'}{\partial y} + \frac{\partial w'}{\partial z} = 0,$$

(z is measured in a direction parallel to the surface and perpendicular to the mean flow) that, since $u' = \dfrac{\partial u'}{\partial x} = w' \dfrac{\partial w'}{\partial z} = 0$ on $y = 0$, $\dfrac{\partial v'}{\partial y} = 0$ on $y = 0$. It follows that,

$$\frac{\partial}{\partial y}\overline{(u'v')} = \overline{u'\frac{\partial v'}{\partial y}} + \overline{v'\frac{\partial u'}{\partial y}} = 0,$$

and

$$\frac{\partial^2}{\partial y^2}\,\overline{(u'v')} = 0 \text{ on } y = 0,$$

suggesting that the leading term in a series expansion for $\overline{u'v'}\left(= -v_T\dfrac{dU}{dy}\right)$ is proportional to y^3. Remembering that the mean velocity increases linearly with distance from the surface in the interval $0 \leqslant y \leqslant 5\dfrac{v}{u_\tau}$, v_T must be of the form,

$$v_T = K_1\,v y_\tau^3, \qquad 0 \leqslant y_\tau \leqslant 5, \tag{9}$$

where $y_\tau = y u_\tau / v$.

Outside the viscous sub-layer and the direct influence of the surface on the turbulent velocity, we may expect the turbulent energy to be related to the local mean velocity to which it largely, although not wholly, owes its production. Provided that y_τ is not too large, say, less than 20, the mean velocity varies nearly linearly with distance from the surface and a similar linear variation may be assumed in $\sqrt{[(v')^2]}$. This argument is borne out by experiment as shown in Fig. 1, where the values of $\sqrt{[(v')^2/U]}$ deduced from measurements made by Laufer[17] tend to a constant value when y_τ is greater than about 5. At the same time, the scale of the turbulent energy-containing eddies, constrained geometrically by the presence of the surface, increases linearly with y and,

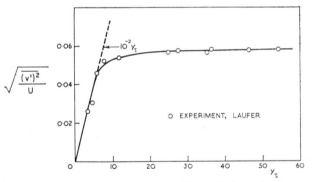

FIG. 1. Ratio of the r.m.s. value of the v'-component of the turbulent velocity near a surface to the local mean velocity.

since the eddy viscosity may be taken to be proportional to the product of the r.m.s. velocity fluctuation and the scale, we are led to a quadratic relation between v_T and y_τ which may be written

$$v_T = K_2 v\,(y_\tau - a)^2, \qquad 5 \leqslant y_\tau \leqslant a. \tag{10}$$

Still further from the wall, but within roughly the inner third of the boundary layer, the linear increase in scale persists whereas the mean velocity remains almost constant, for even when $y_\tau = 20$ the mean velocity has attained roughly half its value in the main stream. Hence v_T increases linearly with distance from the surface and we may write

$$v_T = K_3 v\,(y_\tau - b), \qquad y_\tau \geqslant a. \tag{11}$$

It will be shown in Section 2.2 that an estimate of ν_T in the outer part of the layer, where $\nu_T \gg \nu$, is not required because the concentration there can be related directly to the mean velocity.

Of the six disposable constants in (9), (10) and (11), K_3 can be taken as 0·4, the value suggested by von Kármán for which there is ample experimental support; the others must be determined by comparison with experiment. But we note that there are two relations between the constants which ensure continuity in ν_T at $y_\tau = 5$ and $y_\tau = a$. They are $K_1/K_2 = (5 - a)^2/125$ and $K_2 = 0.4\,(a - b)/(a - a)^2$.

Values of ν_T near a surface can be deduced from the remarkably elegant measurements of Laufer[17] in a pipe and of Schubauer[18] on a flat plate. They are shown in Fig. 2 together with the curve given by (9), (10) and (11), the (rounded-off) values of the constants having been set as follows:

$$K_1 = 10^{-3}, \quad K_2 = 1.2 \times 10^{-2}, \quad a = 1.6, \quad b = 10, \quad a = 20.$$

The broken line in the figure shows the approximation to ν_T/ν introduced by von Kármán[19] for the analysis of heat transfer. The agreement between the points deduced from experiment and the full line is excellent, although it may be argued that as large a number as three disposable constants greatly helps to secure a good fit. However, it must be pointed out that in an attempt to avoid such criticism the fit with experiment was made using three of the experimental points chosen almost at random.

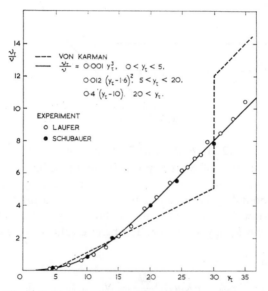

FIG. 2. The variation of eddy viscosity with distance from a surface.

It may be mentioned in passing that the substitution of (9), (10) and (11) into the equation of mean motion,

$$u_\tau^2 = (\nu + \nu_T)\frac{dU}{dy},$$

leads, on integration, to a velocity distribution which agrees well with experiment in the range $0 < y_\tau < 10^3$. In particular, for $y_\tau > 20$,

$$\frac{U}{u_\tau} = 2 \cdot 5 \log (y_\tau - 7 \cdot 5) + 5.6$$

which is close to the usually accepted "intermediate law" for the velocity profile in a turbulent boundary layer on a flat surface.

To summarize the results of this section, Fig. 3 displays pictorially the inner regions of the boundary layer classified according to their diffusivities; the mean velocity and the shallow layer adjacent to the surface through which particles are projected rather than diffused are also shown.

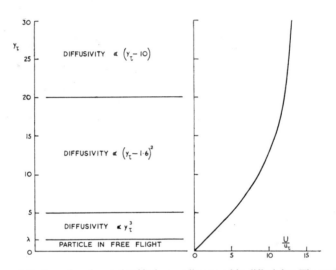

FIG. 3. Regions of the boundary layer classified according to eddy diffusivity. The variation of mean velocity with distance from a surface.

(2.2) *The Rate of Turbulent Transport*

If we defer the question of what happens in the immediate neighbourhood of the surface $y=0$, say in the interval $0 \leqslant y_\tau \leqslant \lambda$, the transport by turbulence across the remainder of the boundary layer can be found from (7), using the expressions for ν_T presented in Section 2.1, in terms of the boundary values of ψ; $\psi = \psi_1$ in the main stream, and $\psi = \psi_0$, say, on $y_\tau = \lambda$. The precise value of ψ_0 will be determined in Section 3.

From (7) and (9),

$$v_0 \psi + \sigma K_1 u_\tau y_\tau^3 \frac{d\psi}{dy_\tau} = N, \quad \lambda \leqslant y_\tau \leqslant 5,$$

which can be integrated to give

$$v_0 \psi - N = A \exp \left[\frac{1}{2\sigma K_1} \cdot \left(\frac{v_0}{u_\tau} \right) \cdot \frac{1}{y_\tau^2} \right], \tag{12}$$

where A is a constant whose value is $(v_0 \psi_0 - N) \exp \left[-\frac{1}{2\sigma K_1} \cdot \left(\frac{v_0}{u_\tau} \right) \cdot \frac{1}{\lambda^2} \right]$, in view of the condition $\psi = \psi_0$ on $y_\tau = \lambda$.

In $5 \leqslant y_\tau \leqslant 20$, from (7) and (10),

$$v_0 \psi + \sigma K_2\, u_\tau\, (y_\tau - a)^2\, \frac{d\psi}{dy_\tau} = N;$$

hence,

$$v_0\psi - N = B \exp\left[\frac{1}{\sigma K_2}\left(\frac{v_0}{u_\tau}\right) \cdot \frac{1}{(y_\tau - a)}\right], \tag{13}$$

with B determined by the condition of continuity in ψ at $y_\tau = 5$ as,

$$A \exp\left\{\frac{1}{\sigma}\left(\frac{v_0}{u_\tau}\right)\left[\frac{1}{50 K_1} - \frac{1}{(5-a)K_2}\right]\right\}.$$

For larger (but not too large) values of y_τ we have from (7) and (11),

$$v_0\psi + \sigma K_3 u_\tau(y_\tau - b) = N, \quad y_\tau \geqslant 20,$$

and so

$$v_0\psi - N = C(y_\tau - b)^{(v_0/u_\tau)/\sigma K_3} \tag{14}$$

To ensure continuity in ψ at $y_\tau = 20$,

$$C = A \exp\left\{\frac{1}{\sigma}\left(\frac{v_0}{u_\tau}\right)\left[\frac{1}{50 K_1} - \frac{15}{(5-a)(20-a)K_2}\right]\right\}(20-b)^{(v_0/u_\tau)/\sigma K_3}$$

In the outer part of the boundary layer it is not necessary to know the magnitude of the eddy diffusivity, provided that the distance from the surface is large enough to ensure that it far exceeds the kinematic viscosity: in which case, it is sufficient to observe that if the equation of motion of the fluid is written as,

$$\frac{v_T}{v} f'(y_\tau) = 1, \tag{15}$$

where $f(y_\tau) = U/u_\tau$, the transport equation,

$$v_0\psi - N = -\sigma \frac{v_T}{v} u_\tau \frac{d\psi}{dy_\tau} = g(y_\tau),$$

say, reduces to

$$g = -\sigma \frac{u_\tau}{v_0} \frac{g'}{f'}. \tag{16}$$

The inequality, $v_T \gg v$, implicit in (15) is amply fulfilled if $y_\tau > 260$, since in these circumstances (11) yields $v_T > 10^2 v$.

On integration, (16) gives

$$v_0\psi - N = D \exp\left[-\frac{1}{\sigma}\left(\frac{v_0}{u_\tau}\right)\frac{U}{u_\tau}\right], \quad y_\tau \geqslant 260. \tag{17}$$

Again, invoking the condition of continuity at $y_\tau = 260$, where $\dfrac{U}{u_\tau} = 19 \cdot 4$, we obtain

$$D = A \exp\left\{\frac{1}{\sigma}\left(\frac{v_0}{u_\tau}\right)\left[\frac{1}{50 K_1} - \frac{15}{(5-a)(20-a)K_2} + 19 \cdot 4\right]\right\}\left(\frac{20-b}{260-b}\right)^{(v_0/u_\tau)/K_3}.$$

In particular, $\psi = \psi_1$ when $U = U_1$, hence

$$v_0 \psi_1 - N = D \exp\left[-\frac{1}{\sigma}\left(\frac{v_0}{u_\tau}\right)\frac{U_1}{u_\tau} \right]. \tag{18}$$

(3) MOTION OF PARTICLES ADJACENT TO THE SURFACE

Any attempt to retain the idea of an eddy diffusivity and, associated with it, the assumption that a particle in its entanglement with eddies moves from one state of quasi-equilibrium to another leads to difficulty as the surface is approached. In the first place the very concept of any eddy diffusivity fails in conviction when the eddy diffusivity has so powerful a spatial variation as to give rise to appreciable changes within a distance comparable with the particle diameter. We are then tempted to adopt a more naïve picture of the transport process and to imagine the particle to be dragged towards the surface in response to and in quasi-equilibrium with the turbulent velocity. But this argument is equally unsuccessful because it is known, see Fig. 1 and Townsend,[9] that when $y_\tau \approx 0$, the r.m.s. velocity fluctuation, $\sqrt{[\overline{(v')^2}]}$, is equal to $10^{-2} u_\tau y_\tau^2$. Hence, when roof deposition is considered, particles cease to move towards the surface when $v_0 = 10^{-2} u_\tau y_\tau^2$. Using (8), it is evident that a particle of density $1\cdot5$ g/cm³ in air cannot approach the roof more closely than about $10^3/u_\tau^{3/2}$ diameters.

It might be argued that a particle is able to traverse the thin layer of fluid adjacent to the surface by way of a dispersive Brownian motion. To examine this possibility we note that for a sphere of diameter d, the Einstein formula for the diffusivity D, as given in standard books such as Kennard,[20] is

$$D = \frac{kT}{3\pi\mu d},$$

where T is the temperature of the fluid, μ is its viscosity and k is the Boltzmann constant ($1\cdot381 \times 10^{-16}$ cm/dyne °K). For air at 293°K, we find $D/\nu = 1\cdot6 \times 10^{-10}/d$ with d measured in cm. Consequently, even for a particle as small as $0\cdot1$ micron in diameter D/ν is $0(10^{-5})$. Now it is easy to show that if Brownian diffusion alone were available to counteract gravity within a distance $0(\nu/u_\tau)$ from a roof-like surface, the rate of deposition would be of order $v_0 \psi_1 \exp\left(-\frac{v_0}{u_\tau}\cdot\frac{\nu}{D}\right)$. Since it is difficult to visualize situations in which u_τ is less than $0\cdot1$ cm/sec, the exponential term is insignificantly small for particle diameters of $0\cdot1$ μ or more.

The remaining methods of particle transport, involving fluid dynamic forces, can also be rejected since they are too weak to outweigh gravity. Without going into detail, the magnitudes of these forces are as follows. (1) The Magnus force, Oseen,[21] due to an angular velocity u_τ^2/ν, proportional to the mean vorticity or the r.m.s. turbulent vorticity in the fluid, is $0\left[\rho u_\tau^2 d^2\left(\frac{u_\tau d}{\nu}\right)\right]$. (2) The force due to mean shear in the fluid, Zierep,[22] is also $0\left[\rho u_\tau^2 d^2\left(\frac{u_\tau d}{\nu}\right)\right]$, on the assumption that a particle, under the initial action of turbulence, is projected into an environment where the mean fluid velocity in the x-direction is less than the particle velocity by an amount $0(u_\tau)$. (3) The pseudo-buoyancy force due to fluctuating pressure gradients (according to a private communication from M. J. Lighthill, it is directed *up* the instantaneous pressure gradient)

is $0\left[d^3\sqrt{\overline{\left(\frac{dp'}{dy}\right)^2}}\right]$: or $0\left[10^{-2}\rho u_\tau^2 d^2\left(\frac{u_\tau d}{\nu}\right)\right]$, since $\sqrt{\left[\overline{\left(\frac{dp'}{dy}\right)^2}\right]}\approx 10^{-2}\rho u_\tau^3/\nu$, Townsend.[9]

Bearing in mind that we argued in Section 3 that $u_\tau d/\nu$ should not exceed $0(10^{-1})$, it follows that the ratio of any of the above forces to the weight of a particle is at most

$0\left(10^{-1}.\dfrac{\rho}{\rho'-\rho}.\dfrac{u_\tau^2}{gd}\right)$. But at the outset of the analysis it was agreed that $\dfrac{\rho}{\rho'-\rho}.\dfrac{u_\tau^2}{gd}$

must be less than about 10^{-1} in order to avoid erosion of the dusty surface, and it therefore appears that at most the forces can only amount to roughly 1/100th of the weight of a particle.

In the light of the failure to account for any massive fluid dynamic force on a particle it must be concluded that the final portion of its approach to the surface is achieved projectile-fashion under the impetus afforded mainly by turbulent velocities some distance from the surface: that is to say, we suppose that the particle acquires a certain velocity at a distance $\lambda\nu/u_\tau$ from the surface (we can assert that λ is of order unity), thence travels towards the surface under the action of *gravity*, *viscous resistance* and the *rapidly decaying turbulent velocity*.

Consider the case of deposition on to a roof. Let y^* be measured vertically upwards from the plane distant $\lambda\nu/u_\tau$ from the surface. The equation of motion of a particle is

$$mv\frac{dv}{dy^*} = \beta\left[cu_\tau\left(\lambda - \frac{y^*u_\tau}{\nu}\right)^2 - v_0\right]\tag{19}$$

in which the instantaneous turbulent velocity has been written as $cu_\tau\left(\lambda - \dfrac{y^*u_\tau}{\nu}\right)^2$;

m is the mass and v the velocity of a particle, and $\beta(=3\pi\mu d)$ is the constant of proportionality between the drag on a particle and its velocity relative to the fluid. β may be conveniently expressed as mg/v_0.

Implicit in (19) is the assumption that the turbulent velocity is perfectly correlated over distances in the y-direction comparable with $\lambda u_\tau/\nu$. It is thought to be reasonable in view of the fact that close to the surface the turbulent structure can only comprise eddies of scale ν/u_τ because an upper limit on their size is imposed by the proximity of the surface and a lower limit by viscous dissipation; moreover, the time of flight of a particle is not of greater order of magnitude than the time taken for the eddies to break up.†

† The time of flight, t_f, is at most $0\left(\sqrt{\left[\dfrac{\nu}{u_\tau g}\right]}\right)$—the maximum time taken by a particle to traverse a distance ν/u_τ under a deceleration g—whereas the time-scale for break-up of the eddies, t_τ, is $0\left(\dfrac{\nu}{u_\tau^2}\right)$. Hence t_f/t_τ is at most $0\left(\sqrt{\left[\dfrac{u_\tau^3}{g\nu}\right]}\right)$, or $0\left[\sqrt{\left\{\left(\dfrac{\rho}{\rho'-\rho}.\dfrac{u_\tau^2}{gd}\right)\left(\dfrac{\rho'-\rho}{\rho}\right)\left(\dfrac{u_\tau d}{\nu}\right)\right\}}\right]$. For dust of density 1·5 g/cm³ in air $\dfrac{\rho'-\rho}{\rho}\approx 10^3$, and since we have already argued that the first and last terms under the radical sign must each be less than 10^{-1}, it follows that t_f/t_τ is less than $0(\sqrt{[10]})$.

Integrating (19) and including the condition $v = cu_\tau\lambda^2 - v_0$ on $y^* = 0$, we obtain

$$\tfrac{1}{2}mv^2 = \tfrac{1}{3}\beta cv\left[\lambda^3 - \left(\lambda - \frac{y^*u_\tau}{v}\right)\right] - \beta v_0 y^* + \tfrac{1}{2}m(cu_\tau\lambda^2 - v_0)^2 \qquad (20)$$

In order that the particle strikes the surface, $v \geqslant 0$ on $y^* = \lambda v/u_\tau$. Hence, from (20), c must exceed the value c_1 given by

$$c_1{}^2 - 2c_1\left[\frac{1}{\lambda^2}\left(\frac{v_0}{u_\tau}\right) - \frac{1}{3\lambda}\left(\frac{u_\tau}{v_0}\right)\left(\frac{gv}{u_\tau{}^3}\right)\right] + \frac{1}{\lambda^4}\left(\frac{v_0}{u_\tau}\right)^2 - \frac{2}{\lambda^3}\frac{gv}{u_\tau{}^3} = 0. \qquad (21)$$

Suppose that the probability density function of the turbulent velocity at any point is Gaussian, then the number of particles which travel in unit time across unit area of the plane $y^* = 0$, where the concentration is ψ_0, with velocity in excess of $c_1 u_\tau\lambda^2$ directed towards the surface is found to be

$$N_R = u_\tau\psi_0\left\{\frac{K_4\lambda^2}{\sqrt{(2\pi)}}\exp\left(-\tfrac{1}{2}\cdot\frac{c_1{}^2}{K_4{}^2}\right) - \tfrac{1}{2}\left(\frac{v_0}{u_\tau}\right)\left[1 - \mathrm{erf}\left(\frac{1}{\sqrt{2}}\cdot\frac{c_1}{K_4}\right)\right]\right\}, \qquad (22)$$

where $K_4 = \dfrac{1}{u_\tau\lambda^2}\cdot\sqrt{\overline{[(v')^2]}}$ $(y_\tau = \lambda)$, and is known from experiment to be 10^{-2}. The suffix R refers to roof deposition.

In the corresponding case of floor deposition, all the particles crossing $y^* = 0$ with velocity directed towards the surface reach the surface, and we find that

$$N_F = u_\tau\psi_0\left\{\frac{K_4\lambda^2}{\sqrt{(2\pi)}}\exp\left[-\frac{1}{2K_4{}^2\lambda^4}\cdot\left(\frac{v_0}{u_\tau}\right)^2\right] + \tfrac{1}{2}\left(\frac{v_0}{u_\tau}\right)\left[1 + \mathrm{erf}\left(\frac{1}{\sqrt{(2)}K_4\lambda^2}\cdot\frac{v_0}{u_\tau}\right)\right]\right\} \qquad (23)$$

(4) THE RATE OF DUST DEPOSITION ON A SURFACE

(22) and (23) can be written

$$N_F = u_\tau\psi_0 G_F; \quad N_R = u_\tau\psi_0 G_R. \qquad (24)$$

Eliminating ψ_0 between (24) and (12), and using (18) we obtain, on substituting numerical values for the constants,

$$N_R = v_0\psi_1\Bigg/\left\{\left(1 + \frac{1}{G_R}\cdot\frac{v_0}{u_\tau}\right)(0\cdot04)^{-1\cdot79\,(v_0/u_\tau)}\right.$$
$$\left.\times\exp\left[-0\cdot714\frac{v_0}{u_\tau}\left(19\cdot5 - \frac{500}{\lambda^2} - \frac{U_1}{u_\tau}\right)\right] - 1\right\}; \qquad (25)$$

$$N_F = v_0\psi_1\Bigg/\left\{1 - \left(1 - \frac{1}{G_F}\cdot\frac{v_0}{u_\tau}\right)(0\cdot04)^{1\cdot79(v_0/u_\tau)}\right.$$
$$\left.\times\exp\left[0\cdot714\frac{v_0}{u_\tau}\left(19\cdot5 - \frac{500}{\lambda^2} - \frac{U_1}{u_\tau}\right)\right]\right\}. \qquad (26)$$

G_R and G_F follow from (22) and (23):

$$G_R = \frac{10^{-2}\lambda^2}{\sqrt{(2\pi)}}\exp\left(-5\times10^3\,c_1{}^2\right) - \tfrac{1}{2}\left(\frac{v_0}{u_\tau}\right)\left[1 - \mathrm{erf}\left(\frac{10^2}{\sqrt{2}}\cdot c_1\right)\right], \qquad (27)$$

$$G_F = \frac{10^{-2}\lambda^2}{\sqrt{(2\pi)}}\exp\left[-\frac{5\times10^3}{\lambda^4}\cdot\left(\frac{v_0}{u_\tau}\right)^2\right] + \tfrac{1}{2}\left(\frac{v_0}{u_\tau}\right)\left[1 + \mathrm{erf}\left(\frac{10^2}{\sqrt{(2)}\lambda^2}\cdot\frac{v_0}{u_\tau}\right)\right]. \qquad (28)$$

c_1 is found from (21):

$$c_1 = \frac{1}{\lambda^2}\left(\frac{v_0}{u_\tau}\right) - \frac{1}{3\lambda}\left(\frac{u_\tau}{v_0}\right)\left(\frac{g\nu}{u_\tau^3}\right) + \left[\frac{1}{9\lambda^2}\left(\frac{u_\tau}{v_0}\right)^2\left(\frac{g\nu}{u_\tau^3}\right)^2 + \frac{4}{3\lambda^3}\left(\frac{g\nu}{u_\tau^3}\right)\right]^{\frac{1}{2}}. \tag{29}$$

Since gravity has no effect on the rate of deposition, N_S, on to a vertical surface, such as a side-wall, N_S can be found as $\lim\limits_{v_0 \to 0} N_F$. Thus,

$$N_S = u_\tau \psi_1 \Big/ \left\{\frac{608}{\lambda^2} - 8\cdot14 + 0\cdot714\,\frac{U_1}{u_\tau}\right\}. \tag{30}$$

The rates of deposition given by (25), (26) and (30) contain a disposable constant λ, about which all that is known at this stage is that it must be of order of magnitude unity. Its precise numerical value can be found only by comparison with experiment, as discussed in the next Section.

(5) COMPARISON WITH EXPERIMENT. THE CONSTANT λ

A series of experiments on the rate of deposition of coal dust (of density 1·4 g/cm³) on to the surfaces of a long wind tunnel of 1 ft square cross-section was made by Dawes and Slack[23] who introduced dust into the airstream and counted, with the help of a microscope, the number of particles deposited on to glass slides of known area in a given time, arranging their count to distinguish between particles of different size. In order to avoid what was claimed to be an inaccurate measurement of ψ_1, they presented the results in the form of N_R/N_F and N_S/N_R as functions of particle diameter.

The skin friction was not measured, but from the stated values of mean airspeed, U_m, over the tunnel cross-section it is possible to estimate u_τ from the standard relation for fully developed turbulent channel flow, e.g. Coles,[24]

$$\frac{U_m}{u_\tau} = 5\cdot76 \log_{10}\left(R.\frac{u_\tau}{U_m}\right) + 10\cdot08,$$

where R is the Reynolds number based on U_m and the half-width of the channel.*

The velocity at the centre of the channel is given by,

$$U_1 = U_m + 2\cdot5u_\tau.$$

u_τ and U_1/u_τ calculated from the above relations and corresponding to the values of U_m quoted by Dawes and Slack are shown in the following Table.

TABLE 2

U_m cm/sec	55·9	99	203
u_τ cm/sec	3·5	6·0	11·0
U_1/u_τ	18·5	19·0	21·0

The experimental results, plotted in the form of N_R/N_F and N_S/N_F against v_0/u_τ are shown in Figs. 4 and 5. v_0 was deduced from the particle diameters given by Dawes

* The corresponding expression for u_τ on an isolated flat surface is $\dfrac{U_1}{u_\tau} = 11\cdot5 \log_{10}\left(R^{\frac{1}{2}}.\frac{u_\tau}{U_1}\right) + 4\cdot4,$ where R is the Reynolds number based on U_1 and the distance from the start of the boundary layer.

and Slack, by introducing, as suggested by them, a shape factor of 1·2. Included in Fig. 4 are some unpublished results, kindly supplied by Dr. Dawes, on wax spheres of density 0·9 g/cm³. The figures also contain curves found from (25)–(30) by setting λ equal to 1·6 (in each figure the curves corresponding to the different values of U_1/u_τ would be almost indistinguishable, and therefore only one has been drawn).

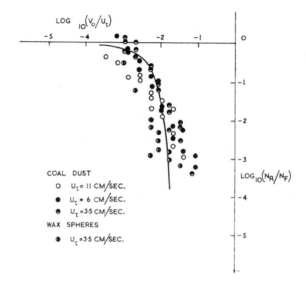

FIG. 4. Ratio of the rates of roof deposition to floor deposition: comparison between theory and the experiments of Dawes and Slack.

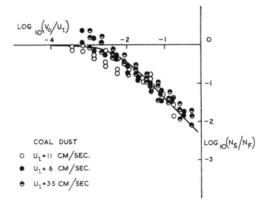

FIG. 5. Ratio of the rates of side-wall deposition to floor deposition: comparison between theory and the experiments of Dawes and Slack.

It should be remarked that the value $\lambda = 1·6$ was selected to give the best fit with the points on Fig. 4 alone. The comparison between the full line and the experimental points in Fig. 5 may therefore be accepted as a genuine test of the theory, which appears to be satisfactory.

To give an idea of the numerical magnitudes of some of the functions appearing in (25)–(30), a few values appropriate to the curves of Figs. 4 and 5, with $U_1/u_\tau = 19$, are shown in the Table below.

TABLE 3

$\dfrac{v_0}{u_\tau} \times 10^4$	1·74	6·95	27·8	111·0	222·0
$G_R \times 10^2$	1·01	0·989	0·830	0·333	0·025
$G_F \times 10^2$	1·02	1·05	1·17	1·67	2·49
$N_R/v_0\psi_1$	22·8	5·50	1·00	0·0489	0·00046
$N_F/v_0\psi_1$	25·0	6·45	2·44	1·07	1·00
$N_S/v_0\psi_1$	23·8	5·94	1·48	0·37	0·19

The scatter of the points in the bottom right of Fig. 4 can be attributed to experimental inaccuracy, for they represent the ratios of a very small number of particles collected on the roof to a much larger number collected on the floor. The scatter towards the top left corner of the figure is, however, thought to be more genuine and is confined to the results of experiments at the highest windspeed and involving the smaller particles, for which it can be shown that the condition stated in the Introduction for the non-erosion of the surface is violated. Since erosion of the particles on the roof is likely to be more severe than those on the floor, the values of N_R/N_F fall below the curve and the cluster of points obtained from experiments at lower windspeeds. A similar defect in the experimental values of N_S/N_F found at the highest windspeed can be observed towards the top left of Fig. 5. Another feature of the experiments that could lead to disparity between the measurements of deposition and the theory is the undoubted existence of a secondary flow in a long duct of square cross-section. It is impossible to account quantitatively for the effect of this transverse flow, although it might be surmised from Fig. 5 to have been small, otherwise the consistency between the experimental data and the theoretical curve would have been destroyed.

The curve in Fig. 4 exhibits a sharp cut-off as v_0/u_τ increases, due physically to the effect of gravity outweighing the impetus from the turbulent fluctuations available to a particle in its upward flight. We should expect the cut-off in N_R to occur when $v_0 \approx 10^{-2}u_\tau\lambda^2$, the r.m.s. value of the v'-fluctuation distant $\lambda v/u_\tau$ from the roof, or roughly when $v_0/u_\tau = 0.03$. Since the probability density of v' is assumed to have a Gaussian distribution, the cut-off will effectively be complete when $v_0/u_\tau = 0.06$. On the other hand, as v_0/u_τ increases, N_F tends to the value v_0/ψ_1, and gravity becomes the dominant cause of deposition. For very small values of v_0/u_τ, when deposition is freed from gravitational influence, N_R and N_F both approach N_S, which is nearly proportional to u_τ.

(6) THE EFFECT OF SPATIAL TEMPERATURE GRADIENTS

The assumption of isothermal flow, on which the preceding analysis was based, deserves reconsideration, since it is well known that small particles tend to flow down temperature gradients—a feature contributing to the deposition of dust on cool surfaces near to hot water pipes or electric lamp bulbs, and an essential process in the operation of thermal precipitators.

An estimate of the force on a spherical particle of diameter d surrounded by fluid in which there is a temperature gradient dT/dy was made by Epstein.[25] In the case of a dust particle whose thermal conductivity is ten times greater than that of air, Epstein's expression for the force is,

$$F = \frac{3}{8} \frac{\rho v^2 d}{T} \cdot \frac{dT}{dy}. \tag{31}$$

A particle under the action of the force F and viscous resistance will drift down the temperature gradient with a velocity whose terminal value is given by,

$$v_T = \frac{1}{8\pi} \cdot \frac{v}{T} \cdot \frac{dT}{dy}. \tag{32}$$

To find the order of magnitude of v_T, consider a flat surface maintained at a temperature T_0 and swept by an airstream whose temperature is T_1. dT/dy is greatest in the viscous sub-layer and equal to Q/k_a, where Q is the rate of heat transfer to or from the surface and k_a is the thermal conductivity of air. But, in the flow past a flat surface on which the boundary layer is turbulent, Q/k_a is given approximately by

$$\frac{\rho C_p}{k_a} \cdot \frac{u_\tau^2}{U_1} \cdot (T_0 - T_1),$$

where C_p is the specific heat of the fluid. It follows that

$$\frac{v_T}{u_\tau} = \frac{0 \cdot 09}{\pi} \cdot \frac{u_\tau}{U_1} \cdot \frac{(T_0 - T_1)}{T_1}, \tag{33}$$

since $\rho C_p/k_a = 0 \cdot 72/v$ for air.

Approximating further by setting $u_\tau/U_1 \approx 0 \cdot 05$, a typical value for the turbulent flow in a channel or past a flat plate, we arrive at

$$\frac{v_T}{u_\tau} \approx 1 \cdot 5 \times 10^{-3} \frac{(T_0 - T_1)}{T_1}, \tag{34}$$

with v_T directed away from the surface if $T_0 > T_1$, and towards the surface if $T_0 < T_1$. If T_1 is taken to be around $300°K$, we see from (34) that even with a temperature difference $(T_0 - T_1)$, as large as $30°K$, v_T/u_τ is only of the order of 10^{-4} which, for the ranges of particle size and friction velocity considered in this paper is negligibly small.

(7) ACKNOWLEDGEMENT

I am indebted to Mr. H. T. Ramsay, Director of the Safety in Mines Research Establishment, for bringing the problem of dust deposition to my attention, and to Dr. Dawes, Dr. Hodkinson and the late Mr. Pereles with whom I profitably discussed the subject. Mr. Pereles had, with my consent, included some of the ideas described here in his 1958 paper on dust deposition.

(8) REFERENCES

1. JORDAN, D. W. *Brit. J. Appl. Phys., Supp.* **3**, 194 (1954).
2. SHIELDS, A. *Mitt Preusz Versuchs. Wass. u. Schiff,* **26** (1936).
3. BAGNOLD, R. A. *The physics of blown sands and desert dunes,* Methuen (1954).
4. CHEPIL, W. S. *Soil Sci.,* **60**, 397 (1945).

5. HURST, H. E. *Proc. Roy. Soc.* A**124,** 196 (1929).
6. RICHARDSON, E. G. *Proc. Roy. Soc.* A**162,** 583 (1937).
7. ROUSE, H. *Proc. 5th Int. Congr. Appl. Mech.*, 550 (1939).
8. VANONI, A. A. *Trans Amer. Soc. Civ. Engng*, **3,** 67 (1946).
9. TOWNSEND, A. A. *The structure of turbulent shear flow*, Cambridge, 1956.
10. SQUIRE, H. B. *Mod. Dev. Fluid Dyn.*, **2,** Chap. XIV, Oxford, 1953.
11. OWEN, P. R. and ORMEROD, A. O. *Aeron. Res. Council*, R. & M. 2875 (1954).
12. PERELES, E. G., S.M.R.E. Res. Report 144 (1958).
13. RIDER N. E. *Phil. Trans Roy. Soc.* A**246,** 481 (1954).
14. PASQUILL, F. *Proc. Roy. Soc.* A**198,** 116 (1949).
15. PROUDMAN, J. *Dynamical Oceanography*, Methuen, 1953.
16. REICHARDT, H. *Zeit. angew. Math. Mech.*, **20,** 297 (1940).
17. LAUFER, J. *Nat. Ad. Cttee Aero., Tech.* Note 2954 (1953).
18. SCHUBAUER, G. B. *J. Appl. Phys.*, **25,** 188 (1954).
19. KARMAN, TH. VON. *Proc. 4th Int. Congr. Appl. Mech.* (1934).
20. KENNARD, E. H. *Kinetic Theory of Gases*, McGraw-Hill, 1938.
21. OSEEN, C. W. *Hydrodynamik, Leipzig*, 1927.
22. ZIEREP, J. *Zeit. Flugwiss.*, **3,** 22 (1955).
23. DAWES, J. G. and SLACK, A. S.M.R.E. Res. Report 105 (1954).
24. COLES, D. *Calif. Inst. Tech. Report* 20–69 (1953).
25. EPSTEIN, P. S. *Zeit. Phys.*, **54,** 537 (1929).

C

THE CLASSICAL COMPUTATIONS OF THE AERODYNAMIC CAPTURE OF PARTICLES BY SPHERES

by H. HERNE
Scientific Department, National Coal Board

(1) INTRODUCTION

A WIDE range of physical problems from diverse practical fields are concerned with the collision between two particles borne in a fluid medium. The fluid flows around the particles and this flow pattern generates viscous forces on them. These viscous forces affect the trajectories of the particles and therefore condition whether the two particles collide or not. The contribution which a theoretical calculation can make is to estimate quantitatively the relative importance of inertial and viscous forces and so to evaluate whether, for given initial conditions, collision between the particles occurs or not.

A number of workers have made such calculations when one particle is spherical and large relative to the other particle. This paper reviews the work which has been published and attempts to assess its accuracy partly by considering the method of calculation and partly by comparing the results with recent similar work in which the author has participated.

(2) THE PHYSICAL PROBLEM

The first step in attempting a mathematical analysis of the practical problem is to identify and to state the process or processes of greatest importance and the physical laws on which these depend. The first physical simplification is to reduce a complex assemblage of particles to two only, immersed in a fluid; the word "particle" is extended here to include, for example, air bubbles in a liquid. This assumption is obviously far less valid for high concentrations of particles, since the perturbing influence of all the other particles except the two considered on the fluid flow pattern is ignored, and the chance of an impact of either particle with a third one is ignored also. This simplification is accepted in all the theoretical studies of this problem.

The second physical simplification which most workers in this field accept is that one particle is much larger than the other and is spherical in shape. Solid particles, which retain their shape, must be approximately spherical for the theory to apply to them; particles of liquid in a gaseous medium approximate to a spherical shape due to surface tension, and Best[1] has shown that particles of water in air can be regarded as spherical when they are less than one millimetre in diameter. Air bubbles in water are approximately spherical when rising under gravity at diameters of up to about 3 mm,[2] although Saffman[3] considers that a diameter of about 1 mm is the limit for spherical shape. The shape of the other particle is not of great importance, since its most important characteristic is its average drag coefficient.

When one particle is much larger than the other, the fluid flow pattern is assumed to be characterized by the flow round the larger, spherical one. Most workers have assumed that the smaller particle does not affect this flow pattern at all. The basic physical problem then becomes that of estimating the trajectory of the smaller particle relative to the larger spherical one when both inertial and fluid forces act on the smaller particle. The larger sphere is moving relative to the fluid under some such force as gravity, for example, so that its path in the fluid sweeps out a tube of cross-section equal to the cross-section of the sphere. If the smaller particle were influenced only by inertia then the two particles would impact if the smaller one were originally within this tube. This is commonly regarded as a collision efficiency of unity. Equally if the smaller particle were influenced only by fluid forces it would be carried out of the swept tube by the flow of the fluid round the larger sphere, giving a collision efficiency of zero. In any given physical circumstance the smaller particle is influenced by both these forces and the collision efficiency is somewhere between unity and zero. The mathematical problem is to evaluate this efficiency of collision quantitatively for all possible initial conditions.

This approach is an essentially simple one and ignores the effect of Brownian movement, any electrical forces due to charge on the particles and any microturbulence in the flow pattern. Furthermore, the theoretical calculation can give only the estimated efficiency of impact or collision; it does not follow that coalescence of the two particles will occur and experiment has shown that particles may, under certain circumstances, bounce apart after collision.

(3) THE MATHEMATICAL PROBLEM

The second step in attempting the mathematical analysis is to express the above simplified physical problem in quantitative analytical terms as differential equations of motion. Further simplifying assumptions are needed at this stage.

(3.1) *Flow Patterns Round the Sphere*

The Navier–Stokes equation for the flow of a viscous fluid are non-linear and cannot be solved rigorously for flow round a single sphere. The flow pattern is characterized by the Reynolds number for the sphere, defined customarily by the product of the sphere diameter and the fluid velocity relative to the sphere, divided by the kinematic viscosity of the fluid. This dimensionless number is a measure of the relative importance of inertial and viscous forces within the fluid. Stokes has shown that for conditions where the inertia is negligible, and where, therefore, the Reynolds number approaches zero, the Navier–Stokes equations can be linearized and solved for flow round a sphere. This analysis is best taken directly from a standard textbook such as Lamb's *Hydrodynamics*, page 597 of the sixth edition.[4] This flow pattern is often termed the viscous flow pattern.

At the other extreme, where the viscous forces are negligible compared with the inertial ones within the fluid, the equations of motion can again be linearized to give a flow pattern commonly called the potential flow pattern. This corresponds to a very large Reynolds number, and is outlined in Lamb's *Hydrodynamics*, page 123.

The evaluation of flow patterns round spheres at finite Reynolds numbers is considerably more difficult. Oseen has produced an approximate set of equations of motion of the fluid which are linear, but which present considerable difficulties in solution. Goldstein[5] has solved Oseen's linearized equations for a sphere at small values of Reynolds number and this solution has been extended by Tomotika and Aoi[6] to give a flow pattern for a Reynolds number of unity. Pearcey and McHugh[7] have extended Goldstein's analysis and have published flow patterns for Reynolds number of 1, 4 and 10. Kawaguti[8] has developed a series solution for a Reynolds number of 20 and a numerical correction to this in a subsequent paper.[9] Lister[10] has evaluated flow patterns for Reynolds numbers of 1, 10 and 20 by relaxation methods, but her results do not give sufficient detail in the cylindrical space defined by the projected section of the sphere in its direction of motion. This work has, however, been extended by Jenson[11] who gives flow patterns round spheres for Reynolds numbers of 5, 10, 20 and 40; these results would be more suitable as a basis for calculations of collision efficiencies. Stewartson,[12] using the Oseen approximation, gives a generalized discussion of the flow round a sphere at higher Reynolds numbers, whilst Proudman and Pearson[13] have given analytical expansions for the flow at finite Reynolds numbers by combining the linearized Stokes analysis near the sphere surface with the Oseen analysis far from the sphere. Kynch[14] studies analytically the flow pattern round two spheres accepting the Stokes linearization and considers more briefly the problems of three and more spheres; his work is directed chiefly to determining the free-falling velocities of the spheres. The results of Pearcey and McHugh, those of Jenson and those of Proudman and Pearson all criticize the results given by Tomotika and Aoi.[6]

Hocking[15] evaluates the drag forces when there are two spheres of comparable size present. His analysis is limited to the Stokes linearization of the Navier–Stokes equations and corresponds therefore to very small Reynolds numbers. His calculations are based on the superposition of two solutions, one when the relative motion of the two spheres is along their lines of centres and one when it is at right angles to this line of centres. Since the solution in the Stokes case is linear the superposition of these two solutions can give the drag forces for any relative motion between the two spheres. However, since this Stokes assumption of no inertial forces is accepted, these solutions are valid for water droplets in air only up to about 60 μ diameter.

The main interest in these different flow patterns is in the down-stream part. Fortunately the calculation of collision efficiency depends very much more on the up-stream flow pattern, which shows considerably less variation from solution to solution.

(3.2) *Viscous Drag on Smaller Particle*

The motion of the smaller particle depends very directly on the fluid forces acting on it. Workers who have attempted to calculate the movement of the smaller particle have almost invariably assumed a Stokes law drag of the fluid on the smaller particle in which the force is directly proportional to the vector of the relative velocity of the particle in the fluid. This assumption is not generally true as regards direction for non-spherical particles however small their Reynolds number. The fact that the drag generally deviates in direction from the relative velocity vector becomes unimportant when an average is taken over all possible orientations of non-spherical particles.

The magnitude of the viscous drag on the particle is taken to be directly proportional to the relative velocity of the particle in the fluid, although many practical measurements, which have been summarized by Goldstein[16] and Davies,[17] show that the actual drag is about 14 per cent greater than that given by the simple Stokes law at a Reynolds number of about unity. Many practical problems involve smaller particles with Reynolds numbers well below unity, for which Stokes law is a valid relationship.

(3.3) *Calculation of Particle Trajectories*

If the fluid forces on the smaller particle are assumed to follow Stokes law, and thus to be linearly proportional to the vector of the relative velocity of the particle in the fluid, the equations of motion of the smaller particle may be written down explicitly in terms of the fluid flow pattern round the larger sphere. After these equations are reduced conventionally to a dimensionless form, the equations of motion are shown to depend on one characteristic dimensionless group called the "particle parameter", P, where

$$P = \rho d^2 U / 9 \eta D$$

where ρ = the density of the particle,

d = the effective spherical diameter of the particle,

U = the fluid velocity relative to the sphere at large distances from the sphere,

η = the absolute viscosity of the fluid and

D = the diameter of the sphere.

The equations of motion of the particle are non-linear since the velocity of the fluid due to the flow pattern round the sphere is itself non-linear. In consequence these equations cannot be solved analytically and all workers in this field have had to develop numerical methods of solution. These have invariably involved the step-by-step solution of individual trajectories of the smaller particle, plotting out its path as it approaches and tends to be swept round the larger sphere.

A trajectory is plotted for the smaller particle when its initial condition at a very large distance from the larger sphere is that it is a distance y, say, from the line through the centre of the sphere and parallel to the relative fluid flow at large distances from the sphere. This particle trajectory either hits or misses the sphere itself. The value of y, y_0 say, which corresponds just to a grazing collision is found by trial and error. Then the collision cross-section or, alternatively, the efficiency of collision, E say, under these physical conditions is said to be y_0^2 / R^2, where R is the radius of the sphere. The main objective of the computation is to evaluate this efficiency, E, for various values of the particle parameter, P.

This definition of efficiency of collision is a direct visualization of the physical conditions when the smaller particle is infinitesimal. If the smaller particle is assumed to have an equivalent spherical radius of a, say, the common assumption is that the particle and the sphere will just collide when the particle trajectory's nearest approach to the sphere surface is a distance a. A full computation gives, therefore, the efficiency of collision as a function of the particle parameter P for a series of values of a/R, the dimensionless equivalent of a.

(4) COMPUTED EFFICIENCIES OF COLLISION

A number of computations have been made of the efficiency of collision under the above conditions. The various results are discussed briefly below and are shown in Figs. 1 and 2. The full lines in Figs. 1 and 2 are the results obtained by Fonda and Herne[18] using the Pilot ACE digital computer at the National Physical Laboratory to evaluate trajectories in viscous and in potential flow patterns round spheres. These results are considered to be the most accurate available within the basic assumptions outlined above. Figure 1 shows the results only for an infinitesimally small particle, although the original work covered the trajectories of particles which approached the sphere at their nearest point by up to 0·1 of the sphere radius. Some further similar work has been carried out for Mason[19] by the National Physical Laboratory for trajectories in the viscous flow pattern having values of P of 0·2, 0·4, 0·6, 0·8, 0·9 and 1·0.

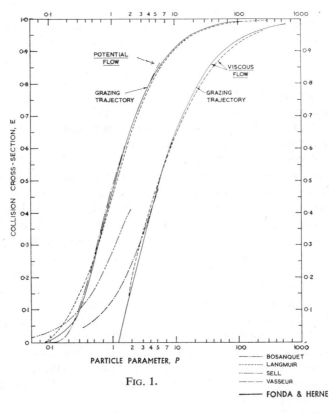

FIG. 1.

BOSANQUET
LANGMUIR
SELL
VASSEUR

FONDA & HERNE

(4.1) *Sell*

Sell[20] gives a long paper on filtration and in his figure 19 he gives the curve for the collision of particles with a sphere. This curve is reproduced in Fig. 1. Sell's paper does not give sufficient details of the calculation to enable any check to be made on its accuracy. By comparison with the more accurate potential flow curves it is obviously only of historical interest.

(4.2) *Langmuir and Blodgett*

The collection of water and ice particles by aircraft was of interest in the last war and Langmuir and Blodgett[21] have evaluated the efficiency of such collision by spheres in potential flow. Their results are given in Fig. 1, where it is clear that they agree closely with the more recent and accurate calculations except at the lower values of the particle parameter, P. The calculations were made on a differential analyser, but Langmuir seems later to have fitted an analytical expression to his numerical results and this may possibly have led to inaccuracies in this region. The original report does not give sufficiently full details to check this.

Later Langmuir[22] evaluated a similar efficiency for viscous flow round the sphere and this also is given in Fig. 1. This result, too, is similar to the more accurate calculation, but again Langmuir seems to have chosen for no apparent real purpose to fit an analytical expression to his calculated points. This work also was carried out on a differential analyser. His estimate of the critical value for the particle parameter, P, of 1·214 is very close to the more accurate value lying between 1·212 and 1·213, determined by Fonda and Herne.

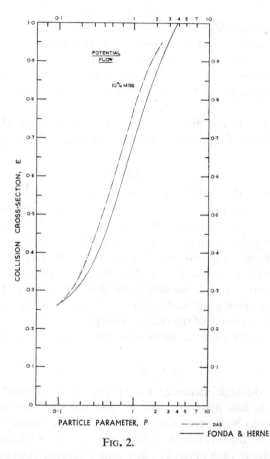

FIG. 2.

Langmuir uses this viscous flow calculation in conjunction with his earlier potential flow calculation to make an inspired guess of the efficiencies of collision against the particle parameter, P, for various values of Reynolds number; these guessed values are given in his figure 1 of the 1948 paper. His equation 23 on which these guesses are based may well have an element of truth in it, but it is quite impossible to justify it rigorously.

(4.3) Vasseur

An aerodynamic calculation by Vasseur[23] seems to have been made without any appreciation of previous work. Vasseur calculated the trajectory of four different sizes of particles from 12 to 40 μ in diameter impinging on a sphere of 20 cm diameter in an air stream of 90 m/s. The sphere diameter is given as 20 cm in his text and as 40 cm in his summary; it is not possible to check this since he does not seem to appreciate the importance of the particle parameter, P. His results are given graphically in Fig. 1, assuming that the sphere diameter was 20 cm. Since his work does not seem to have been aware of previous similar work his results are probably of small relative importance.

(4.4) *Bosanquet*

Stairmand[24] has considered this collision problem in connection with filtration and in an Appendix to this paper Bosanquet has given his own calculations of the "Target Efficiency" of spheres for various different values of a somewhat different form of the particle parameter. Only three of these values have been calculated and the others have been obtained by what is termed interpolation; no details are given of this process.

Bosanquet's results are given in Fig. 1 and these agree closely with the more detailed calculations of Fonda and Herne at low values of the particle parameter, P.

(4.5) *Das*

Das[25] has viewed this collision problem from the meterological viewpoint and has evaluated a few trajectories for the potential flow pattern, considering only those trajectories whose nearest approach to the sphere is 0·1, 0·2 and 0·3 of the sphere radius. Since he gives no details for grazing trajectories, his values for trajectories approaching the sphere to within 0·1 of its radius are given in Fig. 2 together with similar results of Fonda and Herne. Das has not evaluated results for a particle parameter, P, greater than 2. No details are given of his method of computing trajectories; the result given graphically, such as his figure 4, for example, do not inspire confidence in the accuracy of the results. This paper by Das is, however, the only one which attempts to determine trajectories so far from the sphere.

(4.6) *Pearcey and Hill*

Pearcey and McHugh[7] extended the analysis by Goldstein[5] and gave analytical expressions for the flow patterns round the sphere at Reynolds numbers of 1, 4 and 10. This work seems to have been extended to a Reynolds number of 40 by Pearcey and Hill,[26] who use all these results to calculate the collision efficiency between particles of comparable size to each other. The flow pattern around the two particles is obtained by superposing the two separate flow patterns due to each individual particle with the other absent. This is obviously not satisfactory when the two particles approach each other closely and is criticized by Hocking.[27]

It is difficult to compare these results with those of other workers since they are given in a somewhat different form from the usual. It is possible to compute the particle parameter, P, for any point on the curves of their figures 1 or 7 if the densities of air and water are taken to be approximately 1·2. 10^{-3} and 1 g/ml. Their figure 7 is easier to read and was preferred in constructing the following Table which gives the efficiency of collision calculated from the results of Fonda and Herne for a range of values given by Pearcey and Hill. In this Table d_2/d_1 is the ratio of the diameters of the two particles.

TABLE 1

Collision efficiency					Particle parameter, P	Diameter ratio, d_2/d_1
Viscous flow (Fonda and Herne)	Reynolds number (Pearcey and Hill)			Potential flow (Fonda and Herne)		
	1	4	40			
0·06		0 (7)		0·65	1·35	0·060
0·11	0 (7)				1·30	0·119
			0·0001	0·49	1·00	0·016
0·04		0·0001 (1)		0·62	1·20	0·058
0·08	0·0001 (1)				1·21	0·114
			0·01	0·59	1·34	0·019
0·14		0·01 (1)		0·76	1·69	0·067
0·17	0·01 (1)				1·59	0·130
			0·04	0·68	1·84	0·022
0·26		0·04 (7)		0·84	2·30	0·079
0·28	0·04 (7)				2·18	0·154
			0·09	0·77	2·62	0·027
0·42		0·09 (1)		0·97	3·44	0·096
0·41	0·09 (1)				2·78	0·172
			0·16	0·85	3·72	0·032
0·54		0·16 (7)		1·05	4·67	0·112
0·66	0·16 (7)				4·15	0·212
			0·25	0·92	5·34	0·038
0·70		0·25 (1)		1·16	6·88	0·136
			0·36	0·98	7·86	0·046
0·86		0·36 (7)		1·21	8·56	0·152
			0·49	1·04	11·44	0·056
0·96		0·49 (1)		1·33	13·35	0·189
			0·64	1·08	16·61	0·067
1·17		0·64 (7)		1·43	17·79	0·219
			0·81	1·13	25·49	0·083
			1·00	1·20	42·36	0·107

(1) From Fig. 1 of Pearcey and Hill[26].
(7) From Fig. 7 of Pearcey and Hill[26].

In addition to the above tabular discrepancies Hocking[27] finds a large discrepancy between these results of Pearcey and Hill and his own.

(4.7) *Hocking*

Hocking[15] has evaluated the drag forces on two spheres of comparable size for the Stokes approximation to the Navier–Stokes equations for the fluid flow round the spheres. Using these results Hocking[27] has evaluated the collision efficiency for small particles of about 38 to 60 μ diameter to which this Stokes linearization is applicable. Since the accuracy of the flow pattern computations decreases when the ratio of the diameters of the two particles is less than about 0·2 his results, shown graphically in his figure 1, are not given for values of diameter ratio less than 0·2. It is not reasonable, therefore, to compare these results with those of Fonda and Herne. One striking feature of Hocking's results is that collision does not take place if the diameter of the larger particle is less than 36 μ.

(5) CONCLUSIONS

The various solutions of the classical problem of collision between two fluid-borne particles show a reasonable comparison between one another, as evidenced in Figs. 1 and 2. Such calculations are primarily limited by the restricted knowledge of the flow pattern round spheres. The two extreme values of potential flow and viscous flow have most commonly been used to evaluate collision efficiencies, and the work of Fonda and Herne[18] is considered to be the most detailed and accurate of this type of calculation.

The more recent work has been concerned with evaluating detailed flow patterns at finite Reynolds numbers and for flow round more than one sphere. In order to evaluate such flow patterns and to use them for calculating trajectories and efficiencies is a lengthy arithmetical process which is feasible only with the aid of digital computers. However, when digitial computers are available there seems to be little purpose in evaluating the more simplified general treatment since any specific problem which is of interest may be tackled thoroughly and in detail. The results of Fonda and Herne should therefore be used only for first rough calculations as a preliminary to a detailed study of a particular problem. There does not seem to be any need to take this generalized but simplified treatment further.

(6) ACKNOWLEDGEMENTS

This paper is published with the permission of the Director-General of Research of the National Coal Board.

(7) REFERENCES

1. BEST, A. C., *Quart. J.R. Met. Soc.*, **76**, 302 (1950).
2. HABERMAN, W. L. and MORTON, R. K., *U.S. Navy, D.T.M.B. Report*, 802 (1953)
3. SAFFMAN, P. G., *J. Fluid Mechanics*, **1**, 249 (1956).
4. LAMB, H., *Hydrodynamics*, 6th ed. (Cambridge) (1932).
5. GOLDSTEIN, S., *Proc. Roy. Soc.*, **A123**, 225 (1929).
6. TOMOTIKA, S. and AOI, T., *Quart. J. Mech*, **3**, 140 (1950).
7. PEARCEY, I. and MCHUGH, B., *Phil. Mag.* (7th Series), **46**, 783 (1955).
8. KAWAGUTI, M., *Rep. Inst. Sci., Tokyo*, **2**, 66 (1948).
9. KAWAGUTI, M., *Rep. Inst. Sci., Tokyo*, **4**, 154 (1950).
10. LISTER, M., Ph.D. thesis (London) (1953).
11. JENSON, V. G., *Proc. Roy. Soc.* **A249**, 346 (1959).
12. STEWARTSON, K., *Phil. Mag.* (8th Series), **1**, 345 (1956).
13. PROUDMAN, L. and PEARSON, J. R. A., *J. Fluid Mech.* **2**, 237 (1957).
14. KYNCH, G. J., *J. Fluid Mech.*, **5**, 193 (1959).
15. HOCKING, L. M., Ph.D. thesis (London) (1958).
16. GOLDSTEIN, S., *Modern Developments in Fluid Dynamics* (Oxford) (1938).
17. DAVIES, C. N., *Proc. Phys. Soc. Lond.*, **57**, 259 (1945).
18. FONDA, A. and HERNE, H., Paper in preparation.
19. MASON, B. J., *Physics of Clouds* (Oxford) (1957).
20. SELL, W., *Forsch. Ver. dtsch. Ing.*, **347** (1931).
21. LANGMUIR, I. and BLODGETT, K. B., Army Air Forces Technical Report 5418 (1946).
22. LANGMUIR, I., *J. Met.*, **5**, 175 (1948).
23. VASSEUR, M., *Rech. Aéro.*, **9**, 1 (1949).
24. STAIRMAND, C. J., *Trans. Inst. Chem. Engrs. Lond.*, **28**, 130 (1950).
25. DAS, P. K., *Indian J. Met. Geophys.*, **1**, 137 (1950).
26. PEARCEY, I. and HILL, G. W. *Quart. J.R. Met. Soc.*, **83**, 77 (1957).
27. HOCKING, L. M., *Quart. J.R. Met. Soc.*, **85**, 44 (1959).

PARTICLE TRAJECTORIES, COLLISION AND ATTACHMENT IN FROTH FLOTATION

by D. J. Brown
Scientific Department, National Coal Board

Summary—The trajectories of galena, pyrite and coal particles relative to air bubbles are described and theory is shown to predict a smaller deviation for coal particles than actually occurs.

The ease of attachment of particle to bubble is shown to decrease with increase of distance of point of impact from the vertical axis of the bubble. As this distance increases, so do contact time and relative velocity.

The dependence of stable attachment on the relative values of work of adhesion and kinetic energy is discussed, with reference to particle–bubble and also collision of two water drops.

(1) INTRODUCTION

THE froth flotation process consists, essentially, of agitating a suspension of fine solids, together with reagents, in water, blowing air bubbles through the suspension and collecting the particle-laden bubbles as a froth. A simplified system has been used in a study of the second stage—contact and attachment of mineral particles to air bubbles.

A general description of apparatus, methods and results has been given previously.[1]

By the use of a technique involving a Kodak high-speed camera and an arrangement of mirrors, particles and bubbles were photographed from two directions at right-angles to each other, two images being obtained on the same film so that the relative positions of particles and bubbles could be calculated at any time.

Particle trajectories are considered first and discussion of collision and attachment then follows.

The majority of air bubbles used in the experiments had a major axis of 1·4 mm, a minor axis of 1·2 mm and a velocity of approximately 25 cm/sec (the bubble Reynolds number was about 300). The bubbles were produced at a rate of 30 per second. Data

TABLE 1. PHYSICAL PROPERTIES OF COAL, PYRITE AND GALENA PARTICLES

	Gresford coal	Betteshanger coal	Pyrite	Galena
Specific gravity, g/ml	1·29	1·33	5·03	7·60
Weight, g	$8·61 \times 10^{-6}$	$6·89 \times 10^{-6}$	$3·44 \times 10^{-5}$	$5·76 \times 10^{-5}$
Volume, ml	$6·70 \times 10^{-6}$	$5·20 \times 10^{-6}$	$6·84 \times 10^{-6}$	$7·58 \times 10^{-6}$
Length, cm $\times 10^{-2}$	4·0	3·2	3·9	3·2
Breadth, cm $\times 10^{-2}$	2·6	2·3	2·8	2·3
Area, length $\times$ breadth, cm$^2 \times 10^{-4}$	10·4	7·36	10·92	7·36
Thickness, cm $\times 10^{-2}$	1·7	1·7	1·5	1·6
Contact angle, degrees	45 unoiled 72 oiled	56	68	66
Single particle velocity, measured, cm/sec	0·64	0·70	5·2	8·0

35

obtained for bubbles with major axes other than 1·4 mm were so corrected that
horizontal distances from the minor axes were referred to a major axis of 1·4 mm.

Oiled and unoiled coal and xanthate-coated pyrite and galena particles were used
and their physical properties are tabulated. For the purpose of calculation, the mean
particle diameter was taken to be 0·31 mm, 0·22 of the bubble diameter on the
major axis. The major diameter is of importance as it determines the area swept out
by the rising bubble.

(2) TRAJECTORIES

The particles did not fall vertically in water, their paths being affected by the flow
of water round the bubbles. Particle and bubble movement was measured and trajectories were drawn for coal, pyrite and galena. Some of these are shown in Fig. 1. The

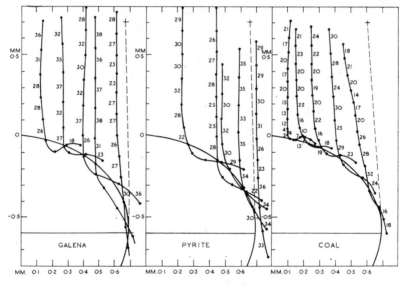

Fig. 1. Particle trajectories.

points show the position of the near edge of the particle at intervals of half a milli-
second. Numbers on the trajectories are the total relative velocities of particle and
bubble in cm/sec. The data for coal are most interesting, in particular the reduction
in velocity for a near top-dead-centre collision and the increase in velocity at the bubble
edge. Values for relative velocity at impact are shown later in Fig. 4.

It is possible to calculate without undue difficulty the deviation of particle path corresponding to the particle just grazing the bubble and then compare it with some of the
experimental trajectories. This has been done in Fig. 1 where the theoretical deviation
assuming potential rather than viscous flow is shown as a dotted line. A straight line
has been drawn between starting and finishing points but the detailed theoretical
trajectory is not, of course, a straight line.

Theory and practice appear to agree reasonably well for galena and pyrite but in the
case of coal, theory under-estimates the deviation which actually occurs.

In the theoretical analysis a number of assumptions were made. These were that
the particle was sufficiently small not to affect the flow pattern of the stream, the

particle Reynolds number was so low that the drag of the fluid on it was given by Stokes' law, the apparent weight of the particle was negligible compared with the viscous force and the motion of the particle proceeded in a single plane. Under such conditions the quantity P is the basic parameter of the problem, where $P = \dfrac{1}{9}\left(\dfrac{a}{R}\right)^2 \dfrac{\rho_1}{\rho_2}$.

N_{Re} and is a measure of the ratio of inertial to viscous effects.

Here, ρ_1 and ρ_2=densities of particle and fluid ($\rho_2 = 1$).

$\qquad a/R$ =ratio of particle to bubble radius=0·22.

$\qquad N_{Re}$ =bubble Reynolds number=307.

The P values for galena, pyrite and coal were 12·5, 8·3 and 2·1 and the values of capture cross-section, $Y_0{}^2$, were obtained from the data of Herne.[2] The values of Y_0 for galena, pyrite and coal were 1·18, 1·16 and 1·07. Here, Y_0 is the initial horizontal displacement from the bubble axis of the centre of the particle which later just grazes the bubble. The value of Y_0 is given in terms of the bubble radius and is for a point sufficiently distant for the particle to be initially unaffected by the bubble.

For the problem involving particle and bubble, one should take into account gravitational forces on the particle and, in addition, deviation from Stokes' law needs to be considered. The equations of motion and method of solution have been described by Herne, but full calculations have not yet been made.

(3) COLLISION

From the trajectories, it was possible to estimate the contact time during which particle and bubble were in apparent contact. Contact time values are shown in Fig. 2 as a function of the horizontal distance of the particle edge from the bubble vertical axis.

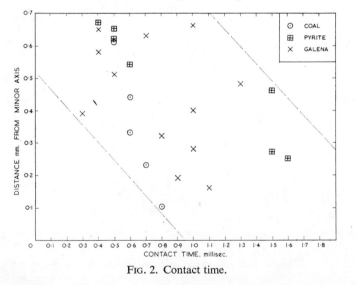

FIG. 2. Contact time.

The variation of contact time with position is slight but definite. W. Philippoff[3] has proposed a method of calculation of contact time in which the mineral particle is pictured as a cylinder of diameter D, which strikes the surface of the bubble. The liquid–air interface acts as an elastic body or spring, the elasticity being caused by the surface tension, and the contact time equation simplifies to $T = 4 \cdot 67(m)^{\frac{1}{2}}/\phi$, where m is the particle mass and ϕ a function containing particle diameter and the Laplace constant. If the contact time is determined by the resolved component of the mass normal to the bubble surface then T should vary with the square root of the cosine of θ, the angle to the normal of the trajectory at impact. The maximum measured variation

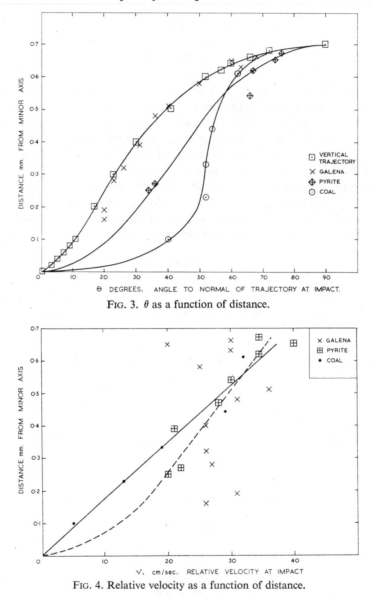

FIG. 3. θ as a function of distance.

FIG. 4. Relative velocity as a function of distance.

of θ is between 0 and 76°, corresponding to $(\cos \theta)^{\frac{1}{2}}$ values of 1 and 0·49. This would give contact times at the bubble centre twice those near the bubble edge. The variation of time with position in Fig. 2 is not therefore surprising, although it must be added that the situation is complicated by the fact that all the particles observed had not exactly the same mass.

The detailed values of θ, the angle to the normal, as a function of position are shown in Fig. 3. As would be expected the highest values are those for coal, followed by pyrite and then galena. Values of relative velocity of particle and bubble at impact are given in Fig. 4. Coal and pyrite show an increase of velocity with displacement of the particle edge from the bubble axis but galena shows no such trend.

(4) ATTACHMENT

By observation and judicious use of all the measured trajectories, the points of contact of the particles on the bubble surface were deduced from the particle positions at a distance 0·5 mm from the bubble top. The fact of attachment or non-attachment of particle to bubble was noted and efficiency of attachment correlated with position of contact. The semi-major axis of the bubble was divided up into seven portions of 0·1 mm and contacts falling in each portion were allocated to the mid-point. The data shown in Fig. 5, therefore, are for the efficiency of attachment corresponding to

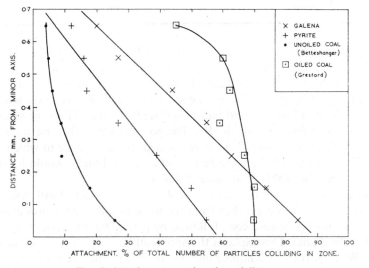

FIG. 5. Attachment as a function of distance.

distances 0·05, 0·15, ... , 0·65 mm from the minor axis of the bubble. In each case, efficiency of attachment falls off with increase in the distance from the axis. The efficiency of attachment is highest for galena and oiled coal and lowest for pyrite and unoiled coal. The data for galena, pyrite and unoiled coal would appear at first sight to show clearly the effect of the difference in specific gravity of the particles but a plot of percentage attachment against $\sin \theta$ (or $\cos \theta$) brings the galena and pyrite results close together, as shown in Fig. 6. Differences in the hydrophobic quality of the various types of particle, as measured by contact angle, complicate the interpretation.

When the particle becomes attached to a bubble under water there is a decrease of free energy, the energy change being in the direction favouring spontaneous adhesion. The free energy decrease is given by the work of adhesion, the product of the air–water interfacial tension, the solid–air interfacial area, and one minus the cosine of the contact angle. Values of work of adhesion and kinetic energy are shown in Table 2. Particle weight, side area and contact angle data were taken from Table 1, the interfacial tension used being 70 ergs/cm².

TABLE 2. WORK OF ADHESION AND KINETIC ENERGY

	Weight, g	Relative velocity, cm/sec	Work of adhesion, ergs	Kinetic energy, ergs
Galena	$5\cdot8 \times 10^{-5}$	33	$3\cdot0 \times 10^{-2}$	$3\cdot2 \times 10^{-2}$
Pyrite	$3\cdot4 \times 10^{-5}$	30	$4\cdot8 \times 10^{-2}$	$1\cdot5 \times 10^{-2}$
Coal		26		
Betteshanger	$6\cdot9 \times 10^{-6}$		$2\cdot3 \times 10^{-2}$	$2\cdot3 \times 10^{-2}$
unoiled Gresford	$8\cdot6 \times 10^{-6}$		$2\cdot1 \times 10^{-2}$	$2\cdot9 \times 10^{-2}$
oiled Gresford			$5\cdot0 \times 10^{-2}$	$2\cdot9 \times 10^{-2}$

The collision process must be divided arbitrarily into two stages. During the first the plane particle approaches the "spherical" bubble and kinetic energy is used in thinning the water film between them. During the second stage, the bubble surface is deformed, again by the available kinetic energy. Once deformation has occurred, the relative velocity of particle and bubble surface is small and thus the kinetic energy available for film thinning is small also. The point at which the first stage ends and the second begins is unknown. If it corresponded to the distance to which a layer of "entrained" water extends from the surface of an air bubble[4] it would be 18 microns from the surface of a bubble of diameter 1·4 mm.

If the water layer between particle and bubble has been thinned sufficiently, and this depends on the kinetic energy, then from the work of adhesion figures attachment is most likely for oiled Gresford coal, followed by pyrite, galena, Betteshanger coal and unoiled Gresford coal. This explains the apparently anomalous results for oiled coal in Fig. 5. When particle and bubble impinge on one another, kinetic energy is transformed into elastic vibrations of the bubble, viscous effects in the region of contact and rotation of the particle. If the kinetic energy on impact is high, then the kinetic energy on recoil may be sufficient to overcome the adhesion forces even if contact has already occurred. From Table 2, if contact has been made over the full area of one side of the particle then disruption is possible if there is little loss of kinetic energy, for galena, Betteshanger coal and unoiled Gresford coal since the kinetic energy term is equal to or exceeds the work of adhesion. Loss of kinetic energy is to be expected, however, and disruption is not very probable. If adhesion has not occurred over the full area, however, then there is a greater possibility of disruption. Attachment and disruption of water drops in air is considered in Appendix 1.

For contact to occur along the length of a particle the water film must recede in a time of about 1 msec. For a mean particle diameter of 0·31 mm, this means recedence velocities of 15 and 30 cm/sec for the cases of radial thinning and thinning from one end, respectively. These velocities are comparable with those found for the spreading of liquids on water to form surface films. Evans has measured the thickness of the water film between a static bubble and a rotating hydrophobic surface at which spontaneous rupture of film and attachment occurred.[5] This thickness was found to be 0.1–$0.2\ \mu$ for internal bubble pressures 500–1500 ergs/cm², in agreement with the data of Russian workers.[6] One would expect it to be largest for the most hydrophobic surfaces.

The efficiency of particle–bubble attachment depends on whether or not water is expelled fast enough from the film during the time of 1 msec to reduce the film thickness to $0.2\ \mu$ approximately.

Philippoff[3] has applied Stefan's equation to this problem, assuming the model of two circular planes moving towards each other. His relationship is

$$\delta = \frac{D^2}{8}\left(\frac{3\pi\eta}{\epsilon v m}\right)^{\frac{1}{2}}$$

where δ=the final film thickness,

D=particle diameter, η=liquid viscosity,

ϵ=coefficient of restitution,

v=relative velocity of particle and bubble,

m=particle mass.

Taking $v=33$ cm/sec, $m=5.8\times10^{-5}g$, $\epsilon=1$,

$D=330\ \mu$ ($\frac{1}{2}$(length+breadth)), then

$\delta=9.5\ \mu$.

This value is much higher than that required for spontaneous rupture of the film. Obviously the model is unsatisfactory. In actual fact, the width of the film separating the interfaces must be larger at the periphery than at the centre during a considerable portion of the drainage period. This leads to a greatly increased rate of drainage and a value of δ sufficiently small for attachment.

The tangential velocity of the particle, relative to the bubble, introduces a further complication since it is no longer the same water film which is being thinned but an ever-changing one. The same amount of work done on the film produces less and less thinning as the tangential velocity increases. This has been demonstrated by Evans.[5] By experiments in which an air bubble pressed against a rotating silica disk in water, he showed that the thickness of the water film between bubble and disk increased as the velocity of rotation of the disk increased.

No attempt has been made in the preceding treatment to define rigorously the water flow around the bubble during collision. The water may pass through the space between particle and bubble or alternatively flow round the particle causing rotation which may influence the thinning of the film. No model has been proposed for the final stage of the thinning process, that at which the bubble surface at the point of contact behaves as a spring struck by the particle and first recedes and then advances. Although the depression of the bubble surface may be measured, it has not been possible to define the relative velocity of particle and bubble surface throughout the time of contact. It is this relative velocity which determines the amount of kinetic energy available for thinning the water film.

(5) CONCLUSIONS

The collision with and attachment to an air bubble in water of coal, pyrite and galena particles has been studied for particles of diameter approximately 0.3 mm and bubbles of diameter approximately 1.4 mm. The measured horizontal deviation

D

of the particle path has been compared with that calculated assuming potential flow. Theory and practice appear to agree reasonably well for galena and pyrite but in the case of coal, theory underestimates the deviation which actually occurs. It is probable that a theoretical treatment proposed by Herne,[2] which allows for gravitational forces on the particle and deviations from Stokes law, will give better agreement.

The efficiency of attachment has been shown to decrease as the point of collision becomes more distant from the vertical axis. It does not depend in any simple manner on the relative velocity. There is evidence for a reduction of contact time with distance of point of impact from the vertical axis but not enough data is available for this to be linked directly with efficiency of attachment.

The model of two circular planes moving towards each other has been shown to be inadequate to describe the process by which the water layer between particle and

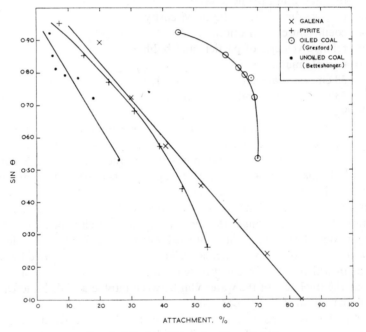

Fig. 6. Attachment as a function of sin θ.

bubble is thinned during collision. It gives a value of the equilibrium distance too high for spontaneous attachment to occur. A new model and theoretical treatment are required. Finally, the importance of the relative magnitudes of work of adhesion and kinetic energy has been illustrated. For the particle–bubble collision studied, kinetic energy values were in general too small for general disruption of adhesion once it had occurred. For the case of two water drops in air, however, the kinetic energy was sufficient to disrupt adhesion already made over quite a large area.

(6) ACKNOWLEDGEMENT

The author wishes to thank the Director-General of Research of the National Coal Board, Dr. Idris Jones, for permission to publish this paper. The views expressed are those of the author and not necessarily those of the Board.

REFERENCES

1. WHELAN, P. F. and BROWN, D. J., *Trans. Inst. Min. Metall.*, **65**, 181–92 (1955–6).
2. HERNE. H., Paper 2 at this Symposium.
3. PHILIPPOFF, W., *Trans. Amer. Inst. Min. (Metall.) Engrs*, **193**, 386 (1952).
4. MIYAGI, O., *et al.*, *Kolloidzschr.*, **81**, 180 (1937).
5. EVANS, L. F., *Industr. Engng Chem.*, **46**, 2420 (1954).
6. DERYAGIN, B. and KUSSAKOV, M., *Acta. Phys.-chim. U.R.S.S.*, **10**, 25 (1939).

APPENDIX

THE UPPER STABILITY LIMIT OF (WATER) DROPS UPON IMPACT

(Based on data of Gorbachev, S. V. and Nikiforova, V. M., Kolloidzschr., 73, 14 (1935))

When a moving water drop (1–1·5 mm diameter) collides with another of the same size at rest, the two may coalesce or recoil with no apparent change depending on:

(1) The angle a between the line joining the centres at the moment of impact and the direction of the moving drop;

(2) The velocity of the moving drop, v.

Coalescence occurs until v exceeds a certain value.

As with particle–bubble collision, the normal component of the velocity is important, a fact not fully recognized in the original paper. Table 3 shows values of v, a and $v \cos a$.

TABLE 3.   NORMAL VELOCITIES ON IMPACT

Experiment	v cm/sec	a degrees	$\cos a$	$v \cos a$
(a) 1	18	13	0·97	17
2	34	21	0·93	32
3	37	26	0·90	33
4	42	37	0·80	34
5	47	48	0·67	31
6	59	53	0·60	35
7	69	62	0·47	32
8	78	79	0·19	15
(b) 1	14	16	0·96	13
2	24	21	0·93	22
3	28	26	0·90	25·
4	37	33	0·84	31
5	49	37	0·80	39
6	56	43	0·73	41
7	63	49	0·66	42
8	76	62	0·47	35
9	90	79	0·19	17

The value of $v \cos a$ at which disruption occurs is reasonably constant. Taking a water drop velocity of 35 cm/sec and a mass of $2·6 \times 10^{-4}$ g (diameter 0·1 cm) the corresponding kinetic energy is 0·32 ergs. Disruption occurs when this is slightly greater than the adhesion forces holding the two water drops together. Provided that the circle of contact has a diameter not greater than 0·035 cm (drop diameter 0·1 cm) then disruption would be expected to occur. The air–water interfacial tension has been taken here as 70 ergs/cm^2.

ELECTRIC CHARGE EFFECTS
IN AEROSOL PARTICLE COLLISION PHENOMENA

By T. Gillespie

Physical Research Laboratory, The Dow Chemical Company,
Midland, Michigan, U.S.A.

INTRODUCTION

The particles of an aerosol may collide with each other, with the particles of another aerosol, or with some fixed surface such as the walls of a smoke chamber, the foliage of a plant, or the fibres of a filter. One might expect electric charges on the particles to have two effects on such collisions. First, they may reduce or increase the number of collisions and, second, they may affect the adhesion of the particles on collision.

In order to assess the role of electric forces, it is necessary to determine the electric charge on the particles and on the surface with which they collide. Attempts to do this have indicated differences between aerosols and hydrosols which make aerosols much more difficult to study quantitatively. The electric charge on the particles of a given hydrosol may vary with the size of the particles but they are all negative or all positive and the particles of a given size have approximately the same electric charge. In an aerosol there are positive particles, negative particles and neutral particles. The particles of a given size may carry a wide range of electric charges. In addition, the electric charge distribution of an aerosol is often time-dependent. It is not surprising, therefore, that much less work has been done on aerosols than on hydrosols which are easier to characterize. Enough work has been done, however, to indicate that the presence of electric charges on aerosol particles can increase the rate of coagulation, can increase the efficiency of filtration by fibrous filters and can ensure the adhesion of particles to surfaces on impact. This article is an attempt to briefly review the presently available information.

MEASUREMENT OF THE ELECTRIC CHARGE DISTRIBUTION OF AN AEROSOL

To measure the electric charge on an aerosol particle, one determines the mobility of the particle in a uniform electric field and then calculates the charge by assuming that the frictional forces are given by Stokes law. Because aerosols are unstable and the electric charge distribution changes with time, it is necessary to measure it with some instrument which assesses a large number of particles in a short time. The instrument developed by Gillespie and Langstroth[1] is suitable for many aerosols.

The instrument is illustrated in Fig. 1. A thin ribbon of the aerosol is drawn up between two vertical and parallel electrodes to which a high d.c. potential difference is applied. The particles are collected in thin strips on glass slides placed on the inside surface of the electrodes. From a knowledge of the position of a particle on the slide, the particle size and the velocity profile of the air through the instrument, the particle charge may be calculated. Neutral particles are caught in a thermal precipitator which is in series with the instrument.

In Fig. 2 some typical results obtained by Gillespie and Langstroth are illustrated. They represent the overall electric charge distribution and do not indicate the fact that there is a different distribution for particles of different size in the aerosol. Even without this additional complication the charge distribution is seen to be very complex and time-dependent.

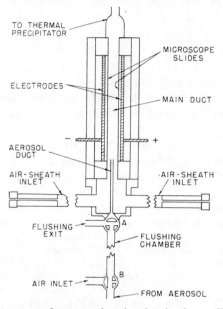

FIG. 1. Diagram of an instrument for measuring the electric charge distribution of an aerosol. (Gillespie and Langstroth.)

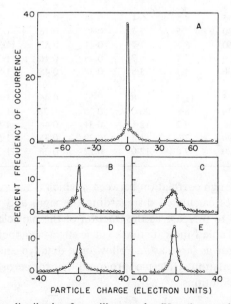

FIG. 2. The electric charge distribution for a silica powder (Vycor) aerosol at 6 min (A), 28 min (B), 60 min (C), 115 min (D), and 200 min (E) after generation. (Gillespie and Langstroth.)

EFFECT OF ELECTRIC CHARGE DISTRIBUTION ON AEROSOL AGING

Gillespie[2] has shown that electric charges play a part in aerosol aging. The magnitude of the electric effects depends upon the average electric charge per particle calculated disregarding the sign, and the fraction of the particles which are charged.

The decrease in the number of particles per unit volume of an aerosol denoted by the symbol n is given at time t by

$$-\frac{dn}{dt} = kn^2 + \beta n \tag{1}$$

where k is a coagulation rate constant and β is a rate constant descriptive of surface loss. Both k and β depend upon the electric charge distribution.

Figure 3 illustrates data obtained by Gillespie for the aging of a Vycor dust in a smoke chamber.

A rigorous correlation of data such as those illustrated in Fig. 3 and the corresponding electric charge distributions is in principle possible, but has never been attempted because of the enormous amount of work involved. Referring to Table 1,

TABLE 1. SOME TYPICAL AGING AND ELECTRIC CHARGE DISTRIBUTION DATA

Aerosol	Time (min)	$\bar{q}$ (Electron units)		Fraction charged		$\frac{\overline{1}}{a} \times 10^{-4}$ cm^{-1}	$k \times 10^8$ (cm³/min)	$\beta \times 10$ min^{-1}
		Pos.	Neg.	Pos.	Neg.			
Ammonium chloride	170	4·4	4·8	0·27	0·46	1·8	5·0	3·0
Magnesium oxide	5	8·3	7·2	0·47	0·48	1·7	19·3	4·7
	60	5·9	5·7	0·44	0·43	1·8	7·8	4·9
Vycor (10 lb/in² air blast)	5	8·5	6·1	0·34	0·29	1·2	13	5·1
	30	7·5	7·7	0·39	0·46	1·2	25	4·0
	60	6·3	7·7	0·41	0·52	1·3	20	4·0
	120	7·1	6·7	0·45	0·46	1·3	14	3·9
	180	4·7	3·8	0·38	0·48	1·8	9	3·9
Vycor (25 lb/in² air blast)	5	11·7	11·8	0·33	0·46	1·6	37	22
	30	8·8	20·0	0·38	0·26	1·6	30	7·7
	60	9·2	12·1	0·31	0·44	1·5	14	5·8
	90	7·6	11·8	0·29	0·35	1·5	10	5·4
	120	9·8	12·0	0·22	0·26	1·5	9	5·2

there appears to be a rough correlation between $\bar{q}$ which is the average electric charge of the charged particles calculated disregarding the sign, and the coagulation rate constant. k also seems to increase as the fraction of the particles which are charged increases. The data in Table 1 indicate that electric effects can increase the coagulation rate constant by a factor as large as 7. Following a detailed analysis of the effect of electric charge on coagulation, Gillespie[2] proposed that for aerosols having symmetrical electric charge distributions

$$k = K_0\left[1 - \frac{f_q^2}{2}\right] + Af_q^2\bar{q}^2\left(\frac{\overline{1}}{a}\right) \tag{2}$$

where K_0 is the coagulation rate constant that would be measured in the absence of electric effects, f_q is the fraction of the particles which are charged, a is the particle radius. A is a complex function of $\bar{q}$, but for the aerosols which have been studied experimentally A is essentially constant and equal to 2×10^{-13} cm³/min/(electron units)²/cm. Figure 4 is a plot of the data in Table 1 as suggested by Equation 2.

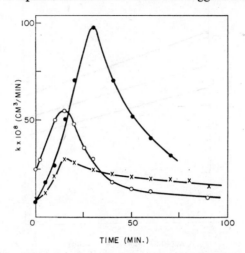

FIG. 3. Variation of the coagulation constant of a Vycor aerosol with time. X, O and ^{0} refer to aerosols produced by air blasts with pressures of 10, 25 and 50 lb/in.² respectively. (Gillespie.)

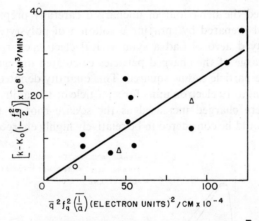

FIG. 4. Illustration of the proportionality between $k-K_0\left(1 - \dfrac{f_q^2}{2}\right)$ and $q^2 f_q^2\left(\dfrac{1}{a}\right)$. $\bullet$, $\triangle$ and O refer to results obtained with Vycor, magnesium oxide and ammonium chloride aerosols. (Gillespie.)

THE ROLE OF ELECTRIC CHARGE DISTRIBUTION IN FILTRATION

The work of Goyer, Gruen and LaMer[3] and of Gillespie[4] has shown that the electric charge on an aerosol particle affects its chances of being caught in a fibre filter. In addition to increasing the efficiency of filtration, one might expect that particle charge would affect the penetration versus particle size curve. This has been confirmed by Gillespie.[4]

Goyer, Gruen and LaMer used carefully prepared homogeneous aerosols in their experiments. These aerosols do not carry electric charges when first prepared. Goyer *et al.* artificially charged the particles to the same extent and measured their penetration through fibre filters. Typical results are illustrated in Fig. 5.

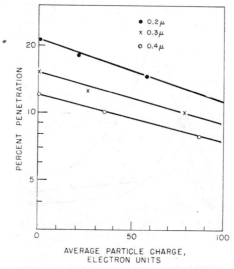

FIG. 5. The effect of electric charge on the penetration of homogeneous aerosols through a paper filter. The figures refer to the radii of the particles. (Goyer, Gruen and LaMer.)

Gillespie[4] assessed the behaviour of uncharged carefully prepared aerosols and a polystyrene aerosol prepared by spraying a solution of polystyrene in carbon tetrachloride. The sprayed aerosol had a symmetrical electric charge distribution. The average electric charge of the charged particles calculated disregarding the sign was proportional to the particle radius squared. This quantity denoted by $\bar{q}$ as above was approximately equal to 19 electron units for a particle of $1\,\mu$ radius. The fraction of the particles which were charged increased as the square root of the particle radius. Such an aerosol would be considered to be relatively highly charged. The behaviour of

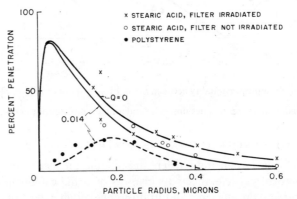

FIG. 6. Penetration curves for wool resin filters. The full and dotted lines illustrate the calculated performance using homogeneous and heterogeneous aerosols respectively. Q refers to the mean electric charge on the fibres calculated disregarding sign. (Gillespie.)

the uncharged and charged aerosols on being drawn through a wool resin filter is illustrated in Fig. 6. The presence of electric charges reduces the penetration and alters the shape of the penetration versus particle size curve. Exposing the filter to X-rays reduces the effective electric charge on the fibres and increases the penetration.

A theory for filtration, taking into account the effect of electric forces on filtration by interception and by diffusion processes, has been developed by Gillespie.[4] Electric effects are most important when the mean velocity through the filter is small. As this velocity is increased they have less effect. Electric charge is most important when the filter fibres are charged. In this case, theory and experiment are in agreement (see Fig. 6). When uncharged aerosols are pulled through filters with uncharged or weakly charged fibres, however, there are a number of anomalous effects which have been attributed to lack of adhesion on contact, by Gillespie.[5]

EFFECT OF ELECTRIC CHARGE ON THE CAPTURE OF PARTICLES BY FALLING DROPS

When a drop falls through an aerosol one might expect the collection efficiency to depend upon the electric charge on the drop, but both theory and experiment indicate that there would be no effect when the relative velocity is large. Gunn and Hitchfield[6] have shown experimentally that the collection efficiency of a 1 mm drop falling through a cloud of droplets (mean diameter, 1 μ) is not affected by charging the drop electrically. Judging from the related problem of filtration and Kunkel's[7] analysis of collection by sedimentation when the interacting particles are of comparable size, no electrical effects would be expected for a drop as large as 1 mm. It would be very interesting to repeat the experiments of Gunn and Hitchfield using much smaller drops with a number of aerosols.

DISCUSSION

From the work that has been done we may conclude that electric charge effects increase the rate of coagulation of highly charged aerosols with symmetrical charge distributions. They also increase the chances of particles being captured in filters when the filtration velocity is not too high. They have little effect on the scrubbing of aerosols by large, rapidly falling drops.

This last conclusion might be altered if there is a question of whether or not the particles stick to the drop on contact or not. When the relative velocity is moderate, Gillespie and Rideal[8] have shown that particles stick to surfaces less strongly if there are no electric charge effects. At high relative velocities inertia would be far more important and no electric effect would be expected.

REFERENCES

1. GILLESPIE, T. and LANGSTROTH, G. O., *Canad. J. Chem.*, **30**, 1056 (1952).
2. GILLESPIE, T. *Proc. Roy. Soc.*, A**216**, 569 (1953).
3. GOYER, G. G., GRUEN, R. and LAMER, V. K., *J. Phys. Chem.*, **58**, 137 (1954).
4. GILLESPIE, T., *J. Colloid Sci.*, **10**, 299 (1955a).
5. GILLESPIE, T., *J. Colloid Sci.*, **10**, 266 (1955b).
6. GUNN, K. and HITCHFIELD, W. R., *J. Met.*, **8**, 7 (1951).
7. KUNKEL, W., *J. Appl. Phys.*, **19**, 1053 (1948).
8. GILLESPIE, T. and RIDEAL, E. K., *J. Colloid Sci.*, **10**, 281 (1955).

DISCUSSION—FIRST SESSION

Deposition from a Turbulent Boundary Layer

Comments on paper by P. R. OWEN

C. N. DAVIES: Mass transfer between a moving fluid and a solid boundary, through a concentration gradient and a turbulent boundary layer, correlates with the Reynolds number if allowance is made for varying Schmidt number, ν/D (kinematic viscosity/diffusion coefficient). This was shown by Lin, Moulton and Putnam (*Ind. Eng. Chem.*, **45**, 636 (1953) who derived a function of ν/D by assuming a distribution of eddy diffusivity in the boundary layer similar to that adopted by Professor Owen.

They also showed that heat transfer can be correlated by substituting the Prandtl number, $C_p\mu/\kappa$, for the Schmidt number in their function.

The following table shows the approximate ranges of the Schmidt and Prandtl numbers which arise in various types of problem involving diffusion or heat convection.

System	ν/D	Pr
Heat convection in gas	—	1
Gaseous diffusion	1	—
Heat in water	—	3–10
Solutes in solution	500–3000	—
Particles in gases:		
radius = $0.01\,\mu$	1100	—
0.1	70,000	—
1.0	1,000,000	—

The gradient of concentration extends at small values of ν/D through what von Kármán called the laminar sub-layer ($y^* = yu_\tau/\nu < 5$) but when ν/D increases the greater part of the concentration difference shifts very close to the surface.

To account for this, and for the high rates of transfer observed, it was necessary to postulate the existence, in the sub-layer, of turbulence of an intensity decreasing as the wall was approached.

The rate-determining process passes over from Brownian or molecular diffusion to eddy diffusion as ν/D changes from 1 to 50,000.

Friedlander and Johnstone (*Ind. Eng. Chem.*, **49**, 1151 (1957)) experimented at still high values of ν/D where Brownian motion is negligible and the rate-determining process is eddy impaction.

They used the formulation of Lin, Moulton and Putnam but instead of integrating the eddy diffusion equation from the surface outwards through the whole boundary layer, they started at a distance from the surface of one particle stop-distance.

This is equal to $v_0 v/g$ and is the distance a particle travels when projected through air at rest with an initial velocity v. The particle size is given by v_0, its terminal velocity of free fall.

For v, like Professor Owen when defining his "free flight", they had recourse to Laufer's observations of the resolute of fluctuating velocity normal to the surface.

These experiments confirmed that eddy diffusion takes place in the sub-layer since, otherwise, particles with a stop-distance less than $y = 5v/u_\tau$ could not be deposited. They also showed an extremely rapid increase of transfer rate with particle size and gas velocity when the stop-distance was less than the thickness of the sub-layer, thus confirming the effect of increasing particle stop-distance.

Professor Owen ingeniously integrates the frequency distribution of normal resolutes of turbulent velocity above a cut-off point below which deposition cannot occur, the point being determined from the equation of motion of the particle by selecting the initial velocity so that it can just reach the surface.

The distance over which free flight takes place, however, is related only to the fluid flow field being set equal to $\lambda v/u_\tau$, where λ is specified as being of order unity, independent of particle size or velocity.

Surely it is certain that the free-flight distance must be about equal to the stop-distance of the particle and thus must vary with particle size and velocity?

A particle will not be affected by eddies which are small compared with its stop-distance. Since eddy size and velocity increase with distance from the surface, large particles will be projected even greater distances, relative to small ones, than are implied by the values of v_0. The approach to the problem using a constant free flight length is not attractive.

That a value of λ near to unity happens to fit the data of Dawes and Slack is a coincidence arising from the small stop-distances of their particles (0·05 cm).

In some deposition problems stop-distances amounting to several cm are encountered without undue departure from Stokes' resistance, so that the turbulence of the main stream rather than that of the boundary layer is the cause of deposition.

Eddies much larger than the stop-distance cannot affect eddy impaction because most of the particles in them remain inside until the eddies expire. They do, however, produce focal deposition and may remove particles from some regions of the flow, thus preventing eddy impaction upon boundaries of such regions.

For eddy impaction only a limited range of the eddy spectrum is operative; the particle responds to eddies comparable in size with its own stop-distance.

SCORER: In order to find the least restrictive conditions for the application of Professor Owen's paper let it first be supposed only that the drag on a particle is proportional to its velocity relative to the air. If the air velocity is v, and y the co-ordinate of the particle, and $-g$ the component of gravity in the y direction, the equation of motion is of the form

$$\ddot{y} = c(v - \dot{y}) - g$$

or

$$\left(\frac{d^2}{dt^2} + c^2 \frac{d}{dt}\right) y = cv(t) - g$$

Let $v(t)$ for a particular dust particle be resolved as follows

$$v(t) = v_0 + \sum_{1}^{\infty} c_n e^{i(2\pi nt/T)}$$

where T is the typical time taken for a particle to be diffused by the turbulence across most of the layer considered by Professor Owen. In time T the periodic parts of the velocity of the environment contribute nothing to y and

$$y = \left(v_0 - \frac{g}{c}\right)\left(T - \frac{1}{c}\right)$$

For this displacement to be the same for all particles except for their displacement due to gravity, viz. gT/c, it is necessary that $T \gg 1/c$, i.e. that the time for diffusion across the layer shall be large compared with the relaxation time of the particle. This is less restrictive than Professor Owen's condition that the representative eddy time should be large compared with the particle relaxation time, if the particles are mostly involved in more than one eddy in traversing the layer.

There is an additional assumption, namely that the absolute velocity of the fluid surrounding the dust particle has the substantially same time spectrum as the velocity of a fluid particle, but this seems reasonable.

It has only been demonstrated that this wider restriction on the particle size is applicable if the drag is proportional to the relative velocity, for only then is the equation linear and the use of the Fourier analysis of the velocity permissible. But provided the relative velocity only exceeds the value to which the Stokes' law is applicable only a small fraction of the time it will be valid.

This means that a particle can be quite readily pictured physically as having a velocity relative to the fluid in its journey and it makes the transition to being flung across the first laminar layer quite acceptable.

Equation 4 in the paper is derived from the equation of continuity of mass and an equation asserting that there is no divergence of particle velocity, by taking the mean values for a sufficiently long period. But clearly there is instantaneously a divergence of particle velocity in the final stage of the journey to the solid boundary. However, equation 4 is a mean equation which can be true even if the precise equations used by Professor Owen to derive it are not true. Indeed one can assert that, if the above restriction on particle size is satisfied, all particles behave during a period long compared with the eddy period, as if they moved with the fluid even though they do not in much shorter periods. Equation 4 can then be simply asserted, the left-hand side being the dust flux towards the boundary which is the definition of N.

OWEN: Particles having an effective Reynolds number less than 1 can hardly exist. The theory applies only to the turbulent boundary layer, not to the free stream outside it. Particles once caught in an eddy are carried along with it.

COHEN: A very simple device, which it is often convenient to use to sample the suspended material in a large gas stream, is a flat plate, covered with a sticky material, held at right angles to the gas flow. Can the methods of calculation discussed be applied to this system and has any experimental work been carried out? The practical point is whether any estimate of (a) particle size distribution of the suspended matter (b) mass concentration, can be obtained from this arrangement.

STAIRMAND: The efficiency of impaction on discs can be calculated in the same way as for spheres and cylinders, as discussed earlier in this Symposium and in Ref. 1 (below). Figure 1 shows the efficiency of collection of various particle sizes on a 3 in. diameter disk, exposed in the dusty gas flowing at 20 ft/sec (the density of the particles is taken as 2 g/cm³, suspended in air at 140°C). From this curve it will be seen that the impaction efficiency is zero at 10 μ, 10 per cent at 20 μ, and 86 per cent at 100 μ.

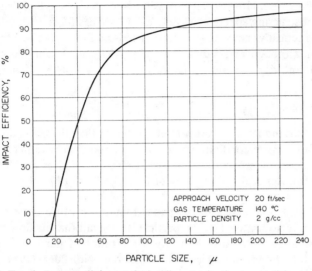

FIG. 1. Impact efficiency of 3 in. diameter impingement disk.

It is clear from these data that an impingement disk cannot collect a representative sample of dust in the size ranges in which Dr. Cohen is interested.

1. Stairmand, C. J., Dust Collection by Impingement and Diffusion, *Trans. Inst. Chem. Eng.*, **28**, 130 (1950) (with Appendix by C. H. Bosanquet).

WALTON: Fonda and Herne's calculations indicate that when a/R is small but finite the collision efficiency falls to an asymptotic value, not to zero, as K diminishes. This asymptotic value increases with a/R and is considerably greater for potential than for viscous flow. On the other hand, Hocking (Paper 12), considers the viscous case only at larger values of a/R and concludes that the efficiency does become zero. The residual value of the efficiency at small values of a/R and K has considerable significance in some circumstances. Perhaps Mr. Herne would comment on his results in relation to those of Hocking, and also for the potential case where the effect of a/R is greater.

Another outstanding problem concerns the effect of Reynolds number on collection efficiency in the transition region, Re 1 to 100 say. This has a critical effect on estimates of the optimum drop size for dust removal by free falling spray, as shown in Paper 10. The theoretical results of Pearcey and Hill for Reynolds numbers within this range, quoted by Mr. Herne, appear incompatible with Fonda and Herne's data for the limiting viscous and potential flow conditions. Langmuir has given an empirical formula for interpolating between these limiting conditions as a function of Reynolds Number. This has been used by Woolcock and myself in Paper 10, and by other authors, in absence of an exact analytical solution. It is to be hoped that the matter will receive further study.

HERNE: There is a limiting value of the particle parameter P below which collision does not occur for an infinitesimally small particle. The value of the particle parameter is 1/8 for the potential flow pattern and between 1·212 and 1·213 for the viscous flow pattern. The former is immediately obvious from the equations of motion in the potential flow case and the latter had been obtained by a detailed numerical analysis of the viscous flow case. However, it is possible in both cases to find trajectories which approach the obstructing sphere as closely as one wishes for any value of the particle parameter P. Practically speaking therefore there is no limiting value at which collision does not occur although at small values of particle parameter the collision cross-section is small and depends almost entirely on the ratio of the diameters of particle and sphere.

Collection Efficiency of a Small Sphere

STAIRMAND: Bosanquet has shown (Ref. 1 above) that the collection efficiency of a sphere can fall to zero for finite values of the impaction parameter Dg/Vf. In his analysis of the theory of impaction (Appendix to Ref. 1) he gives $\eta_T=0$ for $Dg/Vf=16$ for spherical obstacles and for $Dg/Vf=24$ for cylindrical obstacles.

PICKNETT: Mr. Herne states in his paper that the capture cross-sections he has calculated are only accurate when the particle is so small that its flow pattern may be neglected. However, results have been given for ratios of particle to sphere radius, r/R, of up to 0·1 (Fonda and Herne, M.R.E. rep. No. 2068 (1957), also Mason, *Physics of Clouds*, Cambridge University Press) with no indication of the accuracy to be expected.

If these results for viscous flow are expressed in terms of the capture cross-section of a drop of 30 microns radius in air at 0°C, they may be compared with the results given in Hocking's paper at this conference. Herne's results are for r/R values less than 0·1, while Hocking's results are for r/R greater than 0·2, yet despite this lack of overlap it is obvious that the two are in wide disagreement. Either Hocking's capture cross-sections are too low, or Herne's are too high. The latter is the more likely as, on physical grounds, neglect of the effect of flow round the particle should give results which are too high.

The discrepancy between the two sets of data is so great that, at best, it may be said that Herne's results are a wide over-estimate when r/R is greater than roughly 0·01; at worst, the results are inaccurate for all but infinitely small particles. These conclusions are only for the viscous flow solution at very low P values and it may be that, for larger values of P and for the potential flow solution the results are more accurate. However, I do notice that, with $P=100$ and $r/R=0·1$ the capture cross-sections are so large as to imply that the particle is drawn into the fall path of the sphere. This is physically unlikely.

HERNE: I have tried, like Dr. Picknett, to compare the results of Dr. Hocking with our own. Unfortunately, as Dr. Hocking has pointed out, his results are not reliable at the smaller ratios of particle to sphere diameters and I would not dare to hazard a guess at matching up our own results for very small ratios with those of Dr. Hocking for much larger ratios.

I agreed in general that our own results probably over-estimate the collision cross-section, but I would not underwrite any quantitative estimate of how far these are likely to be in error. Dr. Picknett has misread our results in some respect since the capture cross-sections given in all our own work are obtained only when the particle collides with the sphere on its up-stream side. In this simple mathematical model which we have taken the particle is not drawn into the flow pattern downstream of the sphere as it is in the calculation of Pearcey and Hill, for example.

PEARSON: So far we have seen the results of calculation based on (1) a potential flow—the ideal symmetric flow without separation—for infinite Reynolds number; and (2) a Stokes' slow motion flow, also symmetric, for zero Reynolds number, and use has been made of the interpolation formula suggested by Langmuir for inter-mediate Reynolds numbers.

As a more realistic approximation, I suggested using (3) instead of (1), a potential free streamline flow with separation, and (4) instead of (2), a low Reynolds number solution based on Oseen's equation. Both of these solutions take account of what we may term the wake behind the sphere, which is of course the characteristic feature of all finite Reynolds number flows. For small finite Reynolds numbers, a uniformly valid expansion procedure has been outlined by Proudman, I. and Pearson, J. R. A. (*J. Fl. Mech.*, **2**, 237 (1957)). For large finite Reynolds numbers an interesting expansion has been suggested by Stewartson (*Phil. Mag.* (1956)). For Reynolds numbers of order 10 there seems no prospect of using an analytical solution for the flow, and the results of a numerical solution of the non-linear equation would have to be employed.

HERNE: I believe that Dr. Pearson's second suggestion is more valuable than his first, because interest is centred on the collision cross-section appropriate to Reynolds numbers around the 10, or larger, region. If an attempt were made to copy our own procedure and compute trajectories of particles in flow patterns at such Reynolds numbers it would obviously be easier to feed an analytical expression into the digital computor than to have to rely on a tabular series of numerical results, such as are given by relaxation solutions. The flow solutions by Proudman and Pearson would therefore be of interest but, as Dr. Pearson mentioned, these are valid only for the smaller values of Reynolds numbers. One would seem to be forced to the relaxation solutions, such as those of Jenson.

Dr. Pearson's first suggestion of using the potential flow pattern round a semi-infinite cylinder terminated with a hemispherical head would scarcely seem to be worth the trouble of additional computation. The potential flow pattern round the sphere is a symmetrical one which would still represent the limiting case, and trajectories computed in it would not differ greatly, I would guess, from those computed in the flow pattern around the geometry Dr. Pearson suggests.

WALTON: It was one object of our paper to draw attention to the unsatisfactory state of knowledge of collision efficiencies at intermediate Reynolds numbers and it is to be hoped that someone will undertake the task of remedying this on the lines suggested by Dr. Pearson or otherwise. It is desirable to cover Reynolds numbers greater than 10 (up to 100 or more) for which Dr. Pearson indicates that numerical solutions of the flow pattern would have to be employed. The effect of finite particle size is also of practical importance, particularly at high Reynolds numbers and for small values of the particle parameter, and its introduction would further complicate the computations. It should not be overlooked that experimental measurement of collection efficiency, conducted with regard to dimensional theory, may provide a cheaper and more trustworthy solution even though it displays fewer significant figures.

C. N. DAVIES: At a Reynolds number of 10 the behaviour is nearer to potential flow than viscous. When a particle approaches very close to the obstacle, fluid has to be squeezed and this will decide whether collision takes place or not.

Flotation

PEMBERTON: Surface tension will reduce the contact time of the particle. Is surface deformed by impact?

BROWN: The equation given in the paper for the contact time is a simplified one. The full equation is

$$T = \left(\frac{\pi m}{2\gamma\phi^2}\right)^{\frac{1}{2}} \tag{1}$$

where T=the contact time, m=the particle mass, γ=the liquid–air interfacial tension.

Now
$$\phi^2 = \frac{D^2}{4a^2} + \frac{1}{\ln(a/D) + 0\cdot4625} \tag{2}$$

where D = the particle diameter, and

$$a = \text{the Laplace constant} = \left(\frac{2\gamma}{g\rho}\right)^{\frac{1}{2}} \tag{3}$$

Here g= the acceleration due to gravity
and ρ = the liquid density.

A reduction in the interfacial tension would increase T, from the first formula. The reduction of interfacial tension would tend to increase or decrease ϕ^2 (and therefore decrease or increase T) depending on the relative importance of the first and second terms. On balance, however, one would expect a reduced interfacial tension to give an increase in contact time

The deformation of the surface during impact is illustrated by the Fig. 2. The shock of the impact will cause an oscillation of a periodic time longer than the contact time. During the experiments, the bubbles oscillated violently on release from the capillary tube. The oscillation was completely damped, however, before impact and attachment were studied. Figure 3 shows the extent of the oscillation. The bubbles were oblate spheroids with the smallest, vertical dimension in the direction of motion. The volume of each bubble was $4\pi a^2 b/3$, where the lateral breadth was $2a$ and the height $2b$. The radius of the sphere of equal volume was $(a^2b)^{\frac{1}{3}}$. For a liquid sphere, the frequency of oscillation, is given by Rayleigh, *Phil. Mag.*, **5,** 177 (1892):

$$\lambda^2 = \frac{(n+1)(n-1)(n+2)\gamma}{4\pi^2\{(n+1)\rho + n\rho'\}R^3} \tag{4}$$

where R= the radius of a sphere of liquid, density ρ (air), surrounded by an infinite
       mass of other liquid of density ρ' (water),
    n = the order of the harmonic oscillation,
    n = 2 representing the motion of the sphere between an oblate and a prolate
       spheroid,

γ = the interfacial tension.

Since $(n+1)\rho' \ll n\rho$, then for $\rho'=1$, $n=2$, $\gamma=72\cdot75$ dyn/cm at 20°C,

$$\lambda^2 = 22\cdot1 R^{-3} \tag{5}$$

Figure 1 represents a spheroid with $2a=0\cdot17$ cm, $2b=0\cdot14$ cm and $R=0\cdot08$ cm. From equation 5, λ is approximately 200 vibrations/sec and the periodic time about 5 milliseconds. Inspection of Fig. 2 shows this value to be a reasonable one.

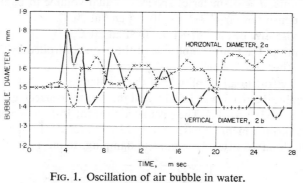

FIG. 1. Oscillation of air bubble in water.

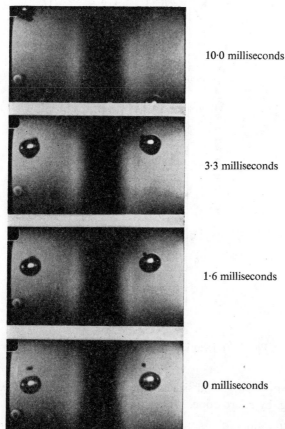

10·0 milliseconds

3·3 milliseconds

1·6 milliseconds

0 milliseconds

FIG. 2. Collision with attachment between bubble and single Galena particle.

E

The effective damping of the oscillation may also be calculated. In the absence of eddying in the air bubble, and neglecting any effect of the exterior fluid, the effect of the viscosity of the air may be represented as (Hughes and Gilliland, *Chem. Eng. Progr.*, **48**, 497 (1952))

$$B = B_0 \exp\left(\frac{-20\mu_i\theta}{\rho d^2}\right) \qquad (6)$$

Where θ = time, d = diameter of sphere of equal volume to bubble,
   ρ = density of air = 1.21×10^{-3} g/cm³ at 20°C,
   μ_i = viscosity of air = 1.84×10^{-6}P at 20°C,
   B_0 = initial fractional amplitude of the drop controlled by the formation or other shock which caused the oscillation,
   B = the fractional amplitude of the oscillation.

The initial bubble diameter was 1·5 mm and the initial displacement was to 1·8 mm, whence, B_0=(1·8−1·5)/1·5=1/5. The calculated time for 16-fold decrease of fractional amplitude, to a displacement of 0·02 mm, is 23 msec for d=1·6 mm. This compares with a value of about 26 msec for complete damping, found from Fig. 3.

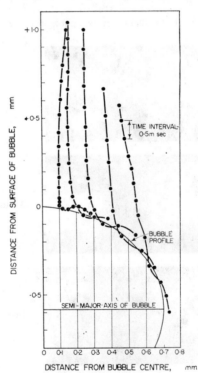

FIG. 3. Trajectories of Gresford coal grains in distilled water.

Electric Charges

CHAMBERLAIN: Charge and size cannot be separated unless the latter is determined separately, e.g. by microscope.

WALTON: Has any estimate been made of the collection efficiencies attainable with artificially produced highly charged spray? Mr. May, in Paper 5(a), indicates that very highly charged rain may double the collection due to impaction. This might perhaps be further enhanced by suitable choice of drop size.

WALTON: (general comment). In relation to the general problem of the aerodynamic forces arising when a small particle approaches closely to a large one, the following estimate of the work required to extrude a viscous fluid from the space between a sphere of radius a and a plane for normal approach may be of interest.

The sphere approaches with a velocity v and at one instant lies at a distance y from the nearest point (pole). Let the separation at a distance r along the plane be $x=y+r^2/2a$. If the velocity of approach of the sphere to the plane is v, the outward flux of fluid at distance r from the pole will be $\pi r^2 v/2\pi r = rv/2$ per unit circumferential length. Treating the problem as one of viscous flow between plane surfaces, the pressure gradient at r is therefore given by

$$\frac{dp}{dr} = -\frac{rv}{2}\frac{12\eta}{x^3},$$

where η is the viscosity of the fluid. Taking the fluid pressure as zero at $r=\infty$, the pressure at r is

$$p = -\int_r^\infty \frac{dp}{dr}\, dr = \frac{3a\eta v}{(y+r^2/2a)^2}$$

and hence the total force on the sphere is

$$F = \int_0^\infty 2\pi r\rho dr = 6\pi a^2\eta v/\,y.$$

If the sphere is of mass m moving with a velocity of approach v_0 at $y_0(\,y_0\ll a)$ and its motion is decelerated by the force F, we have

$$F = -m\frac{dv}{dt} = mv\frac{dv}{dy},$$

since $v = -\dfrac{dy}{dt}$.

SECOND SESSION:

EXPERIMENTAL APPLICATION OF
CAPTURE TECHNIQUES

ASPECTS OF THE DEPOSITION OF RADIOACTIVE AND OTHER GASES AND PARTICLES

by A. C. Chamberlain
A.E.R.E., Harwell

1. INTRODUCTION

SOME studies at Harwell on the deposition of radio-active aerosols from the air to the ground are described. Much of the work has been concerned with fission products formed in the reactors or by nuclear explosions. Iodine-131 is an important fission product which may be present in vapour form. Other fission products are usually found adsorbed on very small particles (condensation nuclei) and iodine may be in this form also. These particles are too small to have appreciable terminal velocity, but are subject to Brownian motion and also to electrostatic forces, by which means they are deposited.

2. SYMBOLS

Symbol	Meaning	Units
d	Representative length (Diameter of sphere, cylinder etc.)	cm
h	Effective height of gas cloud (Meetham[13, 14])	cm
k	von Kármán's constant $(=0.4)$	—
p	Rate of rainfall	mm/hr
s	Radius of raindrop	cm
t	Time	sec
u	Wind velocity	cm/sec
u_1	Wind velocity in free stream	cm/sec
u_*	Friction velocity	cm/sec
v_g	Velocity of deposition $=\omega/\chi$ or Ω/X	cm/sec
$v(s)$	Terminal velocity of raindrop radius s	cm/sec
v_T	Velocity under thermal forces	cm/sec
w	Air velocity in vertical direction	cm/sec
x	Distance in direction of wind	cm
y	Distance laterally along sampling arc	cm
z	Height above ground or other surface	cm
D	Molecular diffusivity	cm²/sec
K	Eddy diffusivity	cm²/sec
$M(s)$	Mass of water per cm³ of air as drops radius s	g/cm³
$N(s)$	Number of drops radius s per cm³ of air	cm⁻³
N_m	Dimensionless constant of mass transfer $=\dfrac{\omega d}{\chi D}$	—
W	Washout ratio $=\dfrac{\text{grammes (or curies) per g of rain}}{\text{grammes (or curies) per g of air}}$	—

λ	Proportional washout per sec	sec^{-1}
μ	Proportional washout per mm rain	mm^{-1}
ν	Kinematic viscosity of air	cm^2/sec
ρ	Density of air	g/cm^3
θ	Schmidt number $=\nu/D$	—
τ	Shearing stress	dyn/cm^2
χ	Volumetric concentration in air	(g or curie)/cm^3
X	Time integral of volumetric concentration ($=$dosage)	(g or curie) sec/cm^3
ω	Rate of deposition per unit surface	(g or curie)/cm^2 sec
Ω	Total deposition per unit surface	(g or curie)/cm^2

3. DEPOSITION OF VAPOUR

3.1 *Radioactive and Stable Isotopes*

Most radioactive nuclides in the atmosphere are accompanied by their stable isotopes, to greater or less extent. Some examples are given in Table 1.*

TABLE 1. EXAMPLES OF RADIOACTIVE VAPOURS IN THE ATMOSPHERE
(figures are orders of magnitude only)

Substance	Amount of stable isotope in air near ground ($\mu g/m^3$)	Radioactive isotope		Amount of radioactive isotope in air near ground ($\mu g/m^3$)	Mode of formation
		Nuclide	Half life		
Iodine	0·1	I^{131}	8·0 d	10^{-4}(†)	Fission, irradiation of tellurium
Sulphur (SO_2)	10	S^{35}	85 d	10^{-12}	Cosmic rays
Carbon (CO_2)	10^5	C^{14}	5600 y	10^{-7}	Cosmic rays, nuclear explosions
Hydrogen (H_2O)	10^6	H^3	12·6 y	10^{-10}	Cosmic rays, nuclear explosions
Zirconium	(?)	Zr^{95}	65 d	10^{-10}	Nuclear explosions

† Maximum at ground level during Windscale accident of 10/10/57.

The behaviour of a radioactive species as regards deposition often depends on the amount of stable element present. This is not because of any differences in the physical behaviour of the radioactive and stable isotopes (there are slight variations in molecular diffusivity) but because adsorption of monomolecular layers by surfaces is usually strong. Measurements of radioactivity enable studies to be made at very low mass concentrations, as shown in Table 1.

Iodine-131 is thus much more likely to be found adsorbed on other aerosols than is carbon 14 for example.

Goldschmidt[1] considers that the stable iodine exists in the atmosphere in a state of equilibrium between the surface of airborne dust and gaseous molecules, an equilibrium which in the presence of much dust may lead even to the practical elimination of truly gaseous iodine.

* The figures quoted are derived from results of Stewart and Crooks[9], Lal and Peters[46], Broecker and Walton[47], Begemann[48] and Peirson, Crooks and Fisher[33].

If adsorption is irreversible the flux ω to the surface does not depend on the amount Ω already deposited. It is convenient then to describe the rate of deposition in terms of the velocity of deposition v_g which can be defined either as

$$v_g = \frac{\omega}{\chi_1} = \frac{\text{Rate of deposition per unit area per sec}}{\text{Volumetric concentration in air at some reference point}}$$

or

$$v_g = \frac{\Omega}{X_1} = \frac{\text{Total deposition per unit area}}{\text{Time integral of volumetric concentration } (=\text{dosage})}$$

If the reference point, where χ_1 or X_1 is measured, is not stated, it must be assumed to be in the free air at some distance from adsorbing surfaces.

3.2 *Laboratory Experiments on Deposition of Iodine-131*

Iodine-131 may be liberated as a vapour in the treatment of irradiated fuel and in the preparation of iodine-131 for medical use. The mass of iodine per unit volume of air is usually extremely low, for example, the maximum permissible level for human inhalation corresponds to about 5×10^{-16} g/cm³ of iodine-131. At such low vapour concentrations, iodine adsorbs strongly on many materials, and it is a constant source of difficulty in handling iodine-131 in the gas or liquid phase to prevent it from adsorbing on surfaces.

All the work on iodine described in this paper has been done with very low volumetric concentrations. Chamberlain[2] performed experiments on the deposition of iodine-131 from an airstream to flat surfaces of various materials in the small wind tunnel shown in Fig. 1. Iodine-131 was prepared as elemental iodine dissolved in carbon tetrachloride solution. The solution was atomized by a spray, and rapidly evaporated leaving a vapour of iodine-131 which was drawn down the tunnel.

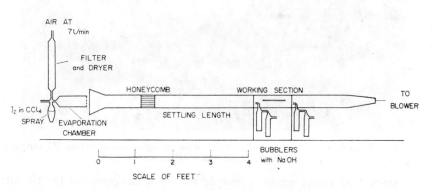

FIG. 1. Deposition experiment in small wind tunnel.

In the working section flat plates were exposed parallel to the airstream, and measurements of the dosage of iodine were made by passing air through bubblers containing caustic soda. Later, F. G. May extended the experiments to higher wind speeds in a larger tunnel with a 1 ft square working section. He liberated the iodine by heating sodium iodide in moist air.

In Fig. 2 is shown the variation of v_g with distance from the leading edge of a plate, on which iodine-131 was deposited from an airstream. As the thickness of the lamina boundary layer increased with distance downwind, the rate of deposition was reduced.

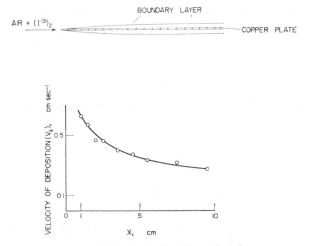

FIG. 2. Diffusion of iodine-131 to flat plate.

A more graphic illustration of the dependence of deposition on the nature of the boundary layer is shown in Fig. 3. This is an autoradiograph of iodine-131 deposited on a flat plate, from an airstream at 400 cm/sec, when a small cylindrical obstacle was fixed perpendicular to the plate. This obstacle caused a break-up of the boundary layer and thereby induced greater deposition of iodine as shown by the plume on the autoradiograph.

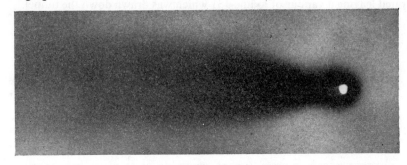

FIG. 3. Autoradiograph of effect of obstacle on flat plate on deposition of iodine-131 vapour from airstream (wind speed 400 cm/sec.).

The transport of matter across a boundary layer is analogous to the transfer of heat in forced convection, and the equations developed for the latter can be applied. In the laminar boundary layer of the flat plate the basic equations are given for example in Goldstein,[3] paras. 53 and 268.

Transfer of velocity or momentum:

$$u \frac{\partial u}{\partial x} + w \frac{\partial u}{\partial z} = v \frac{\partial^2 u}{\partial z^2} \tag{1}$$

with boundary conditions $u=w=0$ at $z=0$, $u=u_1$ at $z=\infty$ and at $x=0$

Transfer of matter:

$$u \frac{\partial \chi}{\partial x} + w \frac{\partial \chi}{\partial z} = D \frac{\partial^2 \chi}{\partial z^2} \tag{2}$$

with the same boundary conditions for u and w, and with $\chi = \chi_1$ at $z = \infty$ and $\chi = \chi_0$ at $z = 0$, where χ_1 and χ_0 are the masses per unit volume in the free air and at the surface respectively. By writing $\chi' = \chi - \chi_0$ the equation can be reduced to the case $\chi_0 = 0$, i.e. where the surface is a perfect sink, and in fact this condition appears to be fulfilled for the deposition of iodine-131 vapour to some surfaces.

Equation 1 can be solved (Blasius, quoted in Goldstein, para. 53) in a form which makes u a function of $zx^{-\frac{1}{2}}$ only. The thickness of the laminar boundary layer is found to increase as $x^{\frac{1}{2}}$ downwind from the leading edge. The shearing stress at the point distance x from the leading edge is:

$$\frac{\tau}{\rho} = 0 \cdot 332 \nu^{\frac{1}{2}} u_1^{\frac{3}{2}} x^{-\frac{1}{2}} \tag{3}$$

or

$$\frac{\tau x}{\rho u_1 \nu} = 0 \cdot 332 \, R^{\frac{1}{2}} \tag{4}$$

where $R = \dfrac{u_1 x}{\nu}$ is the local Reynolds number of flow over the plate.

Equation 3 only applies so long as the boundary layer remains laminar. At a certain value of R the transition to a turbulent layer begins. The value of R at which this happens depends on the degree of turbulence in the main stream, and may be anywhere in the range 10^4 to 10^6.

Equation 2 can also be solved approximately if it is assumed that the variations of χ with height z above the plate is the same as the variation of u with z except for a scale factor. If $\delta'(x)$ is the thickness of the boundary layer for χ and $\delta(x)$ the thickness of the boundary layer for u, it is assumed that $\delta'/\delta = $ constant. This constant is found to be approximately equal to $\theta^{\frac{1}{3}}$ where θ is the Schmidt number ν/D. The rate of deposition ω is then found to be given by

$$\omega = 0 \cdot 332 \, D \theta^{\frac{1}{3}} \nu^{-\frac{1}{2}} \chi_1 u_1^{\frac{1}{2}} x^{-\frac{1}{2}} \tag{5}$$

or

$$v_g = \frac{\omega}{\chi_1} = 0 \cdot 332 \, D \theta^{\frac{1}{3}} \nu^{-\frac{1}{2}} u_1^{\frac{1}{2}} x^{-\frac{1}{2}} \tag{6}$$

or

$$N_m = 0 \cdot 332 \, \theta^{\frac{1}{3}} R^{\frac{1}{2}} \tag{7}$$

where

$$N_m = \frac{\omega x}{\chi_1 D}$$

is a dimensionless mass-transfer number analogous to the Nusselt number of heat transfer.

The experimental correlation of N_m with $R^{\frac{1}{2}}$ is shown in Fig. 4. Experiments, similar to that illustrated in Fig. 2, but with values of u_1 ranging from 38 to 2000 cm/sec are included. At low Reynolds numbers, the correlation between experiment and theory was good, and this in effect showed that diffusion across the boundary layer was the limiting factor on the deposition. The adsorption at the surface of filter paper and also at surfaces of copper and other metals took place as rapidly as the boundary flow would permit. The deposition to filter paper was not increased by treating it with a reactive substance, such as caustic soda, but certain surfaces, particularly paraffin wax, were effective in inhibiting the deposition.

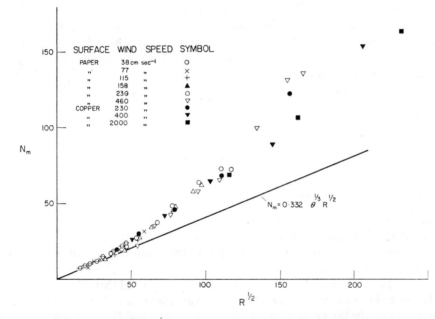

FIG. 4. Correlation of transfer of iodine-131 across boundary layer with Reynolds number.

Chamberlain also did some experiments on the deposition of iodine-131 to leaves of plants in the wind tunnel. The deposition to several broad-leaved species was compared with that to similarly shaped pieces of filter paper attached to the stem of the plant. Since the filter paper was known to act as a "perfect sink" for the vapour, the deposition on the leaf, relative to that on equal area of paper, was taken to be an index of the absorption capacity of the leaf.

In one experiment, the broad bean (*Vicia faba*) was grown in a pot, and the stem of the plant inserted into the wind tunnel through a small hole. The temperature in the wind tunnel was 72°F, with relative humidity 63 per cent and the plant was irradiated by a lamp to promote physiological activity. Paper "leaves" were attached to the stem, and after exposure to radio-iodine vapour (at a very low concentration of stable iodine) the leaves of the plant and the paper "leaves" were removed, and the deposited iodine activity assessed by counting under an end window counter.

The results of this experiment are shown in Table 2, and an autoradiograph of one of the bean leaves and one of the paper "leaves" is shown in Fig. 5. The deposition to the bean leaf was approximately 60 per cent of that to the paper "leaf". Whereas the latter was rather uniformly active, the iodine appears to have entered the bean leaf mainly at points where the skin was damaged. The spot of heavier deposition, just to the left of the mid-rib of the leaf, is associated with a small puncture which had previously been made in the leaf.

TABLE 2. DEPOSITION OF IODINE-131 TO BEAN LEAVES AND PAPER "LEAVES"

Dosage of I^{131} (curie-sec/cm$^3 \times 10^{12}$) $= 260$

Activity on bean leaves (both sides) $= 580, 700$ (mean 640)
(curie/cm$^2 \times 10^2$)

Activity on filter "leaves" (both sides) $= 1300, 1440, 1060,$
(curie/cm$^2 \times 10^{12}$) $730, 1100$ (mean 1100)

v_g to bean leaves (cm/sec) $= \dfrac{\frac{1}{2} \times 640}{260} = 1\cdot2$

v_g to paper "leaves" (cm/sec) $= \dfrac{\frac{1}{2} \times 1100}{260} = 2\cdot1$

Ratio of deposition on bean leaves
to that on paper "leaves" $= 0\cdot58$

FIG. 5. Autoradiograph of bean leaf (right) and paper "leaf" exposed to iodine-131 vapour.

Although the deposition of iodine-131 to the leaf was less than that to paper, it was larger than would have been expected on the basis of the rate at which leaves take in CO_2. The exchange of CO_2 is usually expressed in terms of the net assimilation rate (N.A.R.), for which a typical value is about 0·014 μg CO_2 per cm^2 of leaf surface per sec. Taking the CO_2 content of air as 0·6 μg/cm^3, it follows that the velocity of deposition of CO_2 is about 0·02 cm/sec. The uptake is evidently limited by the rate of reaction at the surface, not by diffusion to the surface.

In other experiments in the wind tunnel, the ratio of the deposition on leaf surfaces to that on filter paper varied from 0·68 to 0·20. The latter result was obtained in an experiment performed in darkness.

It was concluded speculatively that the waxy cutin on the leaf surface inhibits adsorption of the iodine to some extent. When the stomata are open, and at places where the leaf is damaged, diffusion to and adsorption in the mesophyll of iodine is rapid. In discussing the analogous problem of evaporation from a leaf, Monteith[4] finds that transpiration of water from a leaf may be almost as great as from a piece of wet blotting paper of the same size when the stomata are open, but is considerably less when they are closed.

3.3 Field Experiments on the Deposition of Iodine

Chamberlain and Chadwick[5] made measurements of the deposition of iodine-131 vapour in the field. Iodine-131 was prepared as elemental iodine dissolved in carbon tetrachloride, and liberated by atomizing the solution. The amount of stable iodine present was very low, certainly less than 1 mg. The carbon tetrachloride was sprayed up as fine droplets, at a height of 50 cm above the ground; the droplets soon evaporated to leave a vapour of iodine. 30 mc of iodine-131 were used in each experiment but an unknown amount remained adsorbed in the spray.

Measurements were made of the volumetric concentration of iodine in air, at sampling points disposed on arcs 15 or 20 m downwind of the point of release, two sampling heights being used. Air was drawn through bubblers containing caustic soda during the whole period of release. The activity in the bubblers (curies), divided by the rate of flow of air through the bubblers (cm^3/sec) gave a measure of the dosage of activity in air (curie-sec/cm^3). This is denoted in Table 3 by $X(z)$, where z is the height in cm of the sampler above the ground.

Recently, Megaw and Chadwick[6] have done two further field releases (trials 6 and 7). In these experiments, the iodine-131 was prepared as elemental iodine with the addition of 50 mg of stable iodine carrier, by oxidation of the iodide, and was stored as crystalline elemental iodine in a cold trap until required.

It was released by passing air through the cold trap, and the sampling was done on two arcs at 50 and 100 m from the point of release. The volumetric concentration at 100, 60 and 30 cm above ground was measured by drawing the air through a sampling pack consisting of a high efficiency filter followed by a bed of activated charcoal.

The experiments were designed to overcome two disadvantages of the previous series, namely (a) the short period of travel previously used, and (b) the possibility that some droplets of carbon tetrachloride had persisted long enough to reach the samplers.

In both series of trials, at the conclusion of the release of iodine, the amount of iodine-131 deposited on various surfaces was measured, viz.

Surface	Deposition	Units
Grass taken from known area of ground	Ω_G	curies per cm^2 ground
Filter paper placed in Petri dish on ground	Ω_F	curies per cm^2 of paper
Leaves of dandelion (trials 3,4,5), or clover (trial 7) growing in field during release	Ω_L	curies per cm^2 of leaf
Paper "leaves" attached to dandelion or clover	Ω_{FL}	curies per cm^2 of paper "leaf"

The ratio of Ω for any surface to the dosage X in air above it gave the velocity of deposition to that surface.

The measurement of X and Ω in each trial except the first, for which details have already been published[5] are listed in Table 3. In some trials, most of the sampling positions were missed by the plume because of swings of wind. No attempt has been made to analyse the results in terms of Sutton's theory of dispersion of clouds because of uncertainty about the source strengths in trials 1 to 5, and inadequate coverage of the plume in trials 6 and 7.

In Table 4 the meteorological conditions are listed, and the values of v_g are summarized.

The mean values of v_g to grass in the first 5 trials were 2·5 cm/sec. In the last two, in which 50 mg carrier iodine was added to the source, it was 1·6 cm/sec. No systematic difference was found in the values of v_g from the 50 and 100 m arcs in the last two, nor in the results from the centre and edges of the plume in the earlier trials, showing that v_g does not depend on the absolute values of X or Ω.

TABLE 3. MEASUREMENTS OF X AND Ω IN DEPOSITION TRIALS WITH IODINE-131 VAPOUR

Trial 2

$x = 2000$ cm $y = $(cm)	-600	-300	0	300	600	Mean	SE of Mean
$X(50 \cdot \times 10^{12}$	47	100	124	87	33		
$X(12{\cdot}5) \times 10^{12}$	50	88	110	82	43		
Mean	48·5	94	117	84·5	38		
$\Omega_G \quad \times 10^{12}$	145	360	154	168	118		
v_g	3·0	3·8	1·3	2·0	3·1	2·6	0·5
$\Omega_F \quad \times 10^{12}$	53	118	32	38	20		
v_g	1·1	1·2	0·27	0·44	0·52	0·72	0·2

Trial 3

$x = 2000$ cm $y = $(cm)	-900	-600	-300	0	300	600	Mean	SE of Mean
$X(50) \quad \times 10^{12}$	—	32	41	21	21	8·7		
$X(25) \quad \times 10^{12}$	4·6	36	35	26	21	8·5		
Mean	4·6	34	38	23·5	21	8·6		
$\Omega_G \quad \times 10^{12}$	7	80	78	24	33	19		
v_g	1·5	2·4	2·1	1·0	1·6	2·2	1·8	0·2
$\Omega_F \quad \times 10^{12}$	5·4	49	34	17	11·6	7·3		
v_g	1·2	1·4	0·88	0·72	0·55	0·85	0·94	0·1
$\Omega_L \quad \times 10^{12}$	10·0	62	48	18	17	10		
v_g	2·2	1·8	1·3	0·77	0·81	1·2	1·3	
$\Omega_{FL} \quad \times 10^{12}$	8·0	69	94	49	31	19		
v_g	1·7	2·0	2·5	2·1	1·5	2·2	2·0	

TABLE 3—continued

Trial 4

$x = 2000$ cm $y =$ (cm)	−600	−300	0	300	600	Mean	SE of Mean
$X(50)$ $\times 10^{12}$	5·4	—	28	28	11		
$X(25)$ $\times 10^{12}$	4·4	13	21	29	12		
Mean	4·9	13	24·5	28·5	11·5		
Ω_G $\times 10^{12}$	21	40	94	106	44		
v_g	4·3	3·1	3·8	3·7	3·8	3·75	0·2
Ω_F $\times 10^{12}$	3·4	4·7	11·0	11·7	15·6		
v_g	0·69	0·36	0·45	0·41	1·35	0·65	0·2
Ω_L $\times 10^{12}$	4·8	13·1	10·4	47	6·7		
v_g	1·0	1·0	0·44	1·6	0·58	0·92	
Ω_{FL} $\times 10^{12}$	3·4	12·0	39	61	16		
v_g	0·73	1·8	1·6	2·1	1·4	1·5	

Trial 5

$x = 2000$ cm $y =$ (cm)	−600	−300	0	300	600	Mean	SE of Mean
$X(50)$ $\times 10^{12}$	39	147	32	32	13		
$X(25)$ $\times 10^{12}$	76	66	37	14	12		
Mean	57·5	106·5	34·5	23	12·5		
Ω_G $\times 10^{12}$	120	192	78	16	20		
v_g	2·1	1·8	2·3	0·7	1·6	1·7	0·3
Ω_F $\times 10^{12}$	20	37	11·3	4·0	—		
v_g	0·35	0·35	0·33	0·17	—	0·30	0·04
Ω_L $\times 10^{12}$	37	47	23	2·5	—		
v_g	0·64	0·44	0·67	0·11	—	0·46	
Ω_{FL} $\times 10^{12}$	60	110	57	6·7			
v_g	1·0	1·0	1·7	0·29	—	1·0	

Trial 6

$y =$ (cm)	$x = 5000$ cm 0	1200	$x = 10,000$ cm $y =$ 0	2400
$X(100) \times 10^{12}$	7·5	14·4	2·4	4·0
$X(60)$ $\times 10^{12}$	7·0	16·4	2·6	3·7
$X(30)$ $\times 10^{12}$	6·6	13·5	1·9	4·1
Mean	7·0	14·8	2·3	3·9
Ω_G $\times 10^{12}$	14·0	20·7	3·9	7·2
v_g	2·0	1·4	1·7	1·8

TABLE 3—*continued*

Trial 7

$y=$(cm)	$x=5000$ cm			$x=10{,}000$ cm		
	−1200	0	1200	−2400	0	2400
$X(100)\times10^{12}$	9·0	63	22	2·2	24	7·0
$X(60)\ \times10^{12}$	9·2	64	24	3·4	24	6·2
$X(30)\ \times10^{12}$	9·4	64	22	—	22	5·4
Mean	9·2	64	23	2·8	23	6·2
$\Omega_G\ \ \times10^{12}$	13·4	56	22	4·1	32	6·1
v_g	1·46	0·89	0·94	1·2	1·2	1·0
$\Omega_L\ \ \times10^{12}$	3·1	15·8	6·4	0·8	7·5	1·3
v_g	0·34	0·25	0·26	0·29	0·32	0·20
$\Omega_{FL}\ \ \times10^{12}$	8·3	29	10·5	2·4	14·1	2·6
v_g	0·90	0·45	0·46	0·83	0·60	0·42

TABLE 4. SUMMARY OF RESULTS OF DEPOSITION TRIALS WITH IODINE-131 VAPOUR

No. of trial	1	2	3	4	5	6		7	
Date	8.5.49	8.8.50	3.7.51	8.8.51	8.8.51	2.6.59		13.7.59	
Time (G.M.T.)	1620	1500	1100	1500	2000	1340		1340	
Windspeed (cm/sec)									
at $z=200$ cm	520	433	515	408	165	230		387	
at $z=100$ cm.	420	372	442	310	138	164		335	
Friction velocity (cm/sec)	48	35	48	38	15	20		26	
Roughness parameter (cm)	2·8	1·5	1·2	2·4	2·4	5·0		1·0	
Temperature °F	50	65	68	69	61	67		61	
Relative humidity (per cent)	—	61	75	51	78	51		63	
Weather	Sunny	Cloudy	Sunny	Sunny	Dusk	Sunny		Cloudy	
Iodine liberated (mg)	<1	<1	<1	<1	<1	50		50	
Distance of sampling points from source (cm)	$1·5\times10^3$	2×10^3	2×10^3	2×10^3	2×10^3	5×10^3	10^4	5×10^3	10^4
Vegetation cover (mg/cm²)	50	20	26	42	42	108	61	36	42
Velocity of deposition (cm/sec)									
to ground	1·9	2·6	1·8	3·7	1·7	1·7	1·8	1·1	1·1
to leaves	—	—	1·3	0·9	0·5	—	—	0·3	0·3
to paper "leaves"	—	—	2·0	1·5	1·0	—	—	0·6	0·6
to paper in Petri dish	0·6	0·7	0·9	0·6	0·3	—	—	—	—

The values of v_g to the various surfaces generally lie in the decreasing order (1) ground, (2) paper "leaves", (3) leaves, (4) paper in Petri dish. The value of v_g to the ground is enhanced by the fact that the area of grass per cm² of ground is much greater than 1 cm².

The ratio of deposition on the dandelion and clover leaves to that on the similarly shaped and positioned paper "leaves" was in the range 0·5 to 0·7. This was in agreement with the laboratory experiments and showed that they were not vitiated by unnatural conditions indoors.

F

3.4 *Deposition of Iodine-131 at Long Range*

Parker,[7] and Healy *et al.*[8] have made measurements of the deposition of iodine-131 at ranges of up to 30 km from a chemical plant at Hanford, U.S.A., in which irradiated fuel is dissolved up. The average value of v_g was 2·8 cm/sec.

Measurements at even larger ranges were made after the Windscale accident of October 10/11th, 1957, during which about 2×10^4 curies of iodine were released from the stack of a reactor.[9,10,11] The values of v_g found were 0·3 to 0·4 cm/sec in the Lancashire/Yorkshire region and about 0·1 cm/sec in the Harwell area. Even these results may be too high, because the dosages of iodine-131 in air were derived from measurements of the activity of filter papers of types not very efficient for this purpose. It is likely that the iodine was partly or wholly adsorbed on sub-micron nuclei by the time it had travelled to the sampling stations. Such nuclei are much more abundant in air near industrial towns than in desert country such as that near Hanford.

3.5 *Theoretical Velocity of Deposition to Ground Surface*

The boundary layer of flow over grass-covered ground is turbulent, probably with laminar sub-layers over individual leaves. There are satisfactory theories for the turbulent transfer, but it is difficult to assess the role of molecular diffusion in carrying matter over the last few millimetres to the surface. Sheppard[12] proposes an empirical solution in which the diffusivity is the sum of the molecular term D and an eddy term $K(z) = ku_* z$. With the boundary condition $\chi = 0$ at $z = 0$ this leads to an expression for the flux:

$$\omega = \frac{ku_* \chi(z_1)}{\log (ku_* z_1 D^{-1})} \quad \left(z_1 \gg \frac{D}{ku_*} \right) \tag{8}$$

$$v_g(z_1) = \frac{ku_*}{\log (ku_* z_1 D^{-1})} \tag{9}$$

where z_1 is the reference height above the ground at which χ is measured.

Inserting the diffusion coefficient of I_2 vapour (0·08 cm²/sec) into (9), values of v_g are deduced as shown in Table 5.

TABLE 5. THEORETICAL VELOCITY OF DEPOSITION OF IODINE VAPOUR TO GROUND (cm/sec)

Friction velocity cm/sec	Reference height z_1 (cm)		
	50	100	500
20	0·94	0·87	0·74
50	2·12	1·97	1·70

The results of Table 5 only apply when the cloud has travelled a long way from the point of release. v_g is then only slightly dependent on the reference height, because $\chi(z)$ changes rapidly only for very small z.

There is reasonable agreement between theoretical and experimental values of v_g, indicating that the boundary condition $\chi = 0$ at $z = 0$ is at least approximately fulfilled. It has not, however, been possible to correlate the results of the field experiments in detail with theory, because they were not at sufficiently long range to make χ independent of x or y.

4. DEPOSITION OF SULPHUR DIOXIDE

4.1 *Deposition to Ground and to Deposit Gauges*

Meetham[13,14] has investigated the natural removal of SO_2 from the atmosphere. The only direct measurements of the deposition of SO_2 is by analysis of the sulphur in deposit gauges. The deposit gauge is similar to a rain gauge, and collects a representative sample of material dissolved or suspended in rain, but its surface is not representative of the ground as a whole for the collection of gases and fine particulates by diffusion or impaction. Meetham, however, estimated by an indirect method that the yearly deposition of SO_2 over Britain is 3.9×10^6 tons/year, whereas the total computed from the deposition per unit area in deposit gauges is 0.7×10^6 tons/year. Dividing these results by the area of Britain included, 1.7×10^{15} cm², and by the mean volumetric concentration, 41 mg/1000 m³, the rates of deposition and values of v_g given in the first two columns of Table 6 are obtained.

TABLE 6. DEPOSITION OF SULPHUR DIOXIDE

Period	1939–1944		1952 Dec. 5–9	—
Deposition surface	Britain	Deposit gauges	London (in fog)	Cylinder of PbO_2
Volumetric concentration (χ) g/cm³	4.1×10^{-11}	4.1×10^{-11}	2.1×10^{-9}	1.6×10^{-10}
Rate of deposition (ω) g/cm² sec	7.1×10^{-11}	1.3×10^{-11}	1.4×10^{-9}	0.77×10^{-10}
Velocity of deposition (v_g) cm/sec	1.8	0.3	0.7	0.7

Since the deposit gauge is efficient for the collection of rain, it appears that the deposition of SO_2 by rain is not more than one sixth of the total deposition, even if all the sulphate found in the gauges is attributed to washout of SO_2. Meetham[15] suggests that direct absorption at the surface of vegetation and other surfaces is important.

The result $v_g = 0.7$ cm/sec in the London fog of December, 1952, is derived from Meetham's paper[14] which showed that removal of SO_2 by horizontal or upwards transport from the fog zone must have been negligible, so that the rate of deposition can be equated to the rate of emission. The deposition in fog may be partly attributed to the fall of fog droplets with SO_2 in solution.

The final column of Table 6 is derived from the calibration of the lead peroxide cylinder for SO_2 measurements, namely that one mg SO_2 is deposited per day per 100 cm² PbO_2 when the concentration of SO_2 in air is 4.2 p.p.m. by volume (DSIR, quoted by Meade and Pasquill[16]). The value of v_g so found is midway between the values for the deposit gauge and for the ground as a whole. Even allowing for the fact that the surface area of vegetation is greater than that of the ground it covers, and that the lead peroxide cylinder is placed in a screen which reduces the rate of air movement, it is remarkable that the deposition per cm² of ground should be greater than per cm² of lead peroxide. It would be interesting if experiments using sulphur-35 could be done to measure the rate of assimilation on different surfaces and in various conditions.

Washout of SO_2 *and other gases by rain*

Chamberlain[17] has calculated the washout rate of a soluble gas on the assumptions:

(*a*) the rate of absorption is solely controlled by the rate of diffusion of the gas to the raindrop

(*b*) the size spectrum of the raindrops, as a function of the rate of rainfall, is as given by Best[18]

(*c*) the rain falls from a height above the top of the cloud of gas.

The calculation is based on the equation for mass transfer to a small absorbing sphere (Ranz and Marshall[19]).

$$N_m = 2.0 + 0.60\, R^{\frac{1}{2}}\, \theta^{\frac{1}{3}} \tag{10}$$

where $R = \dfrac{2sv(s)}{v}$ is the Reynolds number of air flow round the drop.

The formula for the proportion of the gas washed out per second is:

$$\lambda = \frac{3D}{2} \int_{s=0}^{\infty} \left[2.0\, \frac{M(s)}{s^2} + 0.846\, \frac{M(s)}{s^{\frac{3}{2}}}\, v(s)^{\frac{1}{2}} v^{-\frac{1}{6}} D^{-\frac{1}{3}} \right] ds \tag{11}$$

As the term in brackets includes D to the one-third power only, λ is nearly proportional to the diffusivity of the gas. Alternatively, the washout rate can be expressed as the proportion μ washed out per mm of rain, so that

$$\mu = \frac{3600\,\lambda}{p} \tag{12}$$

when p is the rainfall rate in mm/hr.

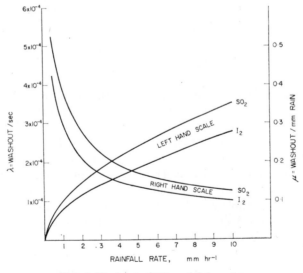

FIG. 6. Washout of SO_2 and I_2 by rain.

In Fig. 6 are shown the calculated values of λ and μ as functions of p for I_2 vapour ($D=0.08$ cm²/sec at 20°C) and SO_2 vapour ($D=0.11$ cm²/sec at 20°C). μ decreases as p increases because the heavier the rain the larger the drops, and large drops are relatively less efficient than small drops in washing-out vapour.

The annual washout of SO_2 can be calculated from the results of Fig. 6. In Table 7 is shown the number of millimetres of rain $A(p)$ falling per annum in each range of p at Harwell during 1951–7, and the value of $\mu(p)$ corresponding to the middle of the range. If the average volumetric concentration of SO_2 in the air during rain is $\chi'(z)$, and an effective height h of the SO_2 cloud is defined so that

$$h\chi_1' = \int_{z=0}^{\infty} \chi'(z)\, dz \tag{13}$$

where χ'_1 is the concentration near the ground, it is easily seen that the annual deposition in rain is:

$$\Omega_p = \Sigma_p \left[A(p)\,\mu(p)\,h\,\chi_1' \right] \tag{14}$$

Assuming that h and χ_1' are independent of the rate of rainfall

$$\Omega_p = h\chi_1' \, \Sigma_p \left[A(p)\,\mu(p) \right] \tag{15}$$

$$= 284\, h\, \chi_1' \text{ g/cm}^2 \text{ year} \tag{16}$$

by inserting the value of $\Sigma A(p)\mu(p)$ from Table 7.

TABLE 7. DEPOSITION OF SO_2 IN AN ANNUAL RAINFALL OF 625 mm

Rainfall rate (p) (mm/hr)	Rain per year at rate p $A(p)$ (mm)	Washout per mm rain $\mu(p)$	$A(p)\,\mu(p)$
0–1	445	0·525	233
1–2	118	0·325	38
2–3	33	0·242	8
3–4	15	0·206	3
4–5	5·6	0·182	1
5–6	4·0	0·164	0·7
>6	5·6	0·12	0·7
Total	625	Total	284

The DSIR survey, on which Meetham's analyses are based, do not enable the mean concentration of SO_2 during rain to be distinguished from the mean annual concentration, but results of Kanno et al.[20] indicate that the former may be about one half the latter.

Inserting $\chi_1' = 2 \times 10^{-11}$ g/cm^3, (one half the figure in Table 6) and taking Meetham's value of 2×10^4 cm for h in country districts of Britain,

$$\Omega_p = 280 \times 2 \times 10^4 \times 2 \times 10^{-11} = 1 \cdot 1 \times 10^{-4} \text{ g/cm}^2 \text{ year}$$

If the deposition in rain is considered as a mean rate averaged over the year, its contribution to the flux is

$$\omega_p = 3 \cdot 5 \times 10^{-12} \text{ g/cm}^2 \text{ sec}$$

Comparison with the results of Table 6, shows that this theoretical washout rate is one quarter of the observed rate of deposition in deposit gauges and one twentieth of the total deposition rate to ground deduced indirectly.

For a vapour which extended to greater heights above ground, washout by rain would be a progressively more powerful mode of removal, and if the vapour extended to the rain forming layer, the absorption in cloud droplets as well as in rain would be effective.

5. DEPOSITION OF ACTIVITY ADSORBED ON NUCLEI

5.1 *Condensation Nuclei*

The natural nuclei in the atmosphere upon which radioactive nuclides may be adsorbed originate in many ways, of which probably the most important are:

(*a*) Sea spray;

(*b*) Dust blown up from the soil;

(*c*) Combustion processes;

(*d*) Volcanic and man-made explosions.

The nuclei have been studied mainly as carriers of ionization in the air,[21] and in that connection are termed Aitken nuclei or large ions, and are found to have mean diameters in the range 0·05 to 0·1 microns.

The decay products of the radioactive gases radon and thoron, being isotopes of polonium, bismuth and lead, are rapidly and probably irreversibly adsorbed on condensation nuclei. The deliberate marking of the nuclei by ThB activity has been used as a method of studying the diffusion and deposition of the nuclei, and the results so obtained are in reasonable agreement with measurements by other methods.[24] Wilkening[22] found that RaB and RaC occurring naturally in the air are attached to nuclei with a median diameter of 0·02 microns. The fission products produced in high-altitude nuclear bomb explosions are believed to attach themselves to particles within the size range 0·02 to 0·2 microns (K. Stewart,[23] and para. 5.3 below).

The effect of attachment to nuclei is to reduce the diffusivity of a radioactive nuclide by about four orders of magnitude, compared with its diffusivity in the atomic or molecular state. Hence the rate at which the activity will diffuse across a boundary layer to an absorbing surface is greatly reduced once it is fixed to a condensation nucleus. An example of this is that the retention of radon and thoron decay products in the human respiratory system is greater when they are generated in nuclei-free air and inhaled in the atomic state than it is when they are first allowed to attach themselves to nuclei.[25]

Deposition of nuclei does, however, occur, four processes being observed:

(i) Diffusion (Brownian motion) leading to fixation at surfaces.

(ii) Electrostatic precipitation.

(iii) Coagulation, followed by fallout under gravity.

(iv) Washout by rain.

In general, radioactivity adsorbed on condensation nuclei, is also precipitated by these methods.

5.2 *Deposition of Nuclei to Flat Plates and to Grass*

The deposition to a flat plate (usually covered with paper) is used as an index of the rate of deposition of particles, but there are disadvantages in this practice, because the boundary layer of flow over a flat plate is different from that over natural surfaces.

In Table 8 the results of some measurements of deposition to flat plates are summarized. In each case plane sheets of about 1 ft² area were exposed horizontally in the open air but protected from rain, and simultaneous measurements were made of the dosage of activity by drawing air through high efficiency filter papers.

TABLE 8. DRY DEPOSITION OF ACTIVITY ON NUCLEI TO HORIZONTAL SURFACES

Period	1953	1953	1957	1959		1957	
Activity	Fission products	RaB and RaC	Fission products	Zirconium-95		Fission products (field expts.)	
Surface	Filter paper	Filter paper	Gummed paper	Filter paper Outdoors	Indoors	Filter paper	Grass
Volumetric concentration curie/cm³	3×10^{-19}	3×10^{-16}	n.s.	$4 \cdot 4 \times 10^{-19}$	$3 \cdot 1 \times 10^{-19}$	Various	
Rate of deposition curie/cm² sec	3×10^{-20}	$1 \cdot 4 \times 10^{-17}$	n.s.	$3 \cdot 9 \times 10^{-20}$	$2 \cdot 3 \times 10^{-21}$	Various	
Velocity of deposition (v_g) cm/sec	0·1	0·05	0·07	0·10	0·007	0·07(U) 0·04(D)	0·20
Reference	Bullas[26]		Stewart[27]	Booker[28]		Megaw and Chadwick[29]	

U=Upwards facing   *D*=Downwards facing

Bullas[26] measured the deposition of radon decay products from the atmosphere to flat surfaces exposed for a few hours at a time. Under the conditions of his work it can be estimated that at least 95 per cent of the decay product atoms would be attached to nuclei. He found values of v_g to depend on the wind velocity. With fresh winds, values of 0·08 and 0·07 cm/sec were found, but in calm weather, v_g was as low as 0·01 or 0·005 cm/sec.

Bullas also measured the deposition of fission product activity from nuclear test explosions. For this purpose he exposed the plates for a week at a time, and allowed a period of several days to elapse after the exposure period before the activity was counted. In three such experiments during December 1953 and January 1954, values of v_g ranging from 0·063 to 0·16 cm/sec, with a mean of 0·10 cm/sec were found. During one period, Bullas also measured the deposition to the underside of the plate, and found 70 per cent as much activity as on the upper surface.

Stewart *et al.*[27] made similar experiments using a plate covered with Vavaseline coating. The dry deposition to the plate of fission product activity from distant nuclear explosions was measured and compared with the activity in air. A mean velocity of deposition of 0·07 cm/sec was obtained.

Booker[28] repeated the experiments once more, but instead of counting the gross beta activity he estimated the deposition of a specific fission product, zirconium 95, by gamma spectrometry of the deposited activity. In addition to exposing filter paper sheets in the open air, he placed similar sheets at a height of 2 m above the floor of various rooms in occupied houses. The volumetric concentration of activity indoors was 80 per cent of that out of doors, but the deposition rate was less than a tenth of that out of doors. This is attributed to the low air velocities indoors.

The experiments of Megaw and Chadwick[29] were carried out in the field. An aerosol was produced by passing an arc between a carbon electrode and an electrode consisting of a piece of irradiated uranium wire. The uranium wire rapidly melted, and a fume was given off consisting mainly of sub-micron particles of uranium oxide, but with some larger particles. Samples taken with a cascade impactor gave 83 per cent penetration to the filter paper stage, as determined by activity, and this would correspond to a particle size of 0·2 microns or less if the density is that of uranium oxide. The fission product activity (with the exception of the krypton, xenon and iodine fractions) was almost certainly contained in or adsorbed on these particles. The total mass of uranium given off as fume was of the order of milligrams.

Arrays of sampling equipment were set up at distances of 50 and 100 m from the source. At each sampling position, flat plates covered on top and bottom with filter paper were exposed. In addition, an attempt was made to measure the deposition to grass surfaces. For this purpose, grass was grown in a greenhouse on a substrate consisting of several layers of filter paper soaked with nutrient solution. The air entering the greenhouse was filtered and the grass was therefore not contaminated with fission products from nuclear explosions. Before the experimental aerosol was released, a 60 cm² plot of grass, supported on a polythene sheet, was placed at each sampling point, with the grass level with the herbage in the field. The dosage of activity in the air near each sampling point was measured by suction through high-efficiency filters.

After the passage of the fission product cloud, the deposition papers, the grass, and the substrate on which it was grown were ashed, and the activity of the ash measured. The velocities of deposition were then computed, with results as shown in the last column of Table 8.

The deposition to downwards facing filter paper at least can be attributed to the turbulent diffusion of the sub-micron constituents of the aerosol. The experiments, therefore, show that the ratio (deposition on grass): (deposition on flat paper surface) for this type of aerosol is about 5:1.

5.3 *Effect of Electrostatic Fields*

It was desirable to investigate what part electrostatic forces might play in the deposition of activity adsorbed on nuclei in the sub-micron size range.

The deposition of fission products from distant nuclear explosions to flat plates under an electrostatic field of 2200 V/cm was measured. The plates, which were 900 cm² in area and covered with paper were placed vertically 5 cm apart in the wind tunnel. A potential of 11,000 V negative was applied to one plate and the other was earthed. Upstream of these plates were placed two similar plates, both earthed, to measure the deposition from the same airstream with no electrostatic field. The activity in the air was measured by the usual method of filter paper sampling, using an asbestos filter paper with high efficiency for sub-micron particles.

The results are shown in Table 9. The nuclei carrying the fission products were driven preferentially to the plate held at negative potential, indicating that most of them carry a positive charge. A correction was made for the deposition by diffusion or impaction to the plates in the electrostatic field, by subtracting the deposition rates to the no-field plates. Under the conditions of the experiment, only a small fraction of the nuclei passing between the plates was deposited, and the deposition rates can be related to the mobility by the equation.

$$\text{Mobility (cm}^2\text{/sec volt)} = \frac{v_g(+) + v_g(-) - 2v_g(0)}{\text{Field strength}} \tag{17}$$

In deducing the mobility in this way, it has been assumed that all the nuclei-carrying fission products are charged, and the mobilities will in fact be underestimated for this reason.* It has also been assumed that the mobility of positively and negatively charged nuclei is the same.

The diffusion coefficient can be deduced from the mobility if it is assumed that the nuclei each carry unit electronic charge, and the diameter can also be deduced if it is further assumed that they are spherical. In fact the nuclei would not be all of the same size, and the diffusion constant and diameter deduced in this way is an average of an ill-defined kind.

The diameters deduced in Table 9 for the nuclei-carrying fission products are slightly larger than the average size of large ions (Aitken nuclei) in the atmosphere. This can be explained by the greater average age of the nuclei-carrying fission products.

TABLE 9. DEPOSITION OF BOMB FISSION PRODUCTS UNDER ELECTROSTATIC FIELD

Period of run	Activity in air curie/cm^3 × 10^{18}	Windspeed in tunnel cm/sec	Velocity of deposition (cm/sec) to flat plates in field			Mobility cm^2/sec volt	Diffusion constant cm^2/sec	Diameter microns
			+2200 V/cm $v_g(+)$	−2200 V/cm $v_g(-)$	Nil $v_g(0)$			
16–23/8/57	0·33	1000	0·71	0·12	0·06	3·5 × 10^{-4}	9 × 10^{-6}	0·08
23–30/8/57	0·27	500	0·44	0·14	0·034	2·3 × 10^{-4}	6 × 10^{-6}	0·10
30/8–3/9/57	0·57	500	0·26	0·07	0·020	1·3 × 10^{-4}	3 × 10^{-6}	0·16

The field at the earth's surface would tend to drive positively charged fission-product-carrying nuclei to the ground, but the magnitude of the field does not seem to be sufficient to produce deposition rates comparable with those tabulated in Table 8. The mean field at Kew is 3·6 V/cm (Chalmers[21]) and this would give a deposition velocity of less than 0·001 cm/sec. Fields as high as 150 V/cm are sometimes

---

* As regards the ordinary nuclei in the air, about 50 per cent are uncharged and of the remainder equal numbers have positive and negative charges.[21] The distribution of charge in the fission-product-carrying nuclei is evidently biassed towards the positive, presumably because of the beta decay of the activity on them. For the same reason, the number of uncharged fission-product-carrying nuclei is probably lower than 50 per cent of the total.

found in thundery weather, but fields of this magnitude would be required continuously to give deposition velocities of the order observed.

Particles of 0·1 microns diameter and density 5 have terminal velocities of 4×10^{-4} cm/sec and this also is small compared with the observed values of v_g. Moreover, the facts

(a) deposition is nearly equal on downward and upward facing surfaces;

(b) v_g is strongly dependent on wind speed

rule out sedimentation as the deposition process.

5.4 Deposition by Thermal Effects

It is well known that dust particles in a room tend to be deposited where warm air is in contact with cold surfaces, and the principle of thermal deposition is also used in the thermal precipitator.

Rosenblatt and La Mer[30] have measured the velocity v_T reached by particles of various sizes in temperature gradients in air. v_T depends only slightly on the diameter of the particle and is given approximately by

$$v_T = \frac{0 \cdot 036}{T} \frac{dT}{dz} \text{ cm/sec}^{-1} \tag{18}$$

where T is the temperature in degrees absolute and $\dfrac{dT}{dz}$ the temperature gradient.

For a particle to attain a velocity equal to 0·1 cm/sec in air at N.T.P., a temperature gradient of 760 deg per cm would be necessary. It is, therefore, very unlikely that thermal forces can account for an appreciable part of the observed natural deposition of activity on small particles.

5.5 Deposition of Nuclei by Diffusion to Surfaces

Equation (6) for deposition of vapours to a flat plate:

$$v_g = 0 \cdot 332 D \theta^{\frac{1}{3}} \nu^{-\frac{1}{6}} u_1^{\frac{1}{2}} x^{-\frac{1}{2}}$$

gives the velocity of deposition at a point x cm from the leading edge of the plate. If l is the length of the plate, the value of v_g for the whole plate, which corresponds to the results of Table 8, is

$$\bar{v}_g = \frac{1}{l} \int_{x=0}^{l} v_g(x) \, dx \tag{19}$$

$$= 0 \cdot 664 D^{\frac{2}{3}} \nu^{-\frac{1}{6}} u_1^{\frac{1}{2}} l^{-\frac{1}{2}} \tag{20}$$

replacing θ by ν/D.

Equation 20 makes v_g depend on the two-thirds power of D, and inserting the values appropriate to the second experiment of Table 9, namely $D = 6 \times 10^{-6}$, $u_1 = 500$, $l = 30$, $\nu = 0 \cdot 147$, the value deduced for v_g is 0·0012 cm/sec, which is again much lower than the observed value for the deposition to plates in zero electrostatic field.

However, it is doubtful whether Equation 5 or 6 applies when the Schmidt number is as high as in the present case.

The way in which v_g depends on D is a function of the nature of the boundary layer. Pasquill[31] performed experiments on the evaporation of various liquids from saturated surfaces. The surfaces were arranged to be part of the wall of a wind tunnel, and at the flow rates used, the boundary layer was fully turbulent. The liquids used by Pasquill had diffusion coefficients varying from 0·05 to 0·28 cm²/sec, and the rates of evaporation, when expressed in the same units as v_g were found to be approximately proportional to $D^{0·22}$, as compared with $D^{0·67}$ theoretically for laminar flow. If v_g to the flat plate varied as $D^{0·22}$ instead of $D^{0·67}$, the theoretical rate of deposition of nuclei would be increased 100-fold.

The observed values of v_g to a flat plate may, therefore, be attributed to diffusion of nuclei across the boundary layer if this is at least partly turbulent or transitional in character.

It is desirable to make measurements of v_g for particles of the size of condensation nuclei when the boundary layer of flow is that obtaining over the earth's surface. No direct measurement has been made, but an upper limit can be deduced from the data on the dry deposition of fission products to the ground, which will be considered later, after the washout in rain has first been considered.

5.6 Washout of Nuclei by Rain

Measurements of the activity of fission products in the air have been made for a number of years. The method has been to attach filters to aircraft flown at various heights, and measurements at ground level have also been made (Stewart et al.[32], Peirson, Crooks and Fisher[33]). Also, the amount of activity brought down in rain has been determined, by analysing the fission product content of deposit gauges. (Stewart et al.,[27,32,34] Peirson and Salmon.[35]) The deposit gauges have a certain efficiency for dry deposition, but the amount deposited on them in the absence of rain was shown by Stewart et al.[27] to represent only a few per cent of the total deposited in rain. This does not, however, prove that the same is true for deposition to the ground, where the boundary layer flow is different.

Recently, Burton and Stewart[36] have analysed the same air filters and deposit gauge material for RaD (Pb 210), the long-lived daughter product of radon.

TABLE 10. WASHOUT OF RaD, Cs[137] AND Zr[95] IN RAIN

Nuclide	RaD	Cs[137]	Zr[95]
Period	1956	July 1958–June 1959	July 1958–June 1959
Rainfall (cm)	62	78	78
Air concentration (χ)			
curies/cm³ at $z=10^2$ cm	$4·0 \times 10^{-21}$	$3·0 \times 10^{-20}$	$3·2 \times 10^{-19}$
at $z=1·2 \times 10^5$ cm	$5·1 \times 10^{-21}$	$7·3 \times 10^{-20}$	$1·1 \times 10^{-18}$
Concentration in rain curies/litre	$2·0 \times 10^{-12}$	$1·5 \times 10^{-11}$	$1·3 \times 10^{-10}$
Rate of deposition (ω) curies/cm² sec	$3·9 \times 10^{-21}$	$3·6 \times 10^{-20}$	$3·3 \times 10^{-19}$
v_g cm/sec	1·0	1·2	1·0
W	430	230	130

$$W = \frac{\text{curies/kg in rain}}{\text{curies/kg in air at } 1·2 \times 10^5 \text{ cm}}$$

Some of the results of these measurements are summarized in Table 10, and salient points are as follows:

(a) There is an increase of χ with z for all three nuclides, but this is more marked for Cs^{137} and Zr^{95}, which are injected into the stratosphere by megaton nuclear explosions, than for RaD, which is derived from the terrestrial exhalation of radon.

(b) If the deposition rate ω, averaged over the year, is divided by the concentration at ground level, values of v_g close to 1 cm/sec are obtained. It is a coincidence that these values are similar to those found for the molecular diffusion of I_2 and SO_2 to the ground, for the mechanism is different, viz. washout by rain.

(c) The washout ratio W, defined as the specific activity (curies/kg) of rain divided by the specific activity (curies/kg) of air at 1200 m, lies in the range 100 to 400. This indicates a high efficiency for removal of the nuclei, as can be seen by deriving the corresponding figure for the removal of water from the atmosphere by rain. Saturated air at 0°C contains 4×10^{-3} g water per g air. Hence the corresponding value of W is 250.

It is unlikely that the uptake of the nuclei to the raindrops occurs while they are falling as rain. It is known that there is a lower limit to the size of particles which are impacted on raindrops, and this is in the range 1–10 microns.[37] It can also be shown by using equation 11 that diffusion of the nuclei to the raindrop during its fall cannot be sufficiently rapid.

It is more probable that diffusion to the cloud droplet may be the effective process. When the droplet is of less than about 10 microns diameter, the second term in equation 10 becomes negligible and the equation reduces to

$$N_m = 2 \tag{21}$$

or

$$\frac{2\omega s}{\chi D} = 2 \tag{22}$$

where ω is the flux to unit area of the drop. The rate of loss of material to the drop is $4\pi s^2 \omega$, which from 22 is equal to $4\pi \chi s D$ (this is equivalent to Langmuir's equation for evaporation from drops, see for example Green and Lane,[38] p. 84). Hence if there are $N(s)$ drops of radius s per cm^3 of air, the rate of removal of nuclei is given by

$$\frac{1}{\chi} \frac{\partial \chi}{\partial t} = 4\pi D \Sigma[sN(s)] \qquad \text{molecular diffusivity.} \tag{23}$$

(it is assumed that the diffusion to each droplet can be calculated independently of the presence of others).

Weickmann and Aufm Kampe[39] have published spectra of cloud droplet sizes for three types of cloud, from which values of $\Sigma[sN(s)]$ can be deduced, with results shown in Table 11. The mean radius was 8–9 microns for all three types of cloud, but the spread in sizes was larger for cumulus congestus and cumulonimbus than for fair-weather cumulus, and there are more drops per cm^3 in the last named type.

Under the experimental conditions, the smallest droplets caught were of radius 1·5 microns. It is possible that the number of small droplets was considerably underestimated, and if this was so the estimates of $\Sigma[sN(s)]$ would be too small also.

Putting $\Sigma[sN(s)]=0.06$ cm^2 in equation 23, and taking D for nuclei as 6×10^{-6} cm^2/sec:

$$-\frac{1}{\chi}\frac{\partial\chi}{\partial t} = 4.5\times10^{-6} \text{ sec}^{-1} \tag{24}$$

which gives

$$\chi = \chi_0 e^{-(4.5\times10^{-6}t)} \tag{25}$$

The mean time before attachment of nuclei to droplets is then $\dfrac{1}{4.5\times10^{-6}}$ secs, or 2.5

days (a similar result, by a slightly different method, has been given by Greenfield[40]).

TABLE 11. SIZES OF CLOUD DROPLETS
(after Weickmann and Aufm Kampe[39])

Type of cloud	Liquid water content g/m³	Droplet concentration cm^{-3}	Median radius (microns)	$\Sigma[sN(s)]$
Fair-weather cumulus	1·0	302	9	0·17
Cumulus congestus	3·9	64	8	0·059
Cumulonimbus	2·5	72	9	0·059

The mean time of residence in the troposphere of fission product activity is about 30 days[32] so that diffusion to cloud droplets would have to be effective for one-tenth the time to account for the observed rate of washout. Putting it another way, the observed rate would be achieved if rain-forming cloud occupied an average 4000 ft of the vertical extent of the troposphere.

An alternative approach is to calculate the time a cloud would have to persist for the droplets to absorb activity to the extent required. The cumulonimbus cloud sampled by Weickmann and Aufm Kampe contained 2·5 g of liquid water per m³ of air, or about 2 g per kg air. If a proportion 4.5×10^{-6} of the activity in the air diffuses to the drops per sec, a period of the order of a day would elapse before the drops acquired a proportion 0·4 of the total activity, corresponding to $W=200$. This time would be reduced if a considerable fraction of the liquid water was in micron-sized drops. It would also possibly be less in the presence of snow flakes.

The mean residence of RaD in the atmosphere is about 14 days.[36] This activity may well be attached to smaller nuclei than the fission product activity, with a higher diffusion constant and thus a higher rate of uptake to cloud droplets.

Yet another possibility is that the uptake of activity occurs during the rapid condensation of vapour on to drop-forming nuclei, by a vapour-wind effect.[41]

5.7 Measurements of Fission Products in Soil

Bryant et al.,[42] Morgan et al.[43] and others have made measurements of the activity of strontium-90 in the soil in Britain and these measurements can be compared with the cumulative total deposition in deposit gauges. If dry deposition by turbulent diffusion to grass contributes an important fraction of the total, the amounts found in the soil should be greater than that deduced from deposit gauge measurements. On the other hand, washout of activity from the soil would tend to operate the other way and give a deficit in the soil assay.

The results of three such comparisons are given in Table 12. The soil samples of Morgan et al.[44] at Sonning, Reading, in 1957 were taken in three horizons, 0–2 in., 2–6 in. and 6–12 in. In a field which had not been ploughed since 1953, the activity in the bottom 6 in. was only one-tenth of that in the top 2 in., but it is still possible that a fraction of the strontium activity may have penetrated below the depth sampled.

TABLE 12. ACTIVITY FOUND IN SOIL AND ESTIMATED FROM DEPOSIT GAUGES

Location	Activity	Time of sampling	Depth of sampling (cm)	Activity (curies/cm² × 10¹²)		Reference
				found in soil	cumulative in rain	
Reading	Sr^{90}	July 1957	30	0·56	0·55	Morgan et al.[34] Stewart et al.[27]
Milford Haven	Cs^{137}	July 1959	14	5·1	3·4	Peirson and Salmon[35]
Milford Haven	$Zr^{95}+Nb^{95}$	July 1959	14	18·2	10·0	Peirson and Salmon[35]

The estimate of cumulative fallout with which these results are compared is derived from measurements of the fallout in rain at Milford Haven, Pembrokeshire, extending back to May, 1954, and measurements of the relative specific activity of rain at various other places in the United Kingdom.[27] From this data the fallout at Reading is calculated, and is found to be very close to the measured soil content.

The soil samples taken at Milford Haven by Peirson and Salmon were taken in two horizons each of 7 cm. Ninety-five per cent of the fission product activity was found in the top horizon. The samples were analysed for Cs^{137}, and $Zr^{95}+Nb^{95}$, by gamma spectrometry, and the activities found were 50 and 80 per cent respectively larger than the cumulative deposit gauge measurements at the same place.

A similar comparison was made by Bergh et al.[45] at two sites near Ski in Norway. The deposit in rain of Sr^{90} and Cs^{137} during the period October 1957–October 1958 was compared with the increment in the soil content between those dates.

At one site, which was on the bare top of a 1000 m hill, the yearly increment in soil was no less than five times the fallout in rain, whereas at the other, more sheltered site, only a fairly small discrepancy was found. The results are, therefore, conflicting. If the discrepancy between Peirson and Salmon's soil measurements and the rain results is to be explained by dry deposition, then the value of v_g for deposition of fission product activity to grass must be between 0·5 and 1 cm/sec, and about ten times the value for deposition of the same activity to flat horizontal plates. The value found in Megaw and Chadwick's experiments, with a similar aerosol size deposited on grass was 0·2 cm/sec, and 0·4 cm/sec was observed for the deposition of Windscale iodine, probably on nuclei, in Lancashire and Yorkshire.

In another paper in this volume, P. R. Owen gives a theoretical treatment for the deposition of particles on surfaces, in which v_g (N_F/ψ_1 in Owen's notation) is derived as a fraction of the terminal velocity of the particle and the friction velocity u_* or u_τ.

For sub-micron particles Owen's results lead to:

$$v_g = 4 \times 10^{-3} u_*$$ (26)

If the average value of u_* for natural flow over the ground is 40 cm/sec, this gives $v_g = 0.16$ cm/sec.

6. SUMMARY AND CONCLUSIONS

Radioactive nuclides are present in air in very low mass concentrations, and are usually subject to rapid and irreversible adsorption at surfaces. Velocities of deposition of order 1 cm/sec are found for the dry deposition of iodine-131 vapour to surfaces in the laboratory and in the field. The mode of deposition is by diffusion, eddy diffusion in the free air and molecular diffusion across laminar boundary layers.

Iodine-131 and other activities are also found adsorbed on condensation nuclei. These nuclei have terminal velocities of the order of 10^{-4} cm/sec or less, but the rate of dry deposition to surfaces is found to be of the order of 10^{-2} to 10^{-1} cm/sec. Activity in this form is also subject to deposition in rain.   The mode of uptake to the rain or cloud droplets is uncertain.

7. ACKNOWLEDGEMENTS

I am indebted to Messrs. D. V. Booker, D. H. Peirson and W. J. Megaw, all of A.E.R.E., Harwell, for access to unpublished results.

REFERENCES
1. GOLDSCHMIDT, V. M. *Geochemistry*, Clarendon Press, Oxford (1954).
2. CHAMBERLAIN, A. C., *Phil. Mag.*, **44**, 1145 (1953).
3. GOLDSTEIN, S. (Ed.), *Modern Development in Fluid Dynamics*, Clarendon Press, Oxford, 1938.
4. MONTEITH, J. L., *The New Scientist*, **5**, 1124 (1959).
5. CHAMBERLAIN, A. C. and CHADWICK, R. C., *Nucleonics*, **11**, 22 (1953).
6. MEGAW, W. J. and CHADWICK, R. C. Unpublished (1959).
7. PARKER H. M., *Proc. Int. Conf. on the Peaceful Uses of Atomic Energy*, **13**, 305 (1955).
8. HEALY, J. W., ANDERSON, B. V., CLUKEY, H. V. and SOLDAT, J. K., *Proc. 2nd Int. Conf. on Peaceful Uses of Atomic Energy*, **18**, 309 (1958).
9. STEWART, N. G. and CROOKS, R. N. *Nature, Lond.*, **182**, 627 (1958).
10. CHAMBERLAIN, A. C. and DUNSTER, H. J., *Nature, Lond.*, **182**, 629 (1958).
11. CHAMBERLAIN, A. C., *Quart. J. R., Met. Soc.*, **85**, 350 (1959).
12. SHEPPARD, P. A., *Quart. J. R., Met. Soc.*, **84**, 205 (1958).
13. MEETHAM, A. R., *Quart. J. R., Met. Soc.*, **76**, 359 (1950).
14. MEETHAM, A. R., *Quart. J. R., Met. Soc.*, **80**, 96 (1954).
15. MEETHAM, A. R., *Atmospheric Pollution*, Pergamon Press, 1952.
16. MEADE, P. J. and PASQUILL, F., *Int. J. Air Pollution*, **1**, 60 (1958).
17. CHAMBERLAIN, A. C., A.E.R.E. HP/R 1261 (available from H.M.S.O.) (1953).
18. BEST, A. C., *Quart. J. R., Met. Soc.*, **76**, 16 (1950).
19. RANZ, W. E. and MARSHALL, W. R., *Chem. Eng. Prog.*, **48**, 141 (1952).
20. KANNO, S., FUKUI, S., IHEDA, H. and ONO, Y., *Int. J. Air Pollution*, **1**, 234 (1959).
21. CHALMERS, J. A., *Atmospheric Electricity*, Clarendon Press, Oxford, 1949.
22. WILKENING, M. H., *Rev. Sci. Instrum.*, **23**, 13 (1952).
23. STEWART, K. *Trans. Faraday Soc.*, **52**, 162 (1956).
24. CHAMBERLAIN, A. C., MEGAW, W. J. and WIFFEN, R. D., *Geofisica Pura e Applicata (Milan)*, **36**, 233 (1957).
25. CHAMBERLAIN, A. C. and DYSON, E. D., *Brit. J. Radiol.* **29**, 317 (1956).
26. BULLAS, D. O. Unpublished (1953).

27. STEWART, N. G., OSMOND, R. G. D., CROOKS, R. N. and FISHER, E. M. R., A.E.R.E. HP/R 2354 (available from H.M.S.O.) (1957).
28. BOOKER, D. V. T. To be published (1959).
29. MEGAW, W. J. and CHADWICK, R. C., A.E.R.E. HP/M 114 (1957).
30. ROSENBLATT, P. and LA MER, V. K., *Phys. Rev.*, **70**, 385 (1946).
31. PASQUILL, F., *Proc. Roy. Soc. A.*, **182**, 75 (1943).
32. STEWART, N. G., CROOKS, R. N. and FISHER, E. M. R., A.E.R.E. HP/R, 2017 (available from H.M.S.O.) (1956).
33. PEIRSON, D. H., CROOKS, R. N. and FISHER, E. M. R. *Nature, Lond.*, **186**, 224 (1960).
34. STEWART, N. G., OSMOND, R. G. D., CROOKS, R. N., FISHER, E. M. R. and OWERS, M. J., A.E.R.E. HP/R 2790 (available from H.M.S.O.) (1959).
35. PEIRSON, D. H. and SALMON, L., *Nature*, **184**, 1678 (1959).
36. BURTON, W. M. and STEWART, N. G. *Nature, Lond.*. **186**, 584 and A.E.R.E. HP/R 2084 (1960).
37. HOCKING, L. M., *Q.J. Roy. Met. Soc.*, **85**, 44 (1959).
38. GREEN H. L. and LANE, W. R., *Particulate Clouds: Dusts, Smokes and Mists*, Spon, London, 1957.
39. WEICKMANN, H. K. and AUFM KAMPE, H. J., *J. Met.*, **10**, 204 (1953).
40. GREENFIELD, S. M., *J. Met.*, **14**, 115, (1957).
41. FACY, L., *Arch. for Meteorol. Geophys. & Biochim.*, **8**, 229 (1958).
42. BRYANT, F. J., CHAMBERLAIN, A. C., MORGAN, A. and SPICER, G. S., *J. Nucl. Energy*, **6**, 22 (1957).
43. MORGAN, A., COX, G. W. and TAYLER, R. B., *2nd Int. Conf. on Peaceful Uses of Atomic Energy*, **18**, 503 (1958).
44. BRYANT, F. J., MORGAN, A. and SPICER, G. S., A.E.R.E. HP/R 2730 (available from H.M.S.O.) (1958).
45. BERGH, H., FINSTAD, G., LUND, L., MICHELSON, O. and OTTAR, B., Forsvarets Forskningsinstitut Report K 219, Lillestrom, Norway (1959).
46. LAL, D. and PETERS, B., *2nd Int. Conf. on Peaceful Uses of Atomic Energy*, **18**, 533 (1958).
47. BROECKER, W. S. and WALTON, A., *Science*, **130**, 209 (1959).
48. BEGEMANN, F., *Proc. 2nd Int. Conf. on Peaceful Uses of Atomic Energy*, **18**, 545 (1958).

THE SIZE OF WOOD SMOKE PARTICLES

by W. W. FOSTER*
Torry Research Station, Aberdeen, D.S.I.R.

1. LIST OF SYMBOLS

a=radius of spherical particle.

b=number of cylinders of length l in which charged particles are deposited.

$\beta = (Fc_0/2\pi k_0 \eta d)(n^2 e^2/a^4)$.

c_0=mass concentration of aerosol at time $t=0$.

δ=density of each particle.

e=elementary charge

E=electric field strength.

F=slip factor for correcting Stokes' drag.

I'=current due to deposition of charged particle inside cylinders.

k_0=dielectric constant of medium.

l=length of individual cylinders in which charged particles are deposited.

M=rate of deposition of charged particles at position x.

M_c=mass of particles deposited in charging unit in time t.

n=number of elementary charges on a particle.

η=viscosity of medium.

P=rate of deposition of charged particles in cylinder of length x.

P_b=mass of charged particles deposited on b cylinders in time t.

P_c=mass of particles entering charging unit in time t.

r=radial position in cylinder.

R=radius of cylinder in which charged particles are deposited.

ρ=charge concentration of smoke.

t=time.

t_c=time for smoke to pass from charging unit to centre of set of cylinders.

t_u=time for smoke to pass from smoke box to centre of charging unit.

v=velocity of particle in an applied electric field.

V=velocity of medium carrying smoke.

W=rate of deposition of charged particles in a given length of cylinder.

x=distance.

2. INTRODUCTION

THE smoke generated when wood is heated in air contains a considerable range of compounds resulting from the distillation and degradation of the celluloses, lignins, resins and tannins. Visible particles which are formed when the smoke cools appear to equilibrate rapidly with the ambient vapours. When the present studies of wood smoke deposition began it seemed that the overall rate of deposition of smoke on fish might depend on the size of the particles. Attempts were therefore made to determine the structure of the particles, the average size and the size distribution.

* Member of the staff of the Herring Industry Board.

G

In most industrial smoke generators wood sawdust and shavings are burned to provide heat for the process of destructive distillation. The wood which has suffered degradation becomes fuel during the final phase of combustion. This self-propagating method of smoke generation is very difficult to control even when a controlled draught of air is directed at the glowing sawdust.[1] In the present experiments smoke was generated by agitating sawdust fed into a blast of air which was at a temperature of $314 \pm 2°C$.[2,3]

3. MICROSCOPE EXAMINATION

Smoke cooled down to room temperature was sampled in three ways: by means of a cascade impactor;[4] by gravitational settling in a chamber about 10 cm high; and by an electrical method, the particles being charged with the same sign and allowed to disperse by mutual repulsion. The particles were deposited on glass slides coated with silicone "Repelcote" water repellent to prevent uneven spreading. Light microscope examination showed that the images of the particles appeared to be circular and there was no evidence of the occurrence of loose agglomerates. All indications were that the particles were originally spherical and that coagulation resulted in coalescense. Similar results were found for particles of tobacco smoke,[5,6] tar fogs,[7] and resin smokes.[8]

Wood smoke particles are not very volatile and were shadowed with aluminium under vacuum to increase the image contrast without seriously affecting their size. Examined under oil the particles dissolved leaving aluminium replicas. Fig. 1 shows photomicrographs of typical samples of smoke collected by the three methods described

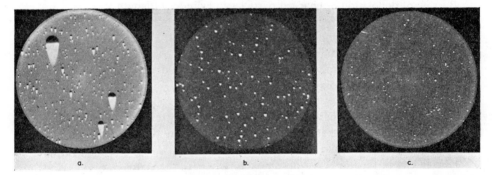

FIG. 1. Aluminium shadow-cast wood smoke particles ($\times 1300$).
Sampling method: (*a*) Cascade impactor; (*b*) Gravitational settling; (*c*) Electrical deposition.

above. The efficiency of collection in the cascade impactor decreases as the size decreases, being less than 50 per cent for particles of radius less than about 0.2μ;[4] it was found that about 95 per cent of the weight of particles is collected by the electrical method; and in gravitational settling nearly all the particles are collected on the horizontal surface, only a very small fraction diffusing to the walls.

The absence of large particles in the samples obtained by gravitational settling and electrical deposition therefore suggests that those present in the cascade impactor sample are artifacts, possibly resulting from coagulation during the passage of smoke through the instrument.[9] The size distribution of the particles obtained by gravitational settling appeared to be fairly uniform and the average size was larger than that of particles collected by electrical deposition. This is attributable to Brownian motion tending to prevent the gravitational settling of small particles and also giving rise to coagulation. Electrical deposition of particles takes place within a fraction of a second before appreciable coagulation occurs. Although about 5 per cent of the total weight of particles is deposited in the charging unit, and some of these might be large ones, it is considered that for aerosols such as wood smoke the size distribution found by depositing particles electrically is nearer to the actual distribution than is found when using the other two methods.

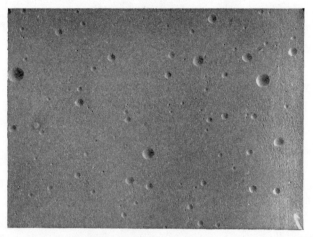

FIG. 2. Gold–palladium shadow-cast wood smoke particles (× 20,000).

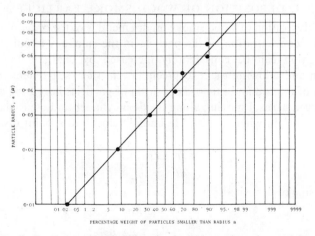

FIG. 3. Log, normal probability plot for 224 wood smoke particles.

It can be seen from Fig. 1 that many of the particles deposited electrically are so small as to be below the limit of resolution of the light microscope. Samples were therefore examined in an electron microscope. Since wood smoke particles dissolve the supporting film (Formvar) used on the microscope grids it was necessary to deposit them on evaporated carbon films. Figure 2 shows a typical electron photomicrograph of particles shadowed with 40–60 per cent gold–palladium at an angle of

20° to the plane of the supporting carbon film. Assuming that each particle formed the segment of a sphere, and that the angle of wetting was 20°, the original radius of each sphere would have been about one fifth of the diameter of the deposited droplet.

For a typical sample of wood smoke, the values of cumulative weight per cent are plotted against the corresponding size on a log normal probability mesh in Fig. 3. The size distribution obtained from the straight line drawn through the points is shown in Fig. 4.

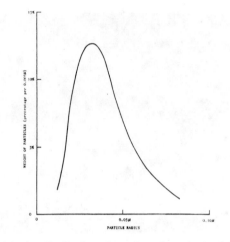

FIG. 4. Particle size distribution of wood smoke—obtained from Fig. 3.

4. DEPOSITION OF WOOD SMOKE PARTICLES

The rate of deposition of wood smoke on dry metal is of the order of 0·005 mg/cm² h when the mass concentration of the particle in the smoke is about 0·25 mg/1. The rate of deposition can be considerably increased by charging the particles with the same sign and allowing them to precipitate in their self-generated electric field. The equation of motion and rate of deposition of particles have been calculated for a unipolar charged aerosol moving along inside a cylinder and continually replenished at an arbitrary origin where $x=0$.[3] The radial velocity at a point distant r from the axis is

$$\frac{dr}{dt} = \frac{r\rho e}{3k_0\eta} \cdot \frac{nF}{a} \tag{1}$$

The mass of smoke deposited per unit time at x is

$$M = \frac{\beta R c_0}{2(1 + \beta x/V)^2} \tag{2}$$

and if P is the total mass of smoke deposited per unit time between $x=0$ and x,

$$P = \pi \frac{R^2 c_0 \beta x}{1 + (\beta x/V)}$$

or

$$x = \pi R^2 c_0 V \left(\frac{x}{P}\right) - \frac{V}{\beta} \tag{3}$$

Where V is the velocity of the smoke along the cylinder, defined in the present experiments as the rate of flow of smoke divided by the cross-sectional area of the cylinder. The other symbols are defined before the main text.

Equations similar to 1, 2 and 3 apply for a charged cloud moving between parallel sheets or over an earthed plane of infinite extent.

Any particular portion of the target acquires a net charge only from deposited particles. If the target is earthed and a mass W deposits in unit time, the current to earth is

$$I' = \frac{3Wne}{4\pi\delta a^3} \tag{4}$$

Equations 3 and 4 have been used to determine a and n for wood smoke particles.[3] In these experiments fresh smoke from the generator passed first through a box of capacity 50 l. at a rate of about 1 l/sec and then through a concentric cylinder corona field. The charged particles were directed along a stainless steel tube consisting of short cylindrical sections joined together by Sellotape. Particles leaving the tube were collected in an electrical precipitator. The amount of smoke on each section was determined by weighing.

If P_b is the mass of smoke particles deposited in time t on b cylinders each of length l, then from Equation 3,

$$b = \pi R^2 c_0 Vt(b/P_b) - \frac{V}{l\beta} \tag{5}$$

From the plot of b against b/P_b c_0 and β can be found and n^2e^2F/a^4 determined; ne/a^3 can be found using Equation 4; and the average radius a and charge ne can be calculated.

It was found that in all experiments there was a linear relationship between b and b/P_b and that the gradient of this line $(\pi R^2 c_0 Vt)$ was usually about 10 per cent less than the actual mass of particles entering the corresponding set of cylinders. These two observations offer strong support for the theory.

5. EFFECT OF POLARITY AND RATE OF CHARGING ON PARTICLE RADIUS

The polarity and magnitude of the voltage applied to the corona electrode were varied to determine whether, for wood smoke, these factors had any effect on the average particle radius calculated from the results of precipitation inside cylinders. Results obtained with smokes of about the same age before charging (t_u) and after charging (t_c) are compared. Since t_u varied only from about 0·9 to 1·1 sec and t_c varied only from about 0·25 to about 0·75 sec it is considered that possible effects due to coagulation which might have arisen in separate experiments can be ignored. As the charging rate increased, the fraction of the total entrant aerosol which was precipitated in the charging unit, M_c/P_c, also increased. According to Table 1, large variations in M_c/P_c appeared to have no effect on the average radius of the emergent aerosol. It would seem from these results that there was no marked tendency for particles of any particular size to be preferentially precipitated during charging, whatever the sign of the charge.

Table 1. Effect of rate charging, indicated by M_c/P_c on particle radius

Positive corona		Negative corona	
M_c/P_c	a	M_c/P_c	a
0·037	0·089	0·073	0·075
0·059	0·106	0·091	0·102
0·109	0·093	0·199	0·100
0·116	0·110	0·457	0·089
0·131	0·102		
0·141	0·118		
0·178	0·103		
0·207	0·090		
0·339	0·098		

6. EFFECT ON PARTICLE RADIUS OF AGEING BEFORE AND AFTER CHARGING

No systematic investigation of the coagulation of samples of the same smoke was made, but results from a number of different experiments appeared to show that the average radius of smoke increased from about 0·10 μ ($t_u \sim 1/$sec) to about 0·14 ($t_u \sim 16$ sec). Assuming that Brownian motion of the particles is the predominant mechanism of coagulation[8,10] particles of radius 0·10 μ would increase to 0·11 μ after 16 sec. This discrepancy between experimental and theoretical results is much larger than is usually found for aerosols. If the particles had grown by the absorption of vapours the mass concentration would have increased by a factor of 2·7 in 16 sec. In fact it was found that the mass concentration tended to decrease by a few per cent as the smoke aged. The divergence from the theoretical value remains unexplained.

In determining the effect of the age of smoke after charging (t_c) on the particle radius, smokes having about the same t_u value were examined, the particle radius being determined in a number of consecutive sets of cylinders. A range of charging conditions was used in these experiments, as indicated in Fig. 5. Although there seems to be no systematic relationship between the rate of charging and the change of particle radius with t_c, there appears to be an overall tendency for the particle radius to increase as the charged smoke ages.

This apparent increase in size could have been due to coagulation or to a tendency for the radial velocity of particles to increase with decreasing size. Equation 1, which gives this velocity, is similar in form to that giving the velocity of particles in an applied field, where

$$v = \frac{Ee}{6\pi\eta} \frac{nF}{a} \tag{6}$$

It follows that since there appears to be no marked tendency for particles of different sizes to move at different velocities during charging (Table 1) it is likely that there should be no tendency on this account for the average radius of charged smoke particles to change as the smoke passes along the cylinder. It is therefore possible that the charged smoke particles were coagulating. This result accords with theoretical discussions[8,11] which show that coagulation due to Brownian motion can never be prevented by the mutual repulsion of charged particles except when each particle has an infinite charge. The measurement of the rate of coagulation of charged aerosols is difficult, chiefly because the particles disperse rapidly on the containing walls. Although the results presented here cannot be considered to be conclusive, it would seem that

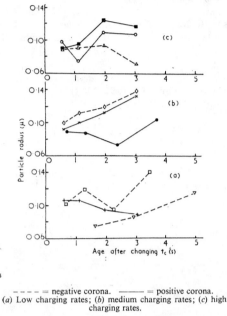

FIG. 5

- - - - = negative corona. ———— = positive corona.
(a) Low charging rates; (b) medium charging rates; (c) high charging rates.

Symbol	Corona conditions	
	V_m (kV)	i (μA/cm)
○	+8·71	·12·2
■	+7·2	4·23
.△	−7·74	.9·67
×	+6·2	1·38
●	+3·68	1·58
◇	−6·69	1·80
+	+5·7 ·	0·39
⊡	−6·0	0·38
.▽	−6·0 ·	0·34

Fig. 5. Effect of ageing on average radius of charged wood smokes.

this method of determining the average radius of charged aerosols might be useful when studying their coagulation, especially when applied to aerosols initially monodisperse or of known size distribution.

7. ACKNOWLEDGEMENTS

The work described was carried out at Torry Research Station of the Department of Scientific and Industrial Research by staff of the Herring Industry Board as part of the programmes of the Board and the Department. The author is indebted to Dr. A. C. Jason for help and advice in the course of this work and also to Mr. W. Hodgkiss and Mr. A. Lees who prepared the electron photomicrographs.

8. REFERENCES

1. CUTTING, C. L., Dept. Sci. Industr. Res., London, Food Investig, leaft. No. 10 (H.M. Stationery Office, 1950).
2. NICOL, D. L., *Brit. Pat.* No. 781,591 (September, 1954); D.S.I.R., London, Food Investig. Bd. Rep., p 41 (1954), p. 31 (1955).
3. FOSTER, W. W., *Brit. J. Appl. Phys.*, **10,** 206 (1959).
4. MAY, K. R., *J. Sci. Instr.*, **22,** 187 (1945).
5. BRANDT, O. and HIEDEMANN, E., *Trans. Faraday Soc.*, **32,** 1101 (1936).
6. DRINKER, P., THOMSON, R. M. and FINN, J. L., *J. Industr. Hyg.*, **8,** No. 7, 307 (1926).
7. BADGER, E. H. M. and WILSON, D. S., *J. Soc. Chem. Ind.*, London (Transactions), **65,** 119 (1946).
8. WHYTLAW-GRAY, R. and PATTERSON, H. S., *Smoke: a study of aerial disperse systems*, London, Arnold, 1932.
9. DAVIES, C. N., AYLWARD, M. and LEACEY, D., *Arch. Industr. Hyg.*, **4,** 354 (1951).
10. SCHMOLUKOWSKI, M. VON, *Z. Phys. Chem.*, **92,** 126 (1917).
11. GILLESPIE, T., *Proc. Roy. Soc.*, A**216,** 569 (1953).

THE IMPINGEMENT OF WATER DROPS ON A SURFACE MOVING AT HIGH SPEED

by D. C. JENKINS and J. D. BOOKER
Royal Aircraft Establishment, Farnborough

1. INTRODUCTION

AN aircraft in flight may encounter water droplets which vary from a few microns in diameter up to several millimetres, and the impact of these droplets on forward-facing surfaces of the aircraft gives rise to several design problems. If the droplets are supercooled they freeze on impact and form an ice deposit. Application of heat to the affected surfaces is the usual method of preventing a dangerous build up of ice, and the heat requirements are governed by the rate at which droplets impinge and the impingement area. The icing hazard largely occurs with the smaller droplets for which a determination of the impingement area and rate of catch involves plotting the droplet trajectories as they approach the surface. The problem of droplet trajectories has been extensively studied, and trajectories determined for a wide range of drop size, speed and surface shape,[1,2,3,4] et al.

Trajectories of the larger drops approximate to straight lines, and impingement occurs on the full forward-facing areas with little deflection of the drops. Rain drops impinging on aircraft windscreens seriously reduce visibility, and one solution to this problem is to find a means of atomizing the drops before they meet the surface. At high aircraft speeds the impact of the rain drops may cause serious damage,[5,6] and the problem is to find materials better able to withstand the impacts. A complicating factor in the study of rain drop impacts is that the velocity fields round the aircraft may cause partial or complete break-up of the drop in some cases before it reaches the surface.[7,8] There is, however, insufficient information available at present to enable this aspect to be completely evaluated.

The particular problem dealt with in this paper concerns the impact of raindrops on a surface moving at high speed. A knowledge of the way a drop breaks up in these impacts is of interest as it may shed light on the mechanism whereby damage can be caused. For this purpose a photographic study has been made of the normal impact between a smooth hard surface and water drops nominally of 2 mm diameter and roughly of spherical shape representing a flight case where rupture of the drop has not occurred. It is found that the water from the impinging drop flows over the surface at a speed considerably in excess of the impact speed. This implies the generation of a very high initial impact pressure in the drop which, together with the high flow velocity, is the source of surface damage.

A "streak" photography technique has been developed by means of which water flow velocities resulting from drop/surface impacts can be readily determined. This has been used to find the flow velocities in impacts of drops on a hardened steel surface at speeds up to 3750 ft/sec. An estimate of the peak impact pressures has been made by calculating the stagnation pressures corresponding to the measured flow velocities. It is found that these calculated pressures correspond quite closely with plane shock wave pressures in water if it is assumed that the water particle velocity behind the shock wave is equal to the impact speed.

2. APPARATUS

Figure 1 shows a diagrammatic arrangement of the apparatus used.[9] The drop, supported on a fine web, was positioned on the axis of a smooth bore air gun so that it would be struck by the flat nose of a projectile which formed the impact surface.

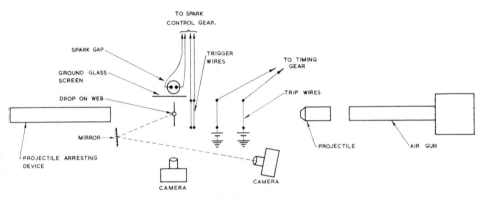

Fig. 1. Diagrammatic arrangement of apparatus.

The projectile velocity could be closely controlled by the air pressure used in the gun, and was measured by the projectile breaking two wires a known distance apart. Illumination of the impact was by means of a spark having an effective light duration in the order of 1 μsec. Triggering the spark was by means of the projectile closing a circuit by striking two crossed wires separated by a small gap. Shadowgraph pictures were obtained by placing a camera and the spark gap on opposite sides of the drop as shown in Fig. 1 with a ground glass screen between the drop and spark to diffuse the illumination. For reflected light pictures the glass screen was replaced by a black flock paper screen and the spark source placed near the camera. The experiments were carried out in a darkened room with the camera shutter being operated manually before and after each shot. By using a variable delay unit in the spark gap apparatus it was possible to take a series of single pictures with the drop and projectile in successive stages of impact. Oblique front views could be taken simultaneously with the side views by means of a mirror and second camera.

3. RESULTS OF SHADOWGRAPH PHOTOGRAPHY

Figure 2 shows a 2 mm diameter drop positioned on the web before firing the gun. Figs. 3 to 8 show in side view successive stages of the normal impact between 2 mm diameter drops and a magnesium alloy surface moving at 1000 ft/sec. At this speed the magnesium alloy surface was undamaged by the impacts. Figs. 9 and 10 show the same process from an oblique front view. From Fig. 3 it can be seen that just before impact the web is blown away pulling out a small protuberance from the back face of the drop which is then unsupported at the moment of impact. During impact the drop is seen to spread radially over the impact surface in the form of a disc, the perimeter of which breaks down first into radial filaments (Fig. 9) and then into a mist of small droplets (Figs. 8 and 10). The disk-type of flow and break down into radial filaments is generally similar to that resulting from drops falling freely on to a horizontal surface.[10,11,12,13]

The trailing web causes a distortion of the rear part of the drop which varies from shot to shot, masking any distortion of this region which may be caused by the impact. A comparison of the position of the rear part of the drop in Fig. 3 with Figs. 4, 5 and 6 shows that movement of this part of the drop during impact is small.

FIG. 2.

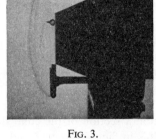

FIG. 3.

FIG. 4.

FIG. 5.

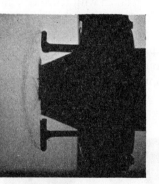

FIG. 6.

FIG. 7.

FIG. 8.

FIG. 9.

FIG. 10.

FIGS. 2–10. Water drop photographs.

By taking the drop and projectile position of Fig. 3 as datum and working to visually similar parts of the disk in successive pictures the rate of radial increase of the disc can be estimated. Taking a constant projectile velocity of 1000 ft/sec the radial velocity of the disc periphery during contact with the impact surface is found to be approximately *3400 ft/sec*. Dr. F. P. Bowden has found similar high radial velocities in the case of the impact of water jets.[14] The pictures suggest that a comparatively large fraction of the water flows at the high speed whereas energy considerations indicate only a small fraction. The appearance of a large volume flow in the pictures may be caused by a break-up of the periphery of the disk into a spray.

4. STREAK PHOTOGRAPHY TECHNIQUE

Water droplets in the outermost edge of the expanding disc have two velocity components, (1) a forward velocity equal to that of the projectile whilst the disc is in contact with the impact surface and (2) a radial velocity over the surface. The droplets thus trace out in space a cone in which the radial component w at any point is given by $w = V \tan \theta$, where V is the projectile velocity and θ is the semi-cone angle at the point. If the impact is photographed in side view using reflected light from a spark source of long enough duration a section of the cone should be recorded as streaks from the moving droplets. This in fact does occur and can be seen in Fig. 11 which shows the impact at 1000 ft/sec taken with reflected light from an Arditron flash tube. Using the upper semi-cone angle, measured close to the drop, and the forward speed of the projectile the radial speed of the disc flow is found to agree with the estimate made using the shadowgraph pictures. It was necessary in taking this reflected light picture to place the light source fairly high above the camera with the result that the lower part of the disc was not properly illuminated. This is considered to be the reason for the small lower cone angle of Fig. 11.

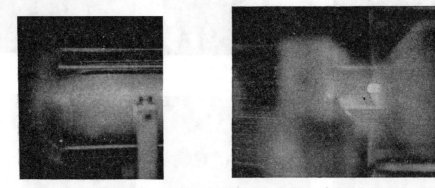

FIGS. 11 and 12. Water drop photographs.

The streak method is particularly useful for finding radial flow velocities in impacts above 1000 ft/sec where the necessary high speed or flash photography would be more difficult to apply. Fig. 12 shows a typical result taken at 2570 ft/sec using a small flash unit which could be placed much closer to the camera than the Arditron unit. On account of a change of apparatus the projectile movement in this case is from left to right of the picture. The spark is triggered some time before impact so that an outline of the drop can be seen as well as the cone trace formed during the impact. Reflected light streaks from the projectile have been suppressed to a certain extent by a matt black treatment, but the outside edge of the projectile is sufficiently well defined to form a datum for the measurement of cone angles.

5. RESULTS OF STREAK PHOTOGRAPHY

Radial flow velocities resulting from the normal impact of 2 mm diameter drops on a steel surface over the impact speed range 300 to 3750 ft/sec have been obtained by the streak technique. The semi-cone angles measured close to the drop, are given in Fig. 13.

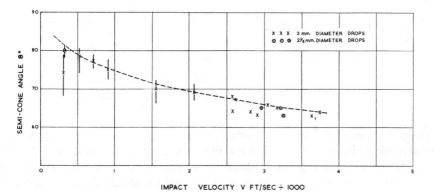
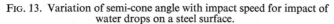

FIG. 13. Variation of semi-cone angle with impact speed for impact of water drops on a steel surface.

Several shots were made at each of a number of speeds up to 2000 ft/sec and for each case the largest and smallest angles found together with an average value have been plotted. Above 1000 ft/sec a gun using a solid propellant was used[15] and above 2000 ft/sec speed control was not sufficiently accurate to ensure several shots at each selected speed. For this reason the results of the individual shots have been recorded. In these tests the spark source was arranged to illuminate the disc completely, the small cone angles occasionally found are, therefore, thought to be due to a lack of symmetry of the radial flow. Allowing for a possible small error in measurement the true angle for any given impact speed is likely to be near the upper angle measured. With the exception of the results at 300 ft/sec the cone angles steadily decrease with increasing impact speed. At 300 ft/sec some rather small cone angles were recorded, but on repeating this case using 2·5 mm diameter drops the average angle increased. It is not clear if this is due to a true drop size effect on the radial velocities or if the larger quantity of water flowing smooths out the flow to a certain extent so that the smallest angles are not found.

Calculated radial velocities using the cone angle results are shown in Fig. 14. It will be seen that very high speeds are reached, approaching 8000 ft/sec at the highest impact speed.

The radial velocity must derive from the pressure generated in the drop on impact, and an estimate of the order of this pressure has been made by calculating the corresponding stagnation pressure for a steady flow. An allowance for compressibility has been made by finding a pressure p such that $\int_0^p \frac{dp}{\rho} = \frac{w^2}{2}$ using density data for water

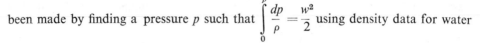

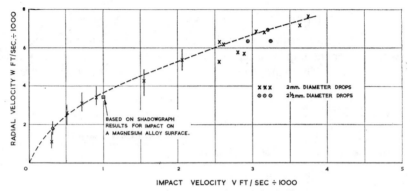

FIG. 14. Variation of radial velocity with impact speed for impact of water drops on a steel surface.

given by Kirkwood.[16] The results are plotted in Fig 15 and show that very high pressures are deduced, reaching 230 ton/in.² at the highest impact speed. Also shown plotted in this figure is a graph of shock wave pressures in water[16] which is based on the relation $p=\rho cv$, where p is the pressure behind the shock wave, ρ is the normal

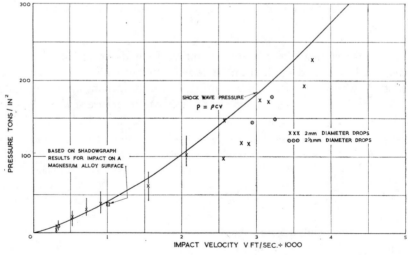

FIG. 15. Variation of impact pressure with impact speed for impact of water drops on a steel surface.

density of water, c is the speed of propagation of the shock wave and v is the speed of the water particles behind the shock wave which, in this case, is assumed to be the same as the impact speed. For comparison the Bernoulli pressure $\frac{1}{2}\rho v^2$ is also shown. The calculated stagnation pressure follows the shock wave pressure, but is somewhat lower at the higher impact speeds. At these speeds slight deformation of the surface occurs which, together with elastic deformation, leads to a reduced shock wave pressure on account of a reduction in the water particle velocity.

6. CONCLUSIONS

The results show that in the normal impact of water drops on a smooth hard surface at high speed some of the water flows radially outwards over the surface at a speed considerably greater than the impact speed. This implies the generation of a high peak impact pressure in the drop.

Calculations of stagnation pressures based on measured radial flow velocities for impacts of water drops on a steel surface at speeds up to 3750 ft/sec suggest that in this case the peak pressure approximates to the shock wave pressure $\rho c v$ where the particle velocity v is taken to be the same as the impact speed.

Depending on the speed water drops striking a surface may induce pressures high in comparison with the static strengths of many materials of aircraft construction of water drops. Also the very high velocity with which the water flows over the surface could induce high shear stresses in the impacted surface and any small surface roughnesses in the way of the flow would be the centre of further damage.

7. ACKNOWLEDGEMENTS

Acknowledgement is made to Mr. W. R. Lane of the Physics Section, C.D.E.E. Porton, for suggesting the web technique for drop support and supplying a suitable material. To Mr. E. G. Cuff of the Photographic Section, C.D.E.E., Porton, for taking the shadowgraph pictures. Also to colleagues at the R.A.E. for valuable discussions, in particular Mr. D. G. A. Rendel of the Mechanical Engineering Department and Mr. W. J. J. Sexton of the Instrumentation Department. (Crown copyright is reserved for this paper.)

8. REFERENCES

1. GLAUERT, M., R. & M. 2025 (1940).
2. LANGMUIR, I. and BLODGETT, K., A.A.F. TR 5418 (1946).
3 TRIBUS, M , University of Michigan, Airplane Icing Information Course, Lecture 3 (1953).
4. BIGG, F. J. and BAUCHEN, J.E., unpublished M.O.S. report.
5. ROBERTSON, R. M., LABISSER, R. J. and STEIN, R. E., Ind. Eng. Chem., 38, 590 (1946).
6. FYALL, A. A., KING, R. B. and STRAIN, R. N. C., unpublished M.O.S. report.
7. ENGEL, O. G., J. Res. Nat. Bur. Stand., 60, No. 3, 245 (1958).
8. JENKINS, D. C., unpublished M.O.S. report.
9. JENKINS, D. C., BOOKER, J. D. and SWEED, J. W., unpublished M.O.S. report.
10. WORTHINGTON, A. M., Proc. Roy. Soc., 25, 261 (1877).
11. SAVIC, P. and BOULT, G. T., NRC of Canada report MT-26 (1955).
12. ENGEL, O. G., J. Res. Nat. Bur. Stand., 54, No. 5, 281 (1955).
13. TSUTSUI, T., Inst. Phys. Chem. Res. Tokyo, 16, 109 (1931); 30, 227 (1936).
14. BOWDEN, F. P. and BRUNTON, J. H., Nature, Lond., 181, 873 (1958).
15. JENKINS, D. C. and BOOKER, J. D., unpublished M.O.S. report.
16. KIRKWOOD, J. G. and MONTROLL, E. W., O.S.R.D., Rep. 676 (1942).

THE DISTRIBUTION OF IMPACTED PARTICLES OF VARIOUS SIZES ON THE BLADES OF A TURBINE CASCADE

by D. L. MARTLEW
(National Gas Turbine Establishment, Pyestock)

Summary—A turbine blade cascade was exposed to an airstream laden with droplets of paraffin wax. Particles in various size groups were counted and the variation of deposition rate with particle size and position on the blade surface estimated.

The airflow in the cascade was calculated and the equations of small particles moving initially with the air were integrated to give their paths. The relative deposition rates were calculated and compared with the measurements. Good general agreement was obtained. The velocities and directions of impact with the blade were also estimated.

1. INTRODUCTION

DAMAGE to gas turbine blading caused by the solid products of combustion of ash forming fuels may occur in several ways. Erosion or corrosion and the formation of aerodynamically harmful deposits may take place. Generally these effects are most severe on those surfaces of the blading which airborne particles reach by direct impact.

The exercise described here was part of exploratory work carried out at N.G.T.E. to discover profitable lines of attack on the problem of blade fouling. The manner in which airborne particles of a range of sizes reach the surface of a turbine blade was investigated. This was done experimentally by counting wax droplets which had been deposited in a cascade, and theoretically by calculating the velocity field in the cascade and integrating the equations of motion of particles moving initially with the airstream.

2. EXPERIMENTAL ARRANGEMENT

The cascade was of a design extensively used in blade fouling work. It used Nimonic blades which were polished in order to remove machining marks. Dimensions were as follows:

Span	2·55 in.
Chord	1·515 in.
Pitch	0·975 in.
Thickness/chord ratio	18·5 per cent
Camber	62/P40
Inlet angle	2°
Outlet angle	−62°

The rig was arranged so that droplets of paraffin wax could be injected in a controlled manner into the airstream upstream of the cascade. The droplets were formed by spraying the molten wax from an airblast atomizer in a separate chamber. A mist of frozen wax spheres was conveyed at low velocity from this chamber to the main air-stream at a point of sudden enlargement in the ducting. This promoted uniform mixing of the wax mist before the flow passed through an accelerating section to the cascade.

All the tests were made at the same conditions; these were an inlet velocity to the cascade of 122 ft/sec, corresponding to an outlet Mach number of 0·23, and a tempera-ture of 30°C. Particles of sizes ranging from 2 to 8 microns were deposited on the blades in sufficient numbers for counting.

The collection of a deposit with sufficient droplets to be counted in the least crowded areas, yet not so dense near the leading edge that individual particles could not be identified was a critical matter and several tests had to be discarded on this account.

The counts were made on the centre blade after removal from the cascade. The blade was mounted on a special stand which enabled any part of the surface to be brought under the objective lens of a microscope. The image was projected on to a screen with a magnification of 1000/1.

The sizes of droplets passing a datum line in a band 50 microns wide as the blade was traversed spanwise were measured in groups increasing geometrically in the ratio $\sqrt{(2)}/1$. The number of droplets in unit area in any size group was calculated from the distance the surface was traversed in order to count 100 droplets. In many cases several adjacent 50 micron bands situated in the central 20 mm span had to be examined to find the required number of particles. Occasionally a size group was so rare that the count had to be curtailed and the deposit density calculated on less than 100 particles with a consequent local reduction in accuracy.

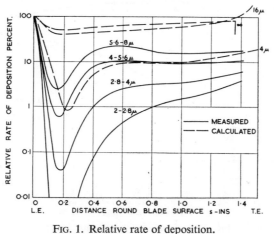

FIG. 1. Relative rate of deposition.

Deposition occurred only on the concave blade surfaces; ten chordwise stations were chosen at which counts were made.

Broadly, the deposit density is at a maximum on the leading edge of the blade. Just behind the nose the curvature of the surface is reversed and in this region deposition is greatly reduced, the reduction being greater for smaller particles. From there to the trailing edge the deposition density rises.

H

3. CALCULATION OF PARTICLE DISTRIBUTION

The paths followed by particles moving within the airstream may be calculated with a knowledge of the aerodynamic drag of the particles and the velocity and direction of the air anywhere in the field of flow.

The present calculation of the particle trajectories was based upon the following assumptions:

(a) The airflow is two-dimensional, potential and incompressible.

(b) The flow round the central blade is sufficiently accurately represented by considering a cascade with only two passages and straight entry and exit end walls.

(c) The drag of the particles is given by Stokes' law.

(d) The particles are moving with the velocity and direction of the airstream at a section one blade pitch upstream of the blade row.

On the assumptions (a) and (b) above, the local flow velocity components, u and v, are conveniently determined from the stream function ψ, using the relations

$$u = \frac{\partial \psi}{\partial y}, \quad v = -\frac{\partial \psi}{\partial x}$$

and

$$\nabla^2 \psi = \frac{\partial^2 \psi}{\partial x^2} + \frac{\partial^2 \psi}{\partial y^2} = 0$$

The boundary conditions are given by ψ=constant along fixed surfaces, i.e. end walls and blades; and $\partial \psi / \partial x$ and $\partial \psi / \partial y$ constant in regions of uniform flow remote from the blading.

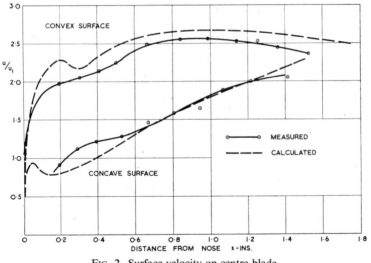

FIG. 2. Surface velocity on centre blade.

Relaxation techniques were used to obtain an approximate solution for ψ over the field of flow. This involved adjusting ψ systematically at the nodal points of a square net covering the field until the finite-difference approximation to $\nabla^2 \psi = 0$ was satisfied at each point to the desired degree of accuracy.

A check on whether this method was giving realistic results was made by calculating the surface velocities on the blade and comparing them with those calculated from pressure measurements. Fig. 2 shows that fair general agreement was obtained.

The non-dimensional equations of motion of a spherical particle moving relatively to the airstream are

$$p \frac{du_1}{dt} = u - u_1; \quad p \frac{dv_1}{dt} = v - v_1$$

$$\frac{dx}{dt} = u_1; \quad \frac{dy}{dt} = v_1$$

where p is given by $p = \frac{2}{9} \frac{\rho}{\rho_a} \left(\frac{a}{L}\right)^2 \left(\frac{LU}{\nu}\right)$.

These equations were derived by Albrecht[1] and G. I. Taylor.[2] The velocity suffix refers to the particle and meanings are attached to other symbols thus:

ρ is particle density
ρ_a is air density
a is particle radius
L is a characteristic length
U is a characteristic velocity (taken here as inlet velocity)
ν is the air kinematic viscosity.

The equations of motion were integrated step-by-step for a succession of suitably small intervals of time. Two particle sizes were considered, 4 and 16 microns diameter, under the conditions of the experimental measurements. The integrations were started one blade pitch upstream ($x_0=0$) for various initial values of y_0 and continued until the blade was reached or until it was clear that it would not be reached.

Figures 3 and 4 show some of the calculated trajectories.

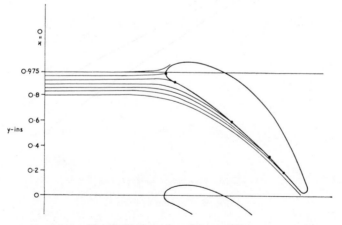

FIG. 3. Trajectories of 4μ particles.

In Fig. 5 are plotted curves of the initial position, y_0, of particles against the distance, s, from the leading edge, round the blade surface, of the point at which impact occurs. The line for $p=$infinity, i.e. very large particles which are undeflected, is included as a limiting case.

If the air upstream of the cascade is uniformly loaded with particles the relative rates of deposition on the blades are given by the slope dy_0/ds of the curves of Fig. 5. These calculated rates are shown, with the experimental results, in Fig. 1. Tolerable agreement is obtained for the 4 micron particles although the calculation gives some-what higher rates than experiment, particularly in the region of minimum deposition.

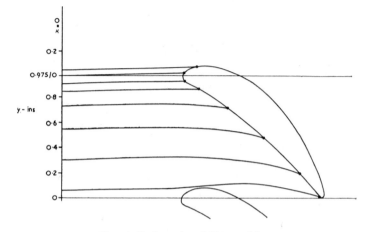

FIG. 4. Trajectories of $16\,\mu$ particles.

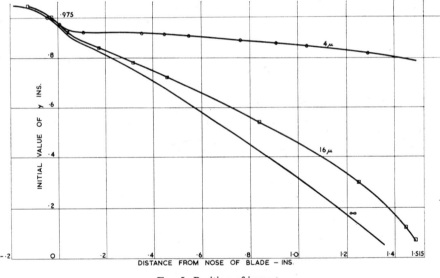

FIG. 5. Position of impact.

Figures 6 and 7 show the velocities and directions of impact with the surface for the two particle sizes. These illustrate how the smaller particles collide at a very shallow angle over the greater part of the concave surface and at velocities approaching the local surface velocity. Larger particles, being deflected and accelerated less by the presence of the blading, tend to impact at less shallow angles and at velocities more nearly that at the entry to the cascade.

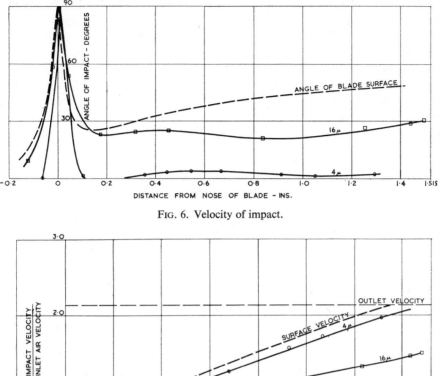

Fig. 6. Velocity of impact.

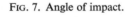

Fig. 7. Angle of impact.

4. DISCUSSION

4.1 *Comparison Between Conditions of Tests and Calculations*

Reasonable agreement has been obtained between the results of measurement and calculation. Nevertheless it is worth looking at some of the ways in which the conditions of experiment and theory differ.

If there is incomplete sticking of particles the calculated deposition rates will be high compared with measurement. That some particles were lost was evident under the microscope from the presence of wax smears. It might be surmised that such losses would be greatest for large droplets, and in those regions where the incidence upon the surface is most shallow. The extent of these losses is difficult to guess, but qualitatively they could account for the differences in question.

No account was taken in the calculations of the existence and effect of boundary layers. An approximate momentum thickness for the concave surface was estimated as 0·012 in. at the trailing edge. The thickness of the retarded layer was several times as great as this, but was nevertheless small compared with the dimensions of the blading, and was unlikely to modify appreciably the paths of particles entering it. Rather thicker boundary layers were present on the convex blade surfaces, even so, these surfaces were so far distant from the paths of airborne droplets that they could have little influence on the trajectories.

The validity of the assumption that the drag of the particles obeys Stokes' law must also be examined. At Reynolds numbers below about 2 measured drag coefficients agree quite closely with those given by Stokes' law and this agreement improves as Reynolds number is reduced.

The greatest relative velocities found in these calculations occurred in the case of a 16-micron particle moving near the nose of the blade, and were of the same order as the inlet velocity. This gives a Reynolds number of about 4, at which the Stokes' law drag coefficient is about 0·63 and the measured one 1·69. This may appear to be a large difference, but it should be noted that this was an extreme case and that it only applied to a small region which the particle took a very short time to pass. It appears, then, that the assumption of viscous drag was of reasonable accuracy. The improvement to be expected from the use of these drag coefficients could not be justified by the increased complexity of the computations.

4.2 *Catch Efficiencies*

The quantity p used in the equations of motion of particles is sometimes known as the impact number.

It has been argued that if a particle has an impact number less than the critical value for a circular cylinder of radius equal to the nose radius of a blade, then the particle cannot reach the nose or any other part of the blade. The critical value for a cylinder is $\frac{1}{8}$, where the impact number is based on the cylinder radius. For the present blading the minimum particle diameter works out at 0·7 microns. This accords with observation in that very few particles of about a micron diameter were found during the counts.

Catch efficiency is defined as the ratio of actual impact rate to the maximum possible rate contained in the band of air which the blade can see looking along the line of approach velocity. For a given airflow pattern, and as long as Stokes' drag law is obeyed, it is a function of impact number only.

For turbine blading the impact number is usually specified in terms of blade chord and outlet velocity. On this basis the catch efficiencies for the two particle sizes considered in this exercise are given in the Table. The limiting case of minimum size for impact is also included.

TABLE 1

Diameter, microns	16	4	0·7
Impact number	1·42	0·088	0·0026
Catch efficiency, per cent	98·7	15·6	0

It is seen, therefore, that for impact numbers near the critical value deposition will occur only near the nose of the blades and particles will be caught only from a very narrow band of incoming air. As impact number increases deposition spreads round the blade and a greater proportion of the burden of the airstream is caught. At an impact number of about 1·45 all the particles will reach a blade, and it is of interest here to note the effect of blade pitch. In Fig. 4 it may be seen how particles narrowly missing one blade are deflected so as to reach the trailing edge region of the next blade actually focusing them on to this region. If the blade pitch were greater this effect could disappear and the impact number at which 100 per cent catch was first attained would be increased. For very large impact number the shoulder of one blade shadows the trailing edge of the next resulting in no deposition there. Again this effect varies with blade pitch.

5. CONCLUSIONS

Reasonable agreement has been obtained between measured and calculated relative rates of deposition for the particular cascade geometry and conditions considered. The inlet velocity was much less than normally used in turbine practice in order to keep the flow simple.

The experiments showed that direct impact occurred only on the concave surface of the blading; no particles at all being found on the convex side except some small ones near the side walls of the cascade where secondary flows were powerful. Large particles, being comparatively undeflected by the flow and the blading, were found to be distributed fairly evenly over the chord. Small particles, much more readily deflected, were found at the nose and rear part of the blade, there being a region behind the leading edge where they failed to deposit. This region became larger in size the smaller the particles.

The details of the particle trajectories revealed by the calculation show particularly how rarely impacts normal to the surface occur. At the extreme nose of the blade impacts are indeed normal, but at a very short distance round the surface particles strike very obliquely and this is even more marked for small sizes. The mechanism by which damage due to deposition on turbines is caused by impact must obviously be sought in terms of collisions occurring very obliquely with the surface.

REFERENCES
1. ALBRECHT, F., *Phys. Z.*, **32**, 48 (1931).
2. TAYLOR, G. I., *Aero. Res. Comm.* R. & M. No. 2024 (1940).

THE ROLE OF DIFFUSION, INTERCEPTION AND INERTIA IN THE FILTRATION OF AIRBORNE PARTICLES

by R. G. DORMAN

Chemical Defence Experimental Establishment, Porton Down, Wilts.

Summary—The Langmuir theory of filtration by diffusion and interception is considered; some simplification is introduced in the calculation of the effect of diffusion and an empirical inertia parameter is added. The modified theory is applied to the interpretation of the experimental results of Ramskill and Anderson for the filtration of di-octyl phthalate particles by glass fibre filters. It is shown that, whilst the interception parameter can be fitted reasonably well to the results, the Langmuir theory over-estimates the effect of diffusion of particles to the finer fibres. The experimental evidence indicates that the inertial parameter depends on the square of the air velocity.

1. INTRODUCTION

THE removal by fibrous filters of fine particulate matter, suspended in an air stream is considered to be due to inertial effects, Brownian motion and direct interception; for large particles gravitational settling may be important and in some cases electrical effects may predominate, but these two latter effects will not be discussed in this paper. Whilst it is a simple matter to describe, in general terms, the effects and relative importance of inertia, diffusion and interception, it is only in recent years that a convincing experimental demonstration has become possible—that is since the production of mono-disperse particulate clouds[1] has been attainable.

Curves of penetration plotted against velocity of air stream for a mono-disperse cloud generally show a rise in penetration as the velocity increases, and diffusional effects decrease, and then with further increase in velocity the penetration decreases as the effect of inertia becomes steadily more important. The construction of a theory which will enable us to calculate the possibility of penetration of any size of particle through any pad or mat of fibres is, however, a much more difficult matter and, whilst the problem has attracted much interest, no really satisfactory practical solution is yet available. It is likely that any useful solution will depend largely on an empirical approach as well as on a theoretical basis and, at present, although a considerable amount of data is available, very little has been presented in a manner suitable for analysis. The major obstacle to progress is probably the measurement of fibre radius, an accurate assessment of which is essential. A fibrous filter contains fibres of different radii, in various degrees of dispersion and orientation and microscopic measurement of fibre radius is not a satisfactory solution. Equations depending on the pressure drop across the filter[2,3] have been suggested to calculate a "mean fibre radius" but depend upon an empirical correction factor. It does not, in any case, follow that the "mean fibre radius" will be the same for each of the three mechanisms of filtration.

Of the many attempts to derive a theory of filtration, admirable reviews of which have been produced by Chen,[4] the best approach to the problems of diffusion and interception seems to be that of Langmuir who considered only low velocities and neglected inertial effects. It is the purpose of this paper to analyse a few results of

112

Ramskill and Anderson[5] using the Langmuir theory, with the addition of an inertia term, as a basis, and to indicate the manner in which future experiments might be designed to obtain the results neecssary to formulate a guide to filter specification.

2. THE FLOW PATTERN ROUND A CYLINDER TRANSVERSE TO THE DIRECTION OF FLOW

Whilst the flow in fibrous filters is likely to be more complicated than the flow round an isolated cylinder, the best approach to a solution of the filtration problem is probably through consideration of the efficiency of a single fibre. Unless the fibres are extremely close to each other the flow to them should not differ greatly from that near to an isolated fibre. For flow in a fibrous filter where the Reynolds number is small, viscous forces play an important part so that Lamb's[6] equations for the viscous flow round a stationary cylinder provide a convenient starting point.

His equations are

$$dr/dt = C_L R_r \sin \theta, \tag{1}$$

$$r d\theta/dt = C_L R_\theta \cos \theta, \tag{2}$$

$$C_L = \frac{v_0}{2 \, [2 - \ln Re]}, \tag{3}$$

where r is the distance from the axis of a cylinder of radius a, θ the angle between the radius vector and the y axis, the flow being in the x direction, and v_0 the upstream air velocity.

$$R_r = 1 - a^2/r^2 - 2\ln (r/a) \tag{4}$$

$$R_\theta = 1 - a^2/r^2 + 2\ln (r/a) \tag{5}$$

The Reynolds number, Re, is defined as

$$2av_0\rho/\eta,$$

where ρ is the air density and η the coefficient of viscosity.

Lamb also gives the drag force on unit length of the isolated cylinder as

$$F = 8\pi\eta C_L, \tag{6}$$

Davies[7] has also investigated the flow round an isolated cylinder and finds the drag force to be the same as that of Lamb, but his equations for the velocity are considerably different and more difficult to handle.

Experiments by Finn[8] using wires of $4\cdot1\,\mu$, $6\cdot5\,\mu$ and $12\cdot6\,\mu$ diameter have confirmed the Lamb equation for the drag force at Reynolds numbers between $0\cdot06$ and $6\cdot0$. For fine fibres of interest in filtration problems Lamb's equations need modification to take slip flow into account and, with this modification, were adopted by Langmuir as the basis for his theory of filtration.

3. FILTRATION BY INTERCEPTION AND DIFFUSION

As the purpose of this paper is to test the relative importance of diffusion and interception on Langmuir's theory with that found in the case of Ramskill and Anderson's[5] results a brief summary of Langmuir's method will be given. In this summary small changes have been made in the approach and some simplification has been introduced in the calculation of diffusion, but the reasoning is, in general, that of Langmuir.

3.1 *Interception*

It is assumed that a massless particle which follows a flow line is caught by interception if its centre passes within a distance r_p of the fibre where r_p is the particle radius. If we assume particles of negligible mass their paths follow the flowlines round the fibre, and from equation 2 it is seen that the volume of gas F, passing within a distance r_p on both sides of the fibre is

$$F = 2C_L \int_a^{a + r_p} R_\theta\, dr \text{ per unit length per second} \tag{7}$$

The slip close to the fibre occurs in a distance approximately equal to λ the mean free path of the gas molecules; introducing this correction into the equation we obtain

$$F = 2C_L \int_a^{a + r_p} \left[1 - \frac{a^2}{(r + \lambda)^2} + 2\ln \frac{(r + \lambda)}{a} \right] dr,$$

$$= 2C_L \left[\frac{a^2}{(a + r_p + \lambda)} - \frac{a^2}{(a + \lambda)} - r_p + 2(a + \lambda) \ln \frac{(a + r_p + \lambda)}{(a + \lambda)} \right.$$

$$\left. + 2r_p \ln \frac{(a + r_p + \lambda)}{a} \right]. \tag{8}$$

Now L, the total length of fibres in unit volume at packing density β, is $\beta/\pi a^2$ so that in a thickness db the total length of fibre is $\beta db/\pi a^2$. For a face velocity v the ratio of volume filtered to the total flow is

$$\frac{FL\, db}{v} = F\beta db/\pi a^2 v = - \frac{dn}{n}, \tag{9}$$

where n is the concentration of particles per cm³ entering the layer. Hence, from the basic filtration equation

$$n = n_0 e^{-\gamma}, \tag{10}$$

which on differentiation gives

$$d \ln n = - d\gamma, \tag{11}$$

we find, for a filter of thickness b,

$$\gamma = FLb/v. \tag{12}$$

In order to calculate γ in a real filter we must know F and L, both of which involve the fibre radius, and the value of C_L or some variant of C_L due to the proximity of other fibres.

Langmuir assumed that he could find a mean fibre radius (r_F) from pressure drop measurements, his equation being

$$r_F^2 = \frac{4M\phi b\beta L(1 - \beta)v_0 \eta}{P}, \tag{13}$$

where $\phi=(\ln 1/\beta+2\beta-\beta^2/2-3/2)^{-1}$ and M is a numerical factor, usually lying between 0·5 and 1·5, which must be determined for individual cases. M varies according to the degree of dispersion and orientation of the fibres in the filter, and low values usually indicate poor distribution.

When the mean fibre radius r_F had been determined, Langmuir considered that a value for C (to be used instead of C_L) could be found from a consideration of viscous forces on the fibres in a filter, all distributed transverse to the flow and having radius r_F, the total length of the fibres being $\beta/\pi r_F^2$. Taking the frictional force, f, per unit length of fibre to be $4\pi\eta C$, he wrote the pressure drop through the filter, P, as

$$P = Lbf = 4\eta b\beta C/r_F^2,$$

so that
$$C = Pr_F^2/4\eta\beta b. \tag{14}$$

(It should be noted here that Langmuir's value for the drag on unit length of fibre is only one half of that given by Lamb.)

The equation for γ, for interception only, is thus:

$$\gamma = FLb/v = \frac{2.Pr_F^2}{4\eta\beta b}\left[\int_a^{a+r_p} R_\theta dr\right]\frac{\beta b}{\pi r_F^2 v},$$

$$= \frac{P}{2\eta\pi v}\left[r_F^2/(r_F+r_p+\lambda) - r_F^2/(r_F+\lambda) - r_p\right.$$

$$\left. + 2(r_F+\lambda)\ln(r_F+r_p+\lambda)/(r_F+\lambda) + 2r_p\ln(r_F+r_p+\lambda)/r_F\right] \tag{15}$$

γ is then sensibly independent of air velocity as pressure drop is almost proportional to the velocity.

3.2 Diffusion

The particles which reach a plane surface in time t from a large volume of smoke in contact with the surface were originally contained in a distance x where

$$x = \left\{\frac{4\Delta t}{\pi}\right\}^{\frac{1}{2}}, \tag{16}$$

and Δ is the diffusion coefficient, the value of which is $1·23\times10^{-6}$ cm²/sec for spheres of $0·15\,\mu$ radius in air at 20°C and 1 atmosphere pressure.

Langmuir then calculated the time that it takes a particle to pass by a fibre from $\theta=60°$ to $\theta°=-60°$ at distance x_0 away from the fibre at $\theta=0$ using Lamb's equation of flow. He then calculated the r.m.s. distance of the particle from the surface during this time as

$$x = 1·120x_0. \tag{17}$$

Inserting these values of x and t in equation 16 a solution for x_0 is found. γ, the index of filtration for very small particles, is then given by

$$\gamma = \frac{x_0^2 P}{r_F\pi\eta v}, \tag{18}$$

where

$$x_0{}^3 = 2\cdot24\eta\,\Delta\beta b/P,$$

so that for very small particles γ is approximately proportional to $v^{-2/3}$.

Introducing the effect of slip and combining the diffusion and interception equations we obtain Langmuir's final equations for filtration of particles of radius r_p,

$$(x_0 + S)(x_0 - r_p)^2 = 2\cdot24\;a\eta\,\Delta\beta b/P, \tag{19}$$

and

$$\gamma = \frac{Px_0}{\pi\eta vr_F}(x_0 + 2S), \tag{20}$$

where $S=0\cdot68\lambda(=0\cdot9\times10^{-5}$ for air at 20°C and 76 cm pressure, according to Langmuir) and a is a constant presumably close to unity to take into account any inaccuracies in the theory.

Langmuir published tables of the various functions from which it is comparatively easy to calculate γ.

4. THE RESULTS OF RAMSKILL AND ANDERSON

Ramskill and Anderson[5] measured the penetration of a monodisperse aerosol of $0\cdot3\mu$ particle diameter (di-octyl phthalate) through sheets of glass fibres at face velocities of from a few cm/sec to 300 cm/sec. Their data included measurements of sheet thickness, packing factor, resistance and a microscopic assessment of the fibre radius. The presentation of their results makes them suitable for calculations of interception and diffusion parameters and comparison with Langmuir's theory. Figs. 1–3 show velocity-penetration curves for four of the filters.

Assuming that diffusion depends basically on equation 16 we consider that, at least to a first approximation, the bandwidth filtered depends on $t^{\frac{1}{2}}$ where t is the time available for diffusion to the fibre. This time depends inversely on the velocity of the particle close to the fibre and hence on the inverse velocity of the main flow. The basic filtration equation then becomes:

$$n = n_0e^{-(D'v^{-\frac{1}{2}} + I')b} \tag{21}$$

where D' and I' are diffusion and interception parameters. The inertial parameter, neglected by Langmuir who only considered low velocities of flow, has been assumed proportional to v by Davies[3] as a result of calculations based on his own viscous flow equation. In consequence a first attempt was made to fit the results of Ramskill and Anderson by the equation

$$n = n_0e^{-(A'v + D'v^{-\frac{1}{2}} + I')b}, \tag{22}$$

where A' is the inertial parameter. This attempt was not successful and secondly the equation was written

$$n = n_0e^{-(A'v^2 + D'v^{-\frac{1}{2}} + I')b}. \tag{23}$$

Expressing the equations in terms of percentage penetration, p, we have

$$\log_{10}p = 2 - Av^2b - Dbv^{-\frac{1}{2}} - Ib. \tag{24}$$

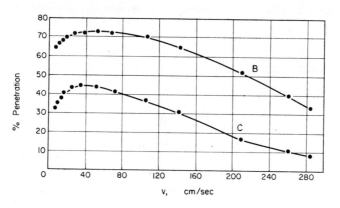

FIG. 1. Filters B and C.

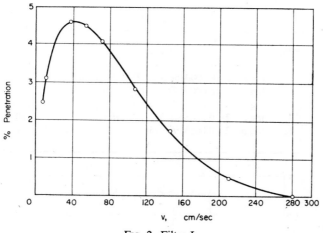

FIG. 2. Filter J.

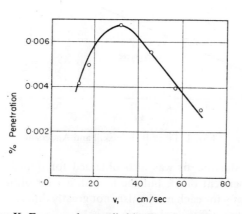

FIG. 3. Filter K. From results supplied by Dr. Ramskill to Mr. Gillespie.

where the inertial, diffusion and interception parameters are now A, D and I. On differentiating

$$\frac{1}{2 \cdot 3 p} \cdot \frac{dp}{dv} = -2Avb + \tfrac{1}{2}Dbv^{-3/2}. \tag{25}$$

Now at v_m, the velocity of maximum penetration,

$$dp/dv = 0,$$

Hence

$$D = 4Av_m{}^{5/2}. \tag{26}$$

If our original functions have been chosen correctly a plot of $2 - \log_{10} p$ against $(v^2 + 4v_m{}^{5/2}v^{-\frac{1}{2}})$ should yield a straight line the slope of which gives A and D whilst the intercept gives I.

Satisfactory straight lines (Figs. 4 to 8) were in fact found for each of the filters and the equations calculated for each are as follows in Table 1.

TABLE 1

Filter	Equation	
B	$\log p = 2 - 0 \cdot 000086 v^2 b - 7 \cdot 71 v^{-\frac{1}{2}} b - 1 \cdot 28 b$	(27)
C	$\log p = 2 - 0.00033 v^2 b - 13 v^{-\frac{1}{2}} b - 10 \cdot 7 b$	(28)
I	$\log p = 2 - 0 \cdot 00012 v^2 b - 9 \cdot 36 v^{-\frac{1}{2}} b - 2 \cdot 22 b$	(29)
J	$\log p = 2 - 0 \cdot 000345 v^2 b - 16 \cdot 7 v^{-\frac{1}{2}} b - 14 \cdot 9 b$	(30)
K	$\log p = 2 - 0 \cdot 0033 v^2 b - 65 v^{-\frac{1}{2}} b - 76 b$	(31)

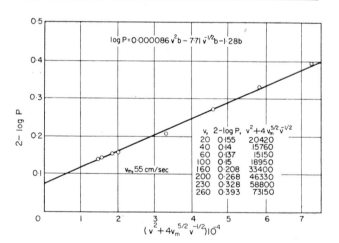

FIG. 4. Filter B, Ramskill and Anderson.

A reasonably satisfactory fit was also obtained for diffusion depending on $v^{-2/3}$ with inertia still dependent on v^2, but the fit with $v^{-\frac{1}{2}}$ for diffusion was rather better and gave the values of γ for each mechanism not greatly different from those calculated on the assumption that diffusion depends on $v^{-2/3}$.

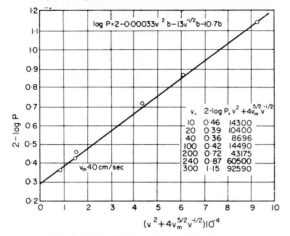

$$\log P = 2 - 0.00033v^2 b - 13v^{-1/2}b - 10.7b$$

v,	2-log P,	$v^2 + 4v_m^{5/2}v^{-1/2}$
10	0.46	14300
20	0.39	10400
40	0.36	8696
100	0.42	14490
200	0.72	43175
240	0.87	60500
300	1.15	92590

v_m 40 cm/sec

FIG. 5. Filter C, Ramskill and Anderson.

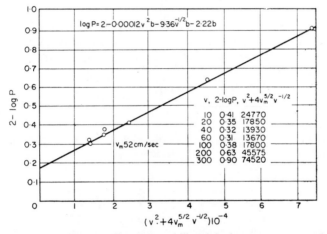

$$\log P = 2 - 0.00012v^2 b - 9.36v^{-1/2}b - 2.22b$$

v,	2-logP,	$v^2 + 4v_m^{5/2}v^{-1/2}$
10	0.41	24770
20	0.35	17850
40	0.32	13930
60	0.31	13670
100	0.38	17800
200	0.63	45575
300	0.90	74520

v_m 52 cm/sec

FIG. 6. Filter I, Ramskill and Anderson.

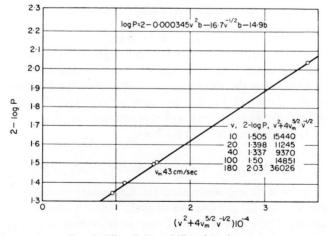

$$\log P = 2 - 0.000345v^2 b - 16.7v^{-1/2}b - 14.9b$$

v,	2-log P,	$v^2 + 4v_m^{5/2}v^{-1/2}$
10	1.505	15440
20	1.398	11245
40	1.337	9370
100	1.50	14851
180	2.03	36026

v_m 43 cm/sec

FIG. 7. Filter J, Ramskill and Anderson.

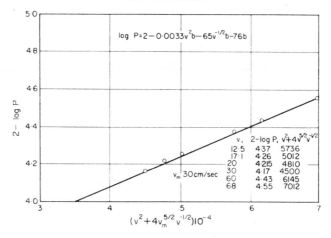

FIG. 8. Filter J, Ramskill and Anderson.

In order to apply the Langmuir theory to these equations we must first estimate the mean fibre radius using equation 13. In these calculations M is taken to be 0·5.

Details for the filters for air velocity of 14·2 cm/sec are shown in Table 2.

TABLE 2

Filter	P (cm water) at 14·2 cm/sec	B	b cm	r_F (Ramskill & Anderson) (μ)	r_F Calc. (μ)	γ (Langmuir) inter-ception	γ (Calc.) inter-ception
B	1·0	0·17	0·051	1·5	2·77	0·22	0·15
C	1·0	0·07	0·028	1·5	0·9	0·59	0·69
I	1·4	0·16	0·081	1·5	2·75	0·31	0·374
J	4·0	0·09	0·074	1·0	0·9	2·35	2·54
K	10·0	0·12	0·046	0·5	0·58	8·15	8·5

Applying the Langmuir theory for γ due to interception with radii as calculated from equation 13 gives values in col. 7 whilst col. 8 gives those found from Table 1. Col. 7 has been calculated from equation 15 with λ equal to $1·0 \times 10^{-5}$ whereas Langmuir took a value for the slip distance of $0·9 \times 10^{-5}$; the difference between the two sets of figures is, however, small. Agreement between cols. 7 and 8 is fairly satisfactory. Correcting all radii to force a fit for interception gives radii of fibres in B, $3·85\,\mu$; C, $0·73\,\mu$; I, $2·15\,\mu$; J, $0·82\,\mu$; K, $0·56\,\mu$.

5. COMPARISON OF DIFFUSION EFFICIENCIES

The value of γ for diffusion was found for Langmuir's theory by the difference between equations 20 and 15 at a velocity of 14·2 cm/sec. A comparison with γ found from the equations 27–31 shows that Langmuir overestimates the importance of diffusion with the error increasing as the fibre radius decreases (Table 3).

With slight simplification to the Langmuir approach the approximate angle $(+\theta°$ to $-\theta°)$ through which the particle passes whilst it may be considered available for diffusion was calculated.

The flow per unit length within a distance r_p of the fibre is given by equation 7, and from Table 1 the ratio of diffusion flow to interception flow can be found. The flow for interception is known to be between the fibre surface and a distance r_p away. From a plot of $\int R_\theta dr$ for each effective fibre radius and different distances from the fibre, it is a straightforward matter to calculate the effective diffusion distance.

The effective time, t, is given by equation 16 and is the time taken by a particle which has diffused across the flow lines from r_p+x to r_p. It is given approximately by

$$t = 2\int_0^\theta \frac{(r_F + x + r_p)d\theta}{v_r \cos\theta} \tag{32}$$

where v_r is the velocity at a distance $(r_p+x/2)$ from the surface of the fibre at $\theta=0°$. Equation 32 assumes that changes in the distance of the particle from the axis are small compared with the distance itself which is in general true.

The integration gives:

$$t = \frac{x + r_p + r_F}{v} \left/ \ln \frac{1 + \sin\theta}{1 - \sin\theta} \right|_0^\theta, \tag{33}$$

and is solved for θ by inserting the value of t obtained from equation 16.

The calculated half angle, θ, through which the particle passes whilst it is available for diffusion to the fibre is given in Table 3, col. 4.

TABLE 3

Filter	γ Langmuir diffusion	γ diffusion from Table 1	$\theta°$
B	0·217	0·24	55
C	0·6	0·22	9
I	0·58	0·42	29
J	2·1	0·76	8
K	6·3	1·4	9

It is of interest to plot θ against r_F for each filter when a smooth curve is obtained, r_F being roughly proportional to θ. A change in θ is probably to be expected from a general consideration of the problem.

6. CONCLUSIONS

There is reasonable agreement between the Langmuir and experimental values for the interception parameter when a value of $M=0·5$ is chosen (equation 13) to calculate the mean fibre radius. The diffusion parameter from experiment does not then agree with that derived from Langmuir's theory, the divergence increasing with decreasing radius. Whilst no comparison could be made with Langmuir's theory, the inertial parameter is important at the higher velocities depending on v^2.

I

There is an extensive literature dealing with air filtration, but no satisfactory theory has so far been put forward and the experimental data are often not easy to interpret. It seems that more experiments on the lines of those of Ramskill and Anderson, which can lead to equations of the type in Table 1, are desirable for ranges of filter materials and particle sizes. From equations similar to those of Table 1, even though they probably represent gross simplifications of the actual mechanism of filtration, it might be possible to approach a solution of the filtration problem by a combination of theory and empiricism.

REFERENCES

1. SINCLAIR, D. and LA MER, V. K., *Chem. Res.*, **44,** 245 (1949).
2. LANGMUIR, I., O.S.R.D. Report No. 865 (1942).
3. DAVIES, C. N., *Proc. Inst. Mech. Eng.*, B1, 185 (1952).
4. CHEN, C. Y., *Chem. Rev.*, **55,** 595 (1955)
5. RAMSKILL, E. A. and ANDERSON, W. L., *J. Colloid Sci.*, **6,** 416 (1951).
6. LAMB, H., *Hydrodynamics*, Camb. Univ. Press, 6th Edn. pp. 606–16, 1932.
7. DAVIES, C. N., *Proc. Phys. Soc.*, **63,** B, 288 (1950).
8. FINN, R. K., *Eng. Exp. Stn.*, University of Illinois Tech. Rep. No. 8, Jan. 1953.

DISCUSSION—SECOND SESSION

Wood Smoke

C. N. DAVIES: Wood smoke contains a number of low-molecular-weight, water-soluble organic compounds which lower the partial water vapour pressure so that atmospheric humidity affects particle size.

FOSTER mentioned that the coagulation coefficient $4kTF/3$, for wood smoke particles of radius about $0 \cdot 10\mu$ had been found to be $2 \cdot 48 \times 10^{-9}$ cm^3/sec whereas the theoretical value is $0 \cdot 55 \times 10^{-9}$ cm^3/sec.

C. N. DAVIES asked whether this discrepancy could have been due to a high relative humidity or to the organic vapours accompanying wood smoke.

FOSTER said that the relative humidity was about 30 per cent, and therefore not likely to have any effect on the rate of coagulation. Furthermore, other people working with similar aerosols, such as tobacco smoke, had apparently not observed such marked differences in theoretical and experimental values.

D. J. BROWN asked whether there had been sufficient turbulence in the smoke to give rise to the increased coagulation rate.

FOSTER said that whilst the uncharged smoke was coagulating it passed along a pipe 8 cm in diameter at an average velocity of about 20 cm/sec and that the turbulence was probably not as great as that in experiments by Langstroth and Gillespie;[1] they had shown that the coagulation constant changed very little up to moderate degrees of turbulence.

STAIRMAND: I am interested in the statement in Dr. Foster's paper (page 92, sec. (4)), that the rate of deposition can be considerably increased by charging the particles and allowing them to precipitate in their self-generated electric field. We have carried out tests in the past in an endeavour to utilize the self-generated field to assist dust collection (in industrial dedusters) without obtaining any marked improvement compared with uncharged particles. We concluded that the effect was quantitatively very small compared with that obtainable by passing the charged particles into an electric field such as that obtaining between charged and earthed plates as, e.g., in a commercial electrostatic precipitator.

In this connection it is worth noting that the rates of dust deposition obtainable in commercial electrostatic precipitators are often in excess of 20 mg/cm^2 per hr, i.e. 4000 times those quoted in Dr. Foster's paper.

FOSTER. Substituting for ρ in equation 1,

$$\frac{dr}{dt} = \frac{rFc}{4k_0\delta\eta} \frac{n^2e^2}{\pi a^4} \tag{7}$$

For very small particles, when diffusion charging predominates, n is approximately proportional to a and dr/dt decreases as a increases. For large conducting particles, field charging predominates, $n \doteqdot 3Ea^2$, and dr/dt is independent of a.

The velocity of a particle in the electric field generated by the particles in a charged cloud may be compared with that in an applied field of strength E using equations 6 and 7. Thus,

$$\frac{dr/dt}{v} = \frac{3rc}{2k_0\delta E}\frac{ne}{a^3} \tag{8}$$

This ratio may be high for aerosols such as wood smoke. For instance, for a typical smoke[3] when $c=0\cdot253$ mg/1, $d=1\cdot3$ g/cm^3, $r=2\cdot50$ cm, $E=1\cdot4$kV/cm ($4\cdot67$ in e.s.u.), $a = 0\cdot116\mu$ and n (calculated) $= 15$, $(dr/dt)/v = 0\cdot72$. When field charging predominates, and r, d and c have the same values as those given above, $dr/dt/v = 2\cdot19 \times 10^{-6}/a$ and is therefore very small when a is greater than about 1μ.

1. Langstroth, G. O. and Gillespie, T., *Canad. J. Res.*, **25**, Section B, 455 (1947).
2. Foster, W. W., *Brit. J. Appl. Phys.*, **10**, 416 (1959).
3. Foster, W. W., *Brit. J. Appl. Phys.*, **10**, 206 (1959).

Collection by Filters

FAIRS: In addition to the various factors affecting fibre filter efficiency already discussed, the nature of the fibre surface must also be considered. Experiments carried out at Widnes[4] on filtration of fine sulphuric acid must (all$<22\mu$; 10 per cent by weight $<1\mu$) have shown that with hydrophobic fibres, i.e. those which collect mists dropwise, filtration efficiencies are obtained which agree closely with those predicted from the Bosanquet Impingement Diffusion equations. In the case of hydrophilic fibres, however, the efficiencies are much lower than the predicted figures. This is certainly due in part to the bunching of the hydrophilic fibres due to attraction of adjacent films of liquid, which has the double effect of increasing the effective fibre diameter and increasing the voidage of the filter bed, both of which lower the efficiency of filtration.

4. Fairs, G. L., *Trans. Inst. Chem. Eng.*, **36**, 476 (1958).

GILLESPIE: The use of mono-disperse aerosols, of the type developed by La Mer and Sinclair, is recommended for this work.

WALTON: Have you carried out any work on the efficiency of single fibres? No. (Dorman.)

WALTON: Are irregularly shaped particles more easy to catch than spheres?

DORMAN: Our experience on comparative efficiencies is limited to aerosols of methylene blue (spheres) and common salt (generally cubical) and shows that when the major diagonal of the salt cube is equal to that of the sphere diameter the penetrations are also equal.

DORMAN: In the discussion, Dr. Stairmand referred to his Paper (Ref. 1, p. 53) dealing with dust collection by impingement and diffusion. Stairmand's approach to the diffusion problem is similar to that of Langmuir and he finds the diffusion parameter to be equal to

$$\left\{\frac{4\Delta}{vr_F}\right\}^{\frac{1}{2}}$$

A dependency on $v^{-\frac{1}{2}}$ is in agreement with Paper No. 9.

His approach to the inertial problem is, however, different from Paper No. 9 in that he considers potential, and not viscous, flow round the fibres. Whilst the velocity distribution for potential flow may hold for high Reynolds number it is not likely to do so for the low values of Reynolds number pertaining to filters composed of very fine fibres.

STAIRMAND: The prediction of the collection efficiency of fibres has been dealt with at length in Ref. 1 (p. 53) and in its Appendix by C. H. Bosanquet. It has been shown that where accurate knowledge of the true size analysis of the mist or dust (in terms of the terminal velocities of the particles) is available, reliable prediction of efficiency can be made. Where difficulties have arisen, these can usually be traced to either inaccurate size analysis data or failure to appreciate that the effective fibre diameter can change, as dust (or mist) deposits on the filter. If allowance is made for these changes, the predictions are accurate. I agree, however, that it is not always easy to study in detail the changes which take place in a filter bed after prolonged use.

C. N. DAVIES: Nowadays, when monofilament materials are available, one would expect better agreement with filtration theory than was obtainable with the short matted fibres in use at the time of Langmuir's work.

Impact of Drops

GILLESPIE: Does the damage caused depend on the impact surface material?

JENKINS: Yes. A single drop will make a perceptible mark on Perspex at 500 ft/sec but requires over 2000 ft/sec to do likewise on mild steel.

EISENKLAM: Have you measured the size of the drops resulting from fragmentation? Lane's work[5] on drops exposed to a blast of air shows a minimum diameter of $15\,\mu$ which might have been the result of experimental limitation.

JENKINS: Not many. In the case of impact at 1000 ft/sec we collected on an oiled slide droplets ranging in size from 5 to $25\,\mu$ diameter.

C. N. DAVIES: Was flow in the boundary layer laminar or turbulent? A turbulent layer could cause appreciable impact on the surface.

MARTLEW: Probably laminar on the under (concave) surface of the blades to which deposition by direct impact was confined.

5. Shatter of drops in streams of air, I.E.C., **43**, 1312 (1951).

THIRD SESSION:

CAPTURE OF PARTICLES BY RAINDROPS

THE SUPPRESSION OF AIRBORNE DUST BY WATER SPRAY

by W. H. WALTON and A. WOOLCOCK*

National Coal Board, Mining Research Establishment, Isleworth, Middlesex

Summary—Measurements of the dust collection efficiency of water drops exposed to an airstream containing homogeneous dust particles (of methylene blue) gave results in good agreement with the theory of Fonda and Herne (and others). The range of variables did not, however, cover the transition from turbulent to viscous flow, nor dust particles of comparable size to the drops. The transition range, especially, merits further experimental study.

Using Fonda and Herne's theoretical data for collection efficiency under potential and viscous flow conditions, and Langmuir's formula for interpolation (as a function of Reynolds number) in the ransition region, estimates have been made of the dust suppression efficiency of both free-falling and projected water sprays as a function of dust size and drop size, with particular reference to mining applications.

Free-falling "gravity" spray has a reasonable efficiency for coarse (>10 microns diameter) dust but the efficiency falls off rapidly in the respirable size range. The optimum drop size for a given quantity of water is estimated to be about 0·5 mm diameter. For a 10 ft height of fall, 22 gal of spray of this size would be required per 1000 ft³ of cloud, for 90 per cent suppression of 3 microns diameter coal dust (density 1·37) and 160 gal at 2 microns. The estimate of optimum size is strongly influenced by the empirical correction made for Reynolds number and it is desirable that the basis for this should be more firmly established.

The collection efficiency of high-velocity drops projected from a pressure nozzle is greater than that of free-falling spray. Ninety per cent suppression down to 2 microns diameter dust should be attainable with a water consumption of 5–10 gal per 1000 ft³ at a pressure of 100–200 lb/in². For a given water consumption and pressure, the drop size of projected spray has little effect on the total amount of dust removed but it critically affects the range of projection, which should match the dimensions of the working space.

It is concluded that gravity spray is not effective for removing respirable dust using the limited height of fall available in mine roadways. High-pressure spray might be effective for treating concentrated clouds near (or ducted from) the source of production.

(1) INTRODUCTION

ONE of the chief means of combating the dust hazard in mining is by the use of sprayed water. This may be used either to wet and immobilize dust before it becomes airborne or to remove airborne dust from suspension. The present investigation is concerned with the removal of airborne dust. The action when an airborne dust cloud is sprayed is very complicated and so, in order to elucidate the fundamental principles involved, the problem was first simplified to the consideration of the action of one water drop moving through a dust cloud and the results then applied to practical situations.

As a water drop traverses a cloud it sweeps out a certain volume of space but not all the dust contained in this volume is hit by the drop. Air is displaced sideways out of the track of the drop and some of the dust particles in this air are also carried out of the path. The fraction of the dust lying in the path of the drop which collides with it and is removed from the cloud is defined as the "collection efficiency" of the drop. This collection efficiency is a function of many factors, principally the size and density

* Now with British Nylon Spinners Ltd., Doncaster.

of the dust and velocity of the drop. The most important aspect of the present investigation is the determination of the variation of collection efficiency with dust size since it is essential that dust suppression methods should be effective against small respirable dust particles as well as against the larger and more readily visible ones.

The problem of the collection efficiency of large particles moving through a cloud of smaller ones is of interest in many fields other than mining, for example, in meteorology and in relation to the spray towers used in chemical engineering. It has been studied theoretically by a number of workers, notably by Langmuir[1] and more recently by Fonda and Herne[2] of the Mining Research Establishment who made use of the electronic digital computer at the National Physical Laboratory. The latter work was undertaken in parallel with the present experimental investigation. Good reviews of the subject have been given by Mason[3] and by Herne.[4]

The theoretical investigation of Fonda and Herne, as of other workers, involves a number of simplifying assumptions required to make the problem mathematically tractable. The ensuing mathematical solution is exact in so far as the initial assumptions are justified. The extent to which failure to satisfy these conditions may affect the result is unknown so that it is important to supplement the theoretical work with direct experiment. A number of experimental investigations have previously been undertaken and are discussed by Mason (*loc. cit.*) but the results tend to be contradictory and inconclusive. This is largely due to the practical difficulties of the problem.

(2) EXPERIMENTAL WORK

2.1 *Preliminary Experiments. Stationary Cloud Method*

The first method used was to produce continuously a cloud of homogeneous dust particles in a closed chamber, thus building up and maintaining a set concentration. A stream of uniform water drops was allowed to fall through this dust cloud and was collected on emergence from the bottom of the chamber. The dust particles were composed of a highly coloured dye, methylene blue, so that the amount picked up by the drops could be obtained by measuring the density of coloration with a spectrophotometer.

The homogeneous cloud of spherical particles was produced by means of a spinning disk sprayer.[5] This consisted of a steel disk floating on an air bearing and rotated at speeds up to 2000 rev/sec by jets of compressed air. The dye solution was fed on to the centre of the disk and centrifuged from the periphery at high speed. When the rate of feed was kept low (below 1 cm³/min) a cloud of uniform droplets was formed whose size could be varied between 50 and 15 microns diameter by varying the speed of the disk. This cloud was dispersed throughout the test chamber where it evaporated to leave residual "dust" particles. An aqueous solution of methylene blue was used when very small particles were required and dust sizes as small as 0·5 micron-diameter could be produced in this way. For large dust sizes a non-volatile solvent, glycerol, was added to the sprayed liquid.

In order to obtain droplets of constant size it was necessary to keep the disk speed constant. The maintenance of a constant air pressure was insufficient for this purpose owing to the varying load on the rotor when fed with liquid. The speed was therefore measured by magnetizing the disk diametrically so that as it rotated an alternating voltage was induced in a small coil mounted on the stator. This voltage was amplified and displayed on a cathode ray oscillograph in comparison with a signal of known frequency from a standard oscillator. The speed was then maintained constant by appropriate manual control of the compressed air supply. The dye solution was fed on to the disk from a 50 cm³ hypodermic syringe driven by a geared-down electric motor to overcome trouble from the blocking of the small bore tubes which had to be used. A gentle upward current of dry air was maintained through the dust chamber in order to keep down the humidity so that the water evaporated rapidly and completely. Figure. 1 shows a sample of 10 microns diameter particles, produced in this way, collected on a membrane filter.

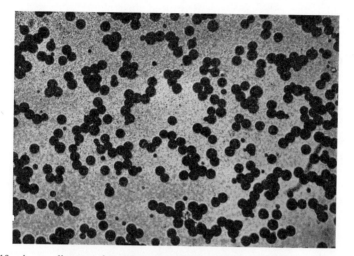

FIG. 1. 10 microns diameter dust particles (methylene blue) collected on membrane filter.

The water spray drops were produced by a micro-burette[6] which gave a stream of drops in succession from the tip of a hypodermic needle over which air was blown at a controlled rate. This stream of drops was directed to fall through a small entrance hole at the top of the cloud chamber, through the dust cloud and out through an exit hole in the bottom. Here the drops were collected in a glass jar mounted at the bottom of a horizontal duct through which was passed a slow horizontal air flow, sufficient to winnow out the dust particles which also fell through the exit hole but not sufficient to affect the motion of the falling drops. The velocity of the drops was measured by photographing their fall with stroboscopic illumination.

The method proved to have a number of practical limitations. The pick-up of dye by the falling drops during their relatively short passage through the cloud (about 3 ft) was small, particularly for small dust (dye) particles and the sensitivity of the method did not permit measurements to be made at dust size below 12 microns diameter. Measurement of the concentration of such large particles in an almost stationary cloud presented difficulties and it was not possible to obtain consistent results or be certain of the absolute accuracy. Sampling was carried out by impinger and by sedimentation cell. With the former there were uncertain orifice losses due to departure from isokinetic conditions; the sedimentation cell method only gave local discontinuous samples. The most satisfactory method was to collect the dust which fell through a known aperture at the bottom of the cloud chamber into a jar containing water into which the dust particles dissolved. Some difficulty was experienced in aiming the water spray drops to pass through the entrance and exit holes to the cloud chamber and hence it was impossible to vary appreciably the height of fall and drop velocity. The larger drops did not attain their terminal velocity in the distance available.

Only a few preliminary results were obtained by this method, these are given in Section 4, Table 2.

2.2 Main Experiments. Stationary Drop Method

In order to overcome the fore-mentioned difficulties a modified technique was adopted in which the roles of water drop and dust cloud were reversed, the dust cloud being carried upwards by an airflow past a stationary drop. This procedure had a number of advantages. The drop velocity relative to the air could be kept constant at any desired value, the difficulty of closely controlling the water spray was removed, isokinetic cloud sampling techniques could be employed and much smaller collection efficiencies were measurable because the effective distance traversed by the drop through the cloud could be increased to any desired value by prolonging the time of passage of the cloud. The method had the disadvantage of yielding a much smaller volume of sprayed liquid containing collected dust material but this was more than off-set by the higher concentration of dust collected in that volume.

FIG. 2. Experimental apparatus, stationary drop method.

The apparatus used is shown in Fig. 2. The rotating disk sprayer (S) was mounted in a glass sided chamber (C) of approximately 8 in. square cross-section through which was passed an upward air-flow. The droplets produced by the sprayer evaporated within the chamber to form the dust particles. The cloud passed from the chamber through a vertical tube (T) $1\frac{5}{8}$ in. diameter containing a flow straightener of corrugated metal foil (Fig. 3) to remove turbulence. At the top of this tube and in the central region of the airflow the water drop was placed, suspended from the lower end of a fine glass capillary tube, Fig. 4. During the course of an experiment the whole flow tube was rotated at intervals to overcome any effects due to possible irregularities in the distribution of airflow over the cross section.

FIG. 3. Flow straightener.

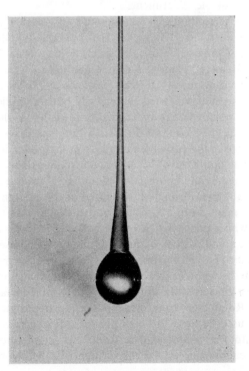

FIG. 4. 2 mm diameter water drop suspended by glass capillary coated with silicone varnish.

The airflow into the dust chamber was measured by the Rotameter (R), Fig. 2, and the velocity in the outlet flow could be calculated from the known diameter of this tube and the flow rate, after allowing for the air used by the sprayer. In the course of the experiment, however, it was found to be more accurate to measure the velocity at the position of the water drop by photographing the upward movement of dust particles under stroboscopic illumination at known frequency. Only particles larger than 20 microns diameter could be recorded in this way and so the calibration of the rotameter obtained when using such particles was assumed also to hold for smaller dust sizes.

The volume of the water drop supported on the end of the glass capillary tube could be controlled by a micrometer syringe connected to the capillary tube. The size of the drop was measured with the aid of the microscope (M). The drop was kept under constant observation during an experiment and its size adjusted as necessary. Even so, it could not be kept absolutely to the required size and the mean of a series of readings of the diameter taken throughout each experiment was taken as the true value. The glass capillaries had to be made as small as $0 \cdot 1$ mm diameter and were formed with a square-cut bell-shaped end coated with a silicone varnish to prevent the water creeping up the sides. It was possible to work with drops down to $0 \cdot 5$ mm diameter, the volume of such a drop being $6 \cdot 6 \times 10^{-5}$ cm^3. The pick up of dust (methylene blue dye) by the drop was again determined by measuring the optical density with a spectrophotometer. The spectrophotometer was modified to deal with 1 cm^3 of solution instead of the 4 cm^3 for which it was designed in order to reduce the degree of dilution necessary. Some dilution was necessary as the liquid of the drop became saturated with dye in the course of the experiment.

With this colorimetric technique it was possible to measure collection efficiencies for dust sizes down to $2 \cdot 5$ microns diameter. The rapid fall in collection efficiency with decreasing size made it impossible to take accurate measurements below this value. An attempt was made to use a more sensitive method in which insoluble spherical particles of carbon black were used as dust particles and counted in the drop under the microscope. The method was tried successfully but was difficult and tedious and so it was not thought worthwhile to proceed with it further at the time.

Measurements of the dust concentration to which the drop was exposed, which caused so much trouble in the earlier technique, was simplified in the present method because the airstream could now be sampled isokinetically. A thin-walled glass sampling tube connected to an impinger was mounted just above and co-axial with the flow tube and air was drawn through at the speed of the emerging dust cloud. In the impinger, which was made from a Drechsel bottle, the air was forced through a fine jet under water in which dust particles were collected and dissolved. A check was carried out for all the combinations of dust size and air speed used in the experiments that no dust penetrated through the impinger. The air velocity into the sampling tube was calculated from its known area and the measured airflow. The airflow as a function of pressure drop across the impinger was determined in a separate experiment with the aid of a Rotameter connected to the upstream side of the impinger. This procedure was used because the high pressure drop across the impinger would introduce errors into the readings of a Rotameter connected in the outlet side. The pressure–flow calibration was checked immediately prior to and after each experiment.

(3) THEORY

It will facilitate presentation and discussion of the experimental results if a brief outline of the theory of the collision processes be given first.

The physical model on which theories have been based comprises a sphere (the drop) of radius R moving at a velocity U relative to a fluid (air) of density ρ_2 and viscosity η. The fluid contains spherical dust particles of radius a and density ρ_1 initially at rest with respect to the fluid. As the sphere moves through the fluid the latter is displaced out of the path and tends to drag the dust particles with it. The latter, however, because of their mass, are not immediately accelerated to the velocity of the fluid but lag behind so that a proportion collide with the sphere; these are the captured particles. Particles whose centres follow paths that pass within a particle radius of the sphere will make contact. The collection efficiency E is defined as the ratio of the number of particles hitting the sphere to the number whose centres initially lay within its track; note that it can exceed 100 per cent for particles of appreciable size. E corresponds to y_0^2, the dimensionless capture cross-section, in Fonda and Herne's notation, but other symbols are the same as used by them.

The above model requires some justification. The water drop has been regarded as a rigid sphere which may be completely characterized by its radius. In practice a falling water drop would tend to be distorted from spherical form by aerodynamic forces and there might be internal circulation which would in turn affect the air flow at the surface. Davies[7] has shown that there is in fact little deformation or circulation in drops of diameter smaller than about 1·5 mm falling in air and that they can be regarded as solid spheres. It has been assumed that the only properties affecting the flow characteristics of the air are its density and viscosity. Since the velocities involved are all low compared with the velocity of sound, compressibility effects can justifiably be neglected. The dust particles have been considered to be spherical for geometrical simplicity in order to avoid the need to consider their orientation. The significance of their mass and of the drag force when their velocity differs from that of the air has already been indicated. These quantities are defined when the size and density of the particles and the properties of the air are known. It will, however, at a later stage be convenient to introduce the drag characteristic of the dust as an independent variable instead of density. The terminal velocity of the dust through the air under the action of gravity has been neglected in the model. This is justifiable if it is small compared with U and if the acceleration of the air and dust by the passage of a water drop is large compared with the acceleration of gravity. In a typical case with a dust of 2·5 microns radius (a) and drop of 0·25 mm radius (R) the terminal velocity of the dust will be about 1 mm/sec and of the drop 200 cm/sec (U), the acceleration will be of the order of $U^2/R = 10^5$ cm/sec². Other assumptions implicit in the model are that only hydrodynamic forces act and that all collisions are effective in capturing dust particles. It should be borne in mind that electrostatic or molecular forces may play a part in some circumstances, also that some dust particles may bounce off without capture. Diffusion of the dust will also be significant when the size is very small.

Theoretical relationships between the variables may be derived by two methods of approach (i) the method of dimensional analysis, which enables general functional relationships to be deduced, and (ii) the strictly analytical approach in which the laws of mechanics are applied to the motions of the dust particles, the drop and the air. The dimensional method will be considered first.

On the basis of the model which has been described the significant variables affecting the collection efficiency are

For the drop	radius R	velocity U
For the fluid	density ρ_2	viscosity η
For the dust	radius a	density ρ_1

The collection efficiency E is a dimensionless quantity determined by the geometrical size and by the pattern of the trajectories of the dust particles relative to the drop. Dynamically similar systems in which corresponding elements of fluid and dust follow similar paths will have equal collection efficiencies. For each such system corresponding to a given collection efficiency there will be a functional relationship between the other variables which satisfies the condition of similitude. We can therefore write

$$E = f(R, U, \rho_2, \eta, \rho_1, a). \tag{1}$$

Since these seven variables involve the three basic units of mass, length, and time, their inter-relationship can be expressed in terms of four, $(7-3)$, dimensionless groups in accordance with Buckingham's Pi theorem,[8] for example,

$$E = f\left(\frac{U\rho_2 R}{\eta}, \ \frac{\rho_1}{\rho_2}, \ \frac{a}{R}\right). \tag{2}$$

Equation 2 reduces the number of parameters on which E is dependent to three. It does not indicate the manner in which E is affected by changes in any one of the variables, but it does show certain simultaneous changes of variables that may be made while E remains constant. Examples of these are listed in Table 1, where n represents a constant multiplier or divisor; line (i), for instance, indicates that the collection efficiency will be unchanged if both U and η are increased by the same factor.

TABLE 1. SIMULTANEOUS CHANGES OF VARIABLES WHICH PRESERVE CONSTANT
COLLECTION EFFICIENCY

	R	U	η	ρ_2	a	ρ_1
(i)		$\times n$	$\times n$			
(ii)	$\times n$	$\div n$			$\times n$	
(iii)	$\times n$		$\times n$		$\times n$	
(iv)			$\times n$	$\times n$		$\times n$
(v)	$\times n$			$\div n$	$\times n$	$\div n$
(vi)		$\div n$		$\times n$		$\times n$

It will be noted in particular that the above results do not throw any light on the effects of change of dust size relative to drop size, or of dust density relative to fluid density. If dust of given density in air is being considered, as in the present experiments, ρ_1, ρ_2 and η will be constant and E will be a function of UR and a/R only.

It may be noted that equation 2 can be expressed in alternative forms with dimensionless groups derived by combination of those used above. For example,

$$E = f\left(\frac{U\rho_2 R}{\eta}, \; \frac{U\rho_1 a^2}{\eta R}, \; \frac{a}{R}\right), \tag{3}$$

a result which will be used later.

If any of the physical variables included in the above analysis were found to be insignificant the number of dimensionless groups would be reduced. For example, if viscous fluid forces predominated and fluid density could be neglected E would be a function of only two groups, which could be written

$$E = f\left(\frac{U\rho_1 a}{\eta}, \; \frac{a}{R}\right), \tag{4}$$

The foregoing analysis has not required any knowledge of the pattern of fluid flow around the dust and drop or placed any restrictions on their sizes except those implicit in the assumption that gravitational forces can be neglected. The model presented, involving two bodies in relative movement in a fluid of any density or viscosity, is still too complex for exact analytical treatment and so further restrictive assumptions must be made. Fonda and Herne, in common with other workers, have assumed that the flow pattern is that of a fluid around a single sphere (the drop) and is undisturbed by the presence of the dust. The dust behaves as a mass point within this flow field and is accelerated by viscous drag of the fluid at a rate proportional to the instantaneous local velocity difference between itself and fluid. The particle behaviour can thus be completely characterized by the quantity $C\eta/m$ where $C = 6\pi a$ so that $C\eta$ is the drag coefficient according to Stokes' Law and m is the particle mass, $= 4\pi a^3 \rho_1/3$. The flow pattern of a fluid around a sphere is only known exactly for the special cases of purely viscous flow (density negligible) and of potential flow (viscosity negligible). Fonda and Herne have calculated the dust particle trajectories within the fluid for each of these regimes and hence found which particles initially in the track of the drop ultimately collide with it. Finite size of dust is introduced by assuming that particles whose trajectories pass within a particle radius of the drop will collide. The results are expressed as curves relating E (or y_0^2) to a dimensionless basic parameter K where

$$K = \frac{U\,m}{RC\eta} \quad \text{or} \quad \frac{2\rho_1 a^2 U}{9\eta R}. \tag{5}$$

for various nearest distances of approach, r_m (measured as a fraction of the drop radius) of the trajectory to the centre of the sphere, for both viscous and potential flow conditions. Collision takes place when $r_m = (a + R)/R$.

One interesting conclusion from the theory is that when $a/R \to 0$ there is a critical value of K below which E is zero. E is generally smaller for viscous than for potential flow at equal values of K because in the former case the fluid streamlines pass further from the sphere due to the stagnation of fluid at the surface, consequently the critical value of K is larger for viscous than potential flow. When a/R is finite E falls to a limiting value (which increases with a/R) as K diminishes.

If dimensional analysis is applied to a system in which it is assumed as above that the dust particles can be characterized by their radius a and by a parameter k, say,

K

representing the acceleration by viscous drag at unit velocity difference (k having the dimension of reciprocal time), then the following relationship is obtained instead of equation 2

$$E = f\left(\frac{U\rho_2 R}{\eta}, \quad \frac{U}{Rk}, \quad \frac{a}{R}\right). \tag{6}$$

k is a function of ρ_1, a and η, and dimensional considerations show that $k \propto \eta/\rho_1 a^2$. It corresponds to Fonda and Herne's quantity $C\eta/m$. If this result is used in equation 6 the latter becomes identical with equation 3. The second term in parenthesis in these equations, U/Rk or $U\rho_1 a^2/\eta R$, is the same as Fonda and Herne's basic parameter, K, apart from a numerical factor. The first term, $U\rho_2 R/\eta$, will be recognized as Reynolds number (divided by two) for the drop. In the two limiting cases of viscous and potential flow around the drop, considered by Fonda and Herne, ρ_2 and η respectively will be ineffective and the Reynolds number term will disappear from the equation. (Note that viscous drag on the dust is still assumed in both cases). It is also legitimate to consider the case where k is finite but a is very small in relation to R so that its influence on the probability of collision from geometrical considerations is negligible. In these circumstances the term a/R disappears from equation 6 leaving E as a function of $U\rho_1 a^2/\eta R$ or K only for the two special flow conditions. The experimental results obtained in the present investigation are plotted as a function of K in Section 4, in comparison with Fonda and Herne's analytical results.

It should be remembered that equation 3 was derived quite generally and without the restrictive assumptions made by Fonda and Herne concerning the purely viscous nature of the drag forces on the dust and the non-disturbance of the flow pattern by the dust particles. The equation has, however, been arranged so that if these assumptions are correct the second term, $U\rho_1 a^2/\eta R$, alone will represent the relationship between the physical variables under certain limiting conditions and the other dimensionless groups will have little effect. If on the other hand, for example, dynamic forces ($\propto$ velocity^2) instead of viscous forces ($\propto$ velocity) acted on the dust particles, equation 3 would still be valid but the relative significance of the groups would be changed. This and other possible disturbing factors are briefly discussed by Fonda and Herne.[2]

Recent theoretical work has attempted to deal with dust and drops of comparable size, and with flow at finite Reynolds number. Hocking[9] has calculated the collision efficiency between free-falling water drops for $a/R > 0.2$, assuming viscous flow. He finds that the efficiency falls to zero as the terminal velocity and size diminish, not to an asymptotic finite value as Fonda and Herne's calculations indicate.

As will appear later, in mining applications of dust spraying interest centres on the transition region between turbulent and viscous flow (turbulent flow approximates to potential flow in front of the drop but not in the wake) so it is necessary to interpolate between the theoretical curves for these states. Langmuir[1] gives the empirical relationship

$$E = [E_v + E_p \, Re/60]/[1 + Re/60] \tag{7}$$

where E_v and E_p relate to the viscous and potential regimes respectively. This interpolation formula will be used in Section 5. Attempts, discussed by Herne,[4] to calculate analytically the collection efficiency at transitional Reynolds numbers have given results which are incompatible with Langmuir's or Fonda and Herne's data for the limiting viscous and potential conditions.

(4) RESULTS

4.1 Stationary Cloud Method

As indicated in Section 2, the experimental errors were large with this method and so only a limited number of experiments were carried out at extreme values of the experimental variables permitted by the method, namely $R=1\cdot3$ mm and $0\cdot25$ mm, $a=24$ microns and 6 microns. The velocity of the water drops falling through the dust cloud could not be varied for a given drop size. The smaller drops were at their terminal velocity but not the larger ones. The results are given in Table 2. The column headed E_{cor} gives corrected values of E which allow for the finite size of the dust; 100 per cent collection efficiency corresponding to the interception of all dust in a cylinder of radius $R+a$ instead of R.

TABLE 2. RESULTS OF PRELIMINARY EXPERIMENTS. STATIONARY CLOUD METHOD
$\eta = 18 \times 10^{-5}$ poise $\qquad \rho_2 = 1\cdot2 \times 10^{-3}$ g/cm³ $\qquad \rho_1 = 1\cdot3$ g/cm³

Water drop radius R (mm)	Velocity U (cm/sec)	Dust Radius a (microns)	Collection efficiency						a/R (10^{-3})	K	Re
			$E\%$					E_{cor} %			
			(i)	(ii)	(iii)	(iv)	Mean				
1·3	330	24	88·4	48·5	130	61·2	82	79	18·5	2·35	570
		6	39·1	32·2	32·4	52·8	37	36	4·6	0·145	
0·25	210	24	99·5	105	122	138	117	96	96	7·7	69
		6	54·7	52·0	66·0	61·5	59	57	24	0·48	

The results show clearly that there is a decrease in collection efficiency with dust size and would at first sight appear to show that smaller drops are more effective than larger, but it must be remembered that the larger drops were falling at much less than their terminal velocity whereas the smaller ones were at their terminal velocity.

4.2 Stationary Drop Method

The ranges of variables, drop size, dust size and drop velocity, attainable by this method were much larger than with the previous one; in particular dust of respirable size (<5 microns diameter) could be used and the drop velocity could be controlled A programme of measurements was carried out using the following values

Dust size, a	2·5, 1·25 μ radius
Drop size, R	1·0, 0·5, 0·25 mm radius
Drop velocity, U	670, 390, 200 cm/sec

these velocities being approximately equal to the terminal velocities of the 1·0, 0·5 and 0·25 mm radius drops respectively. The programme consisted of a fully randomized complete block experiment involving eighteen levels, with two replications. Two sets of observations were made at each replication. In this randomized experiment it proved impossible to reset the variables exactly to their nominal values in each run; the actual values were therefore recorded and used in computing E and K^*. The results are given in Table 3 for each replication, each entry in the Table being the mean of two consecutive sets of observations. Mean values of E and K for the two replications at each level are also given in Table 3, together with the nominal values of R, U, Re^*, a and a/Re. It was shown in the previous section that E should, theoretically, be a function of K, Re and a/r. In Fig. 5 E is plotted as a function of K and, for comparison, the theoretical curves of Fonda and Herne for viscous and potential flow at $a/R=0$ and 0·1 are also given.

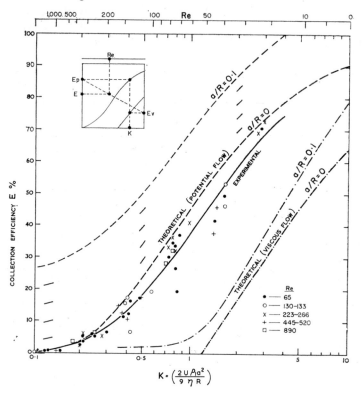

Fig. 5. Plot of experimental results (efficiency versus parameter K) in comparison with Fonda and Herne's theoretical curves.
Use Re scale as shown in inset to give Langmuir's correction for Reynolds number.

It has been suggested that wetting agents added to the sprayed liquid might increase the collection efficiency. Some experiments were therefore carried out in which two equal sized drops were exposed in the apparatus, one of water and the other of wetting agent solution. As expected, no significant difference was found between the collection efficiencies of the drops.

* $K=2\rho_1 a^2 U/9\eta R$ is used instead of the parameter $\rho_1 a^2 U/\eta R$ without numerical coefficient given by dimensional analysis, and Reynolds number $Re=2U\rho_2 R/\eta$ instead of $U\rho_2 R/\eta$, to facilitate comparison with the results of Fonda and Herne and other workers.

A similar set of experiments was carried out to compare dust clouds composed of solid and liquid particles as it was thought this might affect capture on collision, but again no significant difference was found.

(5) DISCUSSION OF RESULTS

Figure 5 and Table 3 show that when E is plotted against K the experimental points lie near to a common curve which follows fairly closely the theoretical line of Fonda and Herne for potential flow and lies between their "potential" and "viscous" curves

TABLE 3. RESULTS. STATIONARY DROP METHOD

$\eta = 18 \times 10^{-5}$ poise $\rho_2 = 1.2 \times 10^{-3}$ g/cm^3 $\rho_1 = 1.37$ g/cm^3

Drop radius R (mm)	Air velocity U (cm/sec)	Dust radius a (microns)	Collection efficiency E %			K			a/R (10^{-3})	Re
			(i)	(ii)	Mean	(i)	(ii)	Mean		
0.25	670	2·5	69·0	72·6	70·8	2·69	2.93	2·81	10	223
		1·25	41·0	33·1	37·0	0·98	0·72	0·85	5	
	390	2·5	53·0	46·2	49·6	1·65	1·66	1·65	10	130
		1·25	19·4	15·8	17·6	0·57	0·39	0·48	5	
	200	2·5	33·5	19·5	26·5	0·80	0·82	0·81	10	65·5
		1·25	6·7	3·9	5·3	0·30	0·21	0·25	5	
0·5	670	2·5	37·7	45·7	41·7	1·40	1·48	1·44	5	445
		1·25	17·5	14·8	16·1	0·49	0·35	0·42	2·5	
	390	2·5	32·3	36·6	34·5	0·79	0·77	0·78	5	260
		1·25	5·7	6·1	5·9	0·28	0·21	0·24	2·5	
	200	2·5	17·5	6·9	12·2	0·40	0·42	0·41	5	133
		1·25	0·8	0·5	0·7	0·15	0·10	0·12	2·5	
1·0	670	2·5	28·3	32·1	30·2	0·70	0·77	0·73	2·5	890
		1·25	6·4	3·5	5·0	0·25	0·18	0·21	1·25	
	390	2·5	10·6	12·6	11·6	0·40	0·37	0.38	2·5	520
		1·25	0·7	0·5	0·6	0·14	0·10	0·12	1·25	
	200	2·5	2·3	2·7	2·5	0·20	0·20	0·20	2·5	266
		1·25	0·2	0·2	0·2	0·07	0·05	0·06	1·25	

except at very small values of E and K. Since dimensional theory indicated that E is a function of a/R and Re as well as of K, the deviation ΔE of the (mean) measured efficiency for each level from the mean experimental curve in Fig. 5 has been examined for correlation with these variables, see Fig. 6 (a) and (b).

The values of Re covered in the present experiments, as shown in Table 3 and Fig. 6 (a), extend from 65 to 890. These lie well outside the region of viscous flow ($Re < 1$); and extend from the upper transition region (where relatively stationary vortices are formed) into the turbulent zone. Under these conditions the flow pattern in front of the drop would be expected to approximate to that given by potential flow theory, although the latter does not correctly represent flow in the wake or indeed account for any resistance to the motion of the drop. The closer approach of the experimental results to the "potential" curve of Fonda and Herne than to the "viscous" curve is therefore to be expected. Figure 6 (a) shows little evidence of a significant Reynolds number effect at the higher values of Re but there is perhaps a suggestion of diminishing collection efficiency at the lower values.

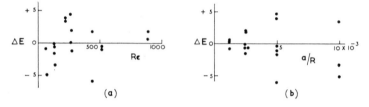

FIG. 6. Deviation of measured collection efficiency (mean value for each level), from mean experimental curve (a) as a function of Reynolds number, (b) as a function of a/R.

In Fig. 7 the deviations $E - E_p$ of the experimental points from the theoretical values for potential flow have been expressed as a fraction of the difference $E_p - E_v$ and plotted against Re for comparison with values calculated from Langmuir's interpolation formula (equation 7). The direction and order of magnitude of the experimentally observed deviations are consistent with Langmuir's formula but the scatter of the points is too great to permit more detailed conclusions to be drawn. A graphical method of carrying out the Langmuir interpolation is shown in Fig. 5.

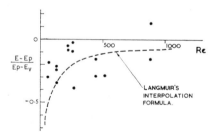

FIG. 7. Fractional deviation of experimental points between theoretical potential and viscous flow curves as a function of Reynolds number in comparison with Langmuir's formula.

Figure 6 (b) shows no correlation between a/R and ΔE for values of a/R in the range $1 \cdot 5 \times 10^{-3}$ to 10×10^{-3}. For the latter value Fonda and Herne's theory for potential flow, gives a change in E of $2 \cdot 5$ approx. (when E is expressed as a percentage) in the middle range of E values, with proportionately smaller figures for smaller values of

a/R. An effect of this magnitude would hardly be observable with the present degree of experimental accuracy. When K is very small the theory predicts that E would fall to an asymptotic value of about 3 per cent for $a/R=10^{-2}$ (proportionate for other values of a/R) instead of being sharply cut off to zero as for $a/R=0$. Although Hocking's later work throws doubt on the asymptotic value, the effect of a/R will be to delay the cut off and this may perhaps explain why the experimental collection efficiency (Table 3) does not fall to zero at the critical value (1/12) of K for zero a/R. The number of observations and the experimental accuracy are insufficient for this effect to show in Fig. 6 (b).

The limited results given in Table 2 for larger sizes of dust are insufficient in number and accuracy to permit any quantitative conclusions to be drawn.

The general conclusion to be drawn from the above is that the experimental results confirm the correctness and completeness of the theoretical model and the calculations made by Langmuir and subsequently with greater refinement by Fonda and Herne, over the range of variables covered by the experiments. It should be noted that this range does not embrace the theoretically interesting and more difficult conditions of intermediate Reynolds numbers and relatively large a/R values, nor values of K much smaller than "critical" for $a/R=0$.

There has been conflicting evidence from other work about the possible significance of other factors not included in the theoretical model discussed above, particularly that some dust-drop collisions may not result in capture of the dust, and that extra dust particles may be drawn into the wake of the drops and captured. See, for example, References 10 and 11. No such effects need be invoked to explain the present observations. Conditions in the wake of suspended drops as used here would, of course, differ from those in free fall.

(6) APPLICATION OF RESULTS TO PRACTICAL CONDITIONS

Previous sections have considered the dust collection efficiency of a single drop moving at a determined velocity. In practical applications of spraying numerous droplets are projected at high velocity from the spray nozzle, are decelerated by air resistance at a rate depending on their size and then, in general, fall to the ground under gravity. The relative importance of the projection and free fall stages in regard to dust removal will vary with circumstances.

6.1 *Spray Falling Under Gravity*

The simplest case that can be envisaged is a curtain of spray in a gallery, falling from roof to floor, and uniformly distributed over its horizontal area A. If a volume of ΔV of water is dispersed into droplets of radius R, the cross-sectional area swept out by the falling drops will be

$$\frac{\Delta V \times \pi R^2}{4\pi R^3/3} = \frac{3\Delta V}{4R}$$

and the effective area denuded of dust will be $3E\Delta V/4R$. The fraction of dust removed from the gallery will therefore be

$$\frac{\Delta n}{n} = \frac{3E\Delta V}{4RA}.$$

This fraction is independent of the concentration n. Continued spraying will result in a logarithmic diminution in concentration, viz.

$$n = n_0 \exp\left(-3EV/4RA\right) \qquad (8)$$

where n and n_0 are the initial and final concentrations respectively and V is the total volume of water sprayed.

Another simple case is that of a dust cloud moving at uniform velocity v along a gallery of rectangular cross-section of width w, passing through a spray curtain uniformly spread across the width and having a total water flow rate Q per unit time. In time t a volume Qt of water will be delivered on an area wvt of the dust cloud. The process is essentially similar to that considered in the previous paragraph, the quotient Qt/wvt or Q/wv replacing V/A in equation 8.

TABLE 4. Values of E and S as functions of drop size and dust size

Water spray falling under gravity in air. Density of dust $1 \cdot 37$ g/cm^3

Calculated from Fonda and Herne's theoretical results with correction for a/R and Langmuir's interpolation formula.

Data in brackets derived from experimental $E-K$ curve of Fig. 5, those for $Re < 65$ lie outside the range of Reynolds number covered by the experiments.

Drop diameter 2R (mm)	Terminal velocity U (cm/sec)	Re	Collection efficiency of drop E (%) Dust diameter, 2a (microns)						Effective capture cross-section per unit volume, S. (cm²/cc) Dust diameter, 2a (microns)					
			2	3	5	10	15	20	2	3	5	10	15	20
0·1	27	1·8	0·1 (0·4)	0·3 (3·8)	2·1 (22)	31 (62)	—	—	0·2	0·5	3·1	46		
0·2	72	9·6	0·3 (0·6)	1·6 (7·0)	6·8 (29)	41 (70)	69 (84)	89 —	0·2	1·2	5·1	31	52	67
0·3	117	23·4	0·4 (0·6)	3·6 (8·0)	12 (32)	49 (71)	73 (85)	88 —	0·2	1·8	6·2	25	36	44
0·5	206	69	1·0 (0·8)	7·0 (9·0)	23 (33)	60 (73)	80 (86)	90 (90)	0·3	2·1	7·0	18	24	27
1·0	403	269	1·1 (0·8)	10 (9·0)	34 (33)	70 (72)	85 (85)	92 (90)	0·2	1·5	5·1	10·5	13	14
1·5	541	543	0·5 (0·6)	7·8 (7·5)	34 (29)	71 (70)	86 (84)	92 (90)	0·05	0·8	3·4	7·1	8·6	9·0
2·0	649	866	0·3 (0·6)	5·9 (5·2)	31 (26)	70 (67)	85 (82)	91 (90)	0·02	0·4	2·3	5·2	6·4	6·8
3·0	806	1613	0·2 (0·4)	4·6 (3·8)	27 (22)	67 (62)	83 (80)	90 (87)	0·01	0·2	1·3	3·3	4·1	4·5

In equation 8 the quantity $3E/4R=S$, say, represents the effective total capture cross-section of unit volume of sprayed liquid and is a measure of its dust collection capacity. Values of E and S for various sizes* of drops falling in air at their terminal velocities are given in Table 4. They refer to the capture of dust particles of density 1·37, which is the density of the methylene blue used in the experimental investigation and is approximately that of coal dust. The main data in the Table have been calculated from Fonda and Herne's theoretical results using their correction for a/R and Langmuir's interpolation formula to allow for the transition from potential to viscous flow. The data in brackets have been derived from the present experimental work by using the smoothed experimental curve of Fig. 5 relating E to K, which makes no allowance for Reynolds number. The lowest value of Re covered by the experimental work was 65 and it will be noted that where this is exceeded in Table 4, i.e. for drops 0·5 mm diameter and larger, there is satisfactory, and often excellent, agreement between the theoretical and experimental figures. As Re decreases it is to be expected that E will move towards the theoretical viscous flow curve of Fig. 5 and that results calculated from the experimental curve will be increasingly in error. Figures derived in this way have been included in Table 4 to illustrate the magnitude of the effect. In view of the good agreement between theory and experiment in the range covered by the latter and the danger of extrapolating the experimental results outside this range, subsequent discussion will be based mainly on the theoretical data.

Several features of the data given in Table 4 are noteworthy. The collection efficiency of spray of given drop size falls rapidly as the dust size diminishes, and is less than 1 per cent for dust smaller than 2 microns diameter for all drops. For given dust size E is approximately constant and S increases inversely proportional to the drop size as the latter falls from 3 mm to 0·5 mm diameter. Below 0·5 mm, S falls with decreasing drop size for dust smaller than 5 microns diameter, but continues to rise for coarser dust. The optimum spray drop size for removal of respirable dust is therefore about 0·5 mm diameter. The fall in the value of S below this size is due to the transition from potential to viscous flow conditions. At large dust sizes this effect is counter-balanced by the increasing significance of direct interception and it appears to be advantageous to use the smallest possible size of spray droplet. The practical limit will be set by the evaporation rate of the spray (see Appendix I) and the need for a reasonable fall-out speed to carry the collected dust out of the air. The deduction of an optimum drop size at about 0·5 mm diameter for dust <5 microns diameter depends on the correctness of Langmuir's interpolation formula.

The importance of the Reynolds number effect in determining the efficiency of gravity spray requires emphasis. It can be seen from Fig. 5 that when E is plotted against log K the theoretical curves for potential and viscous flow are approximately linear and parallel in the range 20 per cent$<E<$60 per cent, E_p-E_v being about 50 per cent. For given dust in air K is proportional to U/R and in the above region an increase in U/R by a factor of two will increase both E_p and E_v by about 21 percentage units. If the velocity U remains constant this change will occur when the drop radius R is halved. Reynolds number ($\propto RU$) will also be halved and in the transition region around $Re=60$ Langmuir's interpolation formula indicates that this will shift E from E_p towards E_v, reducing its value by about 0·17 (E_p-E_v), i.e. 8 percentage units in

---

* In this Section the sizes of drops and dust are given as *diameters*, not radii, in accordance with convention in practical work.

contrary direction to the change of 21 caused by K. The effect of Re is considerably more marked if drops at their terminal velocities are considered, so that both R and U vary. As may be seen from Table 4, the terminal velocities of drops in the size range 0·2 mm to 2·0 mm diameter are, broadly speaking, directly proportional to the size. A decrease in drop size by a factor of two will therefore have little or no effect on K or hence on E_p or E_v. Reynolds number will, however, decrease fourfold and such a change from 120 to 30 will diminish E by $\frac{1}{3}$ (E_p-E_v) or 17 percentage units according to Langmuir's formula. The effect is greatest in the region of $Re=60$ (ca. 0·5 mm diameter drops), diminishing for higher and lower values of Re. For gravity spray, therefore, in the most effective size range, the relationship between drop size and efficiency is dominated by the rapidity of the transition from potential to viscous flow conditions with change of Reynolds number. This is precisely the region in which theory can give least help; further experimental work to verify Langmuir's interpolation formula is desirable.

Curves relating E to drop size for gravity spray have previously been given by Stairmand,[12] based on theoretical data by Bosanquet. These relate to potential flow and zero a/R but appear to have been applied to other conditions, leading to an over-estimation of E for small drops.

From equation 8 it follows that there will be 90 per cent dust removal when $\exp(-3EV/4RA)=0{\cdot}1$, or $3EV/4RA=2{\cdot}3$. Values of V/A, the volume of spray per unit area, required for 90 per cent dust removal from a stationary cloud can therefore be obtained using data for $S=3E/4R$ from Table 4. The results, expressed in practical units of gallons of water per 100 ft², for various drop and dust sizes are given in Table 5.

Table 5. Gravity spray
Spray volume for 90 per cent removal of airborne dust
(Dust density 1·37 g/cm³)

Drop diameter (mm)	Gal of spray per 100 ft² (stationary cloud) or Gal per min per ft width of roadway per 100 ft/min air speed (moving cloud)					
	Dust diameter (microns)					
	2	3	5	10	15	20
0·1	240	90	6·8	1·0		
0·2	240	40	9·2	1·5	0·9	0·6
0·3	260	26	6·8	1·9	1·3	1·1
0·5	160	22	6·7	2·6	2·0	1·7
1·0	230	31	9·2	4·5	3·7	3·5
1·5	940	58	14	6·6	5·5	5·2
2·0	2300	120	21	9·0	7·3	6·9
3·0	4600	230	36	14	11	10

The same data apply to a moving cloud traversing a spray curtain, and represent the spray rate in gallons per minute per foot width of the gallery required to give 90 per cent reduction of dust in a cloud travelling at a velocity of 100 ft/min. In the case of the stationary cloud the rate of spraying is immaterial, only the total volume being significant; for the moving cloud the length of spray curtain in the direction of motion of the air stream is immaterial, the total volume rate of spraying per unit width of gallery being the determining factor.

It will be noted in Table 5 that a moderate control of respirable dust (90 per cent removal at 3 microns diameter and above) by a gravity spray curtain in a 12 ft wide roadway at a (low) air velocity of 100 ft/min would require a water consumption of about 260 gal/min under optimum conditions. The suppression of a stationary cloud in a section of tunnel 12 ft wide by 50 yd long would require 400 gal of water to be sprayed.

6.2 *Projected Spray*

Spray drops travelling at high velocity on leaving a pressure nozzle will have a higher collection efficiency than when falling at lower speed under gravity. It is therefore necessary to estimate the contribution of this phase of their flight to dust suppression.

The velocities U and distances of travel (s) of drops of various sizes projected into air at 3000 cm/sec have been calculated as functions of time from formulae* given by Giffen and Muraszew[13] and from these data velocity was related to distance travelled (Fig. 8). Values of K and Re were next computed for each drop size at various velocities and for different sizes of dust and from these the corresponding values of E were obtained from Fonda and Herne's theoretical data adjusted for a/R and using Langmuir's interpolation formula.

Curves were then drawn of E as a function of distance travelled, Fig. 9, and used to derive mean values, $\bar{E}$ of E over the total projection distance or range of the spray. Similar values for other (lesser) initial velocities were readily derivable for the same data. The results of these calculations are given in Table 6. The total effective volume of air denuded of dust by a single projected drop is $\bar{E}s_0\pi R^2$ where $\bar{E}$ is the mean collection efficiency over the full range s_0, and hence the total effective swept volume per unit volume of liquid sprayed is $3\bar{E}s_0\pi R^2/4\pi R^3 = 3\bar{E}s/4R$. Values of this quantity, which measures the overall efficiency of the spray, are given in the 6th column of Table 6 for initial velocities of 3000 cm/sec and 2000 cm/sec. A projection velocity

---

* (i) Turbulent Flow. $Re > 500$.

$$U = U_0 \bigg/ \left[1 + \frac{0.33\rho_2}{2R\rho_1} U_0 t\right]$$

$$s = \frac{2R\rho_1}{0.33\rho_2} \log_e \left[1 + \frac{0.33\rho_2}{2R\rho_1} U_0 t\right]$$

(ii) Semi-turbulent Flow. $500 > Re > 2$.

$$U = 1 \bigg/ \left[\left(\frac{0.02R\rho_2}{\eta} + \frac{1}{U_0}\right) \exp\left(\frac{30\eta t}{4R^2\rho_1}\right) - \frac{0.02R\rho_2}{\eta}\right]$$

$$s = \frac{2R\rho_1}{0.3\rho_2} \log_e \left[1 + \frac{0.02R\rho_2}{\eta} U_0 \left\{1 - \exp\left(\frac{30\eta t}{4R^2\rho_1}\right)\right\}\right]$$

(iii) Laminar Flow $Re < 2$.

$$U = U_0 \exp\left(\frac{18\eta t}{4R^2\rho_1}\right) \qquad s = \frac{4R^2\rho_1}{18\eta}\left\{1 - \exp\left(\frac{18\eta t}{4R^2\rho_1}\right)\right\}$$

of 3000 cm/sec corresponds to a water feed pressure of about 80 lb/in² for a plain atomizer with a coefficient of discharge of 0·9, or 260 lb/in² for a swirl atomiser with a coefficient of discharge of 0·5. For 2000 cm/sec initial velocity the corresponding pressures would be 36 and 110 lb/in² respectively.

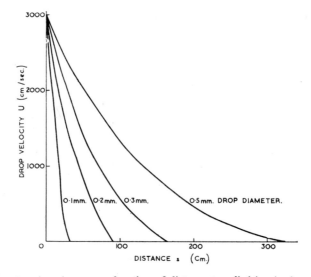

FIG. 8. Velocity of projected spray as function of distance travelled in air, for various drop sizes. (Initial velocity 3000 cm/sec.)

The maximum size of water drop that can be projected through air without disruption is, according to Lane,[14] given by $U^2R=306$, U in m/sec, R (radius) in mm. This gives a maximum drop diameter ($2R$) of 0·68 mm when $U=3000$ cm/sec. The upper size, 0·5 mm, included in Table 6 cannot therefore be greatly exceeded at that velocity.

In the last column of Table 6 there is given the volume of water in the form of projected spray required for 90 per cent removal of dust; the units being gallons of water per 1000 ft³ of cloud. As in the case of gravity spray, it has been assumed that the dust concentration will fall logarithmically so that the total effective swept volume required for 90 per cent removal will be 2·3, i.e. $\log_e 10$, times the volume of cloud treated. This implies a uniform dispersal of spray throughout the cloud, otherwise the scouring action will be wasted on air already cleaned while other parts of the cloud remain unaffected with a consequently reduced overall efficiency.

The main features to be noted from Table 6 are

(i) Drops projected at high velocities have high mean collection efficiencies over their range of projection, values up to 50 per cent being realizable for particles as small as 2 microns diameter, and up to 20 to 30 per cent at 1 micron. The efficiency is greater for small drops than large, particularly for small dust particles, and increases with increasing projection velocity.

(ii) The projection distance or range increases moderately with velocity and strongly with drop size.

TABLE 6. PROJECTED SPRAY. Dust density 1·37 g/cm^3

Initial drop velocity U_0 (cm/sec)	Drop diameter 2R (mm)	Range s_0 (cm)	Dust diameter 2a (microns)	Average collection efficiency over range $\bar{E}$ (per cent)	Total effective swept volume per cm^3 of spray (litres)	Volume of spray per 1000 ft^3 for 90 per cent dust removal (gal)
3000	0·5	330	10	78	7·7	1·9
			5	57	5·6	2·5
			3	39	3·8	3·7
			2	24	2·4	6·0
			1	5	0·5	29
	0·3	163	10	85	6·9	2·1
			5	66	5·3	2·7
			3	49	3·9	3·6
			2	34	2·7	5·2
			1	10	0·8	17
	0·2	89	10	93	6·2	2·3
			5	73	4·9	2·9
			3	57	3·8	3·8
			2	41	2·8	5·2
			1	17	1·2	12
	0·1	30·5	10	110	5·0	2·8
			5	87	4·0	3·6
			3	69	3·1	4·5
			2	55	2·5	5·6
			1	28	1·3	11
2000	0·5	278	10	73	6·0	2·4
			5	50	4·1	3·5
			3	32	2·7	5·4
			2	17	1·4	10·1
			1	2·5	0·2	69
	0·3	135	10	81	5·4	2·6
			5	59	4·0	3·6
			3	41	2·7	5·2
			2	26	1·7	8·2
			1	6	0·4	37
	0·2	73	10	89	4·8	3·0
			5	67	3·7	3·9
			3	50	2·7	5·3
			2	34	1·8	7·7
			1	12	0·7	21
	0·1	23·5	10	107	3·8	3·8
			5	81	2·8	5·0
			3	61	2·2	6·5
			2	46	1·6	8·8
			1	21	0·7	19

(iii) The total dust removal by a given quantity of sprayed water for given velocity and dust size depends on the number of drops formed, the cross-sectional area of each, the range and the average efficiency, all of which are functions of the drop size. Number and collection efficiency on the one hand, and area and range on the other, are affected in opposite senses by change of drop size and so tend to have compensatory effects. In the outcome drop size has little effect on the total dust removal over the dust size range 10 microns to 2 microns diameter, for 1 micron dust finer spray is more effective.

(iv) The total dust removal per unit volume of water sprayed increases with spray velocity (or water feed pressure) for all dust sizes.

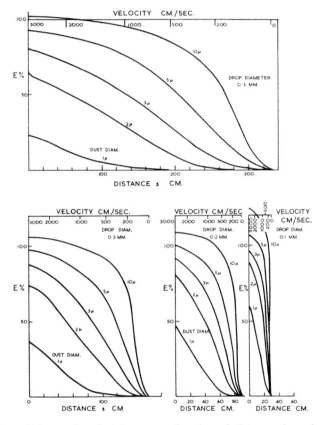

FIG. 9. Collection efficiency of projected spray as function of distance, drop size and dust size.

6.3 Comparison of Gravity Spray and Projected Spray

If the data for gravity spray in Table 5 be considered to relate to 10 ft distance of fall, the volume of cloud in 100 ft² sprayed area will be 1000 ft³ and so a direct comparison can be made with the values for a similar volume given in the last column of Table 6.

For coarse (10-micron diameter) dust gravity and projected spray (3000 cm/sec) are about equally effective at a drop diameter of 0·5 mm, *ca.* 2 gallons of water being needed per 1000 ft³ for 90 per cent dust removal. At smaller drop sizes the efficiency of the gravity spray for this dust increases somewhat whereas that of the projected spray diminishes slightly. In the respirable range of dust, <5 microns diameter, the best results for gravity spray are achieved with 0·5 mm diameter drops, but at this drop size the volume of water needed rises steeply as the dust becomes smaller, being 4·7 gal at 5 microns, 18 gal at 3 microns and 240 gal at 2 microns diameter. With projected spray the rise is considerably less, the corresponding figures being 2·5, 3·7 and 6·0 gal for 0·5 mm diameter drops, drop size in the range 0·5 mm to 0·1 mm diameter has little effect. For 1 micron diameter dust gravity spray is quite ineffective but projected spray has a fair efficiency, about 12 gal of water being required per 1000 ft³ for 90 per cent removal using 0·1 or 0·2 mm diameter drops, rising to 29 gal at 0·5 mm.

It appears from the above that in ordinary mining applications of airborne dust spraying any effect on respirable dust will be achieved in the high-velocity projection zone in the vicinity of the spray nozzle rather than from relatively slow gravitating spray. The drop size of the spray for a given water consumption and pressure is relatively unimportant except in so far as it affects the distance of projection of the spray and thereby the efficient intermingling of spray and dust, provided always that the spray nearly reaches its full range before impaction on the bounding walls. When spraying in a confined space drop size and hence range should be adjusted to suit. The highest practicable water pressure should be used. With good design it appears to be possible to achieve a useful control of respirable dust in the size range 1 to 5 microns diameter at a water consumption of about 5 to 10 gal per 1000 ft³ of air treated. This might find effective application in circumstances where small volumes of dust cloud at high concentration are encountered, particularly near sources of dust production.

All the above data relate to dust of density 1·37 and are applicable to coal. Rock dust of greater density will be removed more readily, approximately equal efficiencies being obtained at equal values of $\rho_1 a^2$, although this simple relationship will tend to break down when a/R is large or E is small.

(7) CONCLUSIONS

The main conclusions to be drawn from this work are as follows.

Experimental measurements of the collection efficiency of water drops for airborne dust particles of methylene blue over the range drop diameter 0·5 mm to 2 mm, dust diameter 2·5 microns to 5·0 microns and drop velocity 200 cm/sec to 670 cm/sec, gave results in close agreement with theoretical predictions. The collection efficiency in this range could satisfactorily be represented as a function of a single dimensionless parameter involving dust size and density, drop size, velocity, and the viscosity of air. The measurements, however, covered only small values of the ratio dust size/drop size and large values of Reynolds number for the drop. Theory indicates that these quantities at larger and smaller values respectively should also affect the efficiency independently of the previously mentioned parameter. The effect of Reynolds number is of particular interest in relation to the dust collection efficiency of spray falling under gravity and merits further study.

Estimates of the efficiency of free-falling or gravity spray indicate that the optimum drop size for removing respirable (<5 microns diameter) dust, for given water consumption, is about 0·5 diameter. The collection efficiency of single drops of this size is high ($>$60 per cent) for coal dust particles (density 1·37) greater than 10 microns diameter but falls rapidly in the respirable dust size range, being 23 per cent at 5 microns, 7 per cent at 3 microns and about 1 per cent at 2 microns diameter. The quantity of water required to achieve 90 per cent suppression of a dust cloud in a 10-ft high gallery by spray falling at its terminal velocity from the full height of the gallery is, per 1000 ft³ of dust cloud, 2·6 gal for 10 micron dust, 6·7 gal at 5 microns, 22 gal at 3 microns, and 160 gal at 2 microns. 260 gal of water per min would be needed for moderate control of respirable dust (90 per cent suppression at 3 microns) in a cloud flowing at an air speed of 100 ft/min in a 12 ft wide gallery. For comparison, the standard N.C.B. spray delivers about ½ gal of water per min. The above data relate to *spherical* dust particles.

Spray drops projected at high velocity from a pressure nozzle have enhanced collection efficiencies for small particles, the mean efficiency over the projection range being as great as 55 per cent for 2-micron diameter dust and 28 per cent for 1 micron, for 0·1 mm diameter drops projected at 3000 cm/sec. Although the projection range increases rapidly with drop size for spray of a given initial velocity or supply pressure, the total dust collection by a given quantity of sprayed water is practically independent of the drop size between 0·1 and 0·5 diameter. It is estimated that 90 per cent suppression of coal dust down to 2 microns diameter could be achieved with a water consumption of 5 to 10 gal per 1000 ft³ of dust cloud. A high water supply pressure is advantageous and drop size should be chosen so that the projection range suits the confines of the working space.

Under normal mining conditions gravity spray is not an effective means of removing respirable dust from the air. High-velocity spray from a pressure nozzle might provide a practicable way of treating concentrated clouds near the source of production or ducted therefrom.

(8) ACKNOWLEDGMENTS

The authors wish to thank Mr. J. F. Holdsworth who assisted with the statistical design and analysis, Mr. E. Brunt and Mr. G. Knight who assisted in the experimental work and Miss P. M. T. Miles who carried out some of the arithmetical calculations. The paper is published by permission of the Director General of Research in the National Coal Board.

(9) REFERENCES

1. LANGMUIR, I., *J. Met.*, **5**, 175 (1948).
2. FONDA, A. and HERNE, H., "Hydrodynamic Capture of Particles by Spheres". Private communication (1957).
3. MASON, B. J., *The Physics of Clouds*, Oxford, Clarendon Press (1957).
4. HERNE, H., Paper 2, this symposium.
5. WALTON, W. H. and PREWETT, W. C., *Proc. Phys. Soc., Lond.*, B, **62**, 341 (1949).
6. LANE, W. R., *J. Sci. Instrum.*, **24**, 98 (1947).
7. DAVIES, C. N., Symposium on Particle Size Analysis.   Supplement to *Trans. Instn. Chem. Engrs*, Lond., **25** (1947).
8. BUCKINGHAM, E., *Phys. Rev.*, **4**, 345 (1914).
9. HOCKING, L. M. Paper 12, this symposium.
10. McCULLY, C. R., FISHER, M., LANGER, G., ROSINSKI, J., GLAESS, H. and WERLE, D., *Industr. Engng. Chem.*, **48**, 1512 (1956)

11. PEMBERTON, C. S. Paper 13, this symposium.
12. STAIRMAND, C. J., *Heat. Vent. Engr.*, **26,** 343 (1953).
13. GIFFEN, E. and MURASZEW, A., *The Atomisation of Liquid Fuels*, London, Chapman and Hall (1953).
14. LANE, W. R., *Industr. Engng. Chem.*, **43,** 1312 (1951).

APPENDIX I

EVAPORATION OF FALLING WATER SPRAY

The life and distance of fall before complete evaporation of water drops of various sizes have been calculated, using Frössling's[1] equation for the rate of evaporation of a ventilated drop and allowing for changing drop size and velocity during fall. Both life and distance are inversely proportional to the difference between the vapour pressure of the drop and the partial pressure of water vapour in the air, the vapour pressure of drop being the saturation vapour pressure of water at the wet bulb temperature. This vapour pressure difference between drop and air when measured in millimeters of mercury is numerically equal, to a close approximation, to one half the wet bulb depression measured in centigrade degrees.

TABLE AI. LIFE AND DISTANCE OF FALL BEFORE COMPLETE
EVAPORATION OF WATER DROPS IN AIR, FOR WET BULB
DEPRESSION OF 10°C (5 mm Hg VAPOUR PRESSURE DIFFERENCE)

(For other humidities, life and distance vary inversely as the wet bulb depression)

Drop diameter (mm)	Life (seconds)	Distance of fall (cm)
0·01	0·10	0·014
0·02	0·38	0·23
0·04	1·5	3·4
0·1	8·3	102
0·2	27	1040
0·4	82	7400
1·0	230	72000

REFERENCE

1. FRÖSSLING, N., *Beitr. Geophys.*, **52,** 170 (1938).

L

THE THEORETICAL COLLISION EFFICIENCY OF SMALL DROPS

by L. M. HOCKING*
University College, London

(1) INTRODUCTION

THE calculations to be described here apply to collisions occurring between small spheres of different radii falling under gravity. The cause of the collisions is the differential rate of fall, and the spheres are small enough for the Stokes approximation to the hydrodynamical equations to be used. For drops of water falling in air, this limits the size of the drops to $30\,\mu$ radius but the drops formed by condensation in a cloud are mainly within this limit so that the results are of use in determining the initial rate at which drops can grow by coalescence in non-freezing clouds. The collision efficiency E, from which the rate-of-growth can be found, is defined as follows. If two drops of different radii are falling in isolation, the centre of the smaller drop, which we shall call the droplet, must lie within a certain horizontal circle a great distance below the larger drop if it is not to be swept round the drop but collide with it. The ratio of the area of this circle to the cross-section of the drop is E.

It is comparatively simple to determine E when the droplet is very much smaller than the drop.[1] When the drop and droplet are of comparable size, the determination of E is more difficult as the drop can no longer be considered to fall undisturbed by the presence of the droplet. Pearcey and Hill[2] made the first attempt to calculate E for collisions between drops of comparable size. Their method is to start with the Oseen flow for a single moving sphere and to find the flow pattern for the two moving spheres by superposition of the flow patterns for each sphere moving in isolation. This method is obviously considerably in error when the spheres are close together. The method of the present calculations is to determine the forces on the spheres from the solution of the Stokes equations for two moving spheres, making complete allowance for their mutual influence. The solution was found by a method essentially equivalent to that subsequently given by Kynch.[3]

(2) THE EQUATIONS OF MOTION

As the Stokes equations are linear, the flow for two spheres moving with arbitrary velocities can be found by superimposing the flows for two spheres moving along and perpendicularly to their line of centres. If the radii of the spheres are a_1 and a_2 and the distance between their centres is r, the drag forces can be found in powers of a_1/r and a_2/r to as high a degree as required. It was considered sufficient to take the terms up to and including the seventh power, the next three terms making very little difference even when the spheres are close together. The accuracy decreases when the spheres are of very different sizes and close together, so that the ratio of the radii, a_2/a_1, for

* The substance of this paper has appeared in *Q. J. Roy. Met. Soc.*, **85**, 44–50 (1959).

which the expressions for the drag forces can be used should be greater than about 0·2.

If the velocities of the spheres along the line of centres are U_1 and U_2 and η is the viscosity of air, the drag forces on the spheres are in the direction of the line of centres and to the accuracy required are $-6\pi\eta a_1 L_1$ and $-6\pi\eta a_2 L_2$ where

$$L_1 = L_1(U_1, U_2, a_1, a_2, r)$$

$$= \frac{U_1(4r^7 - 15a_1^3 a_2 r^3 - 8a_1^5 a_2 r + 30a_1^3 a_2^3 r) - U_2(6a_2 r^6 - 2a_2(a_1^2 + a_2^2)r^4 + 75a_1^3 a_2^4)}{4r^7 - 9a_1 a_2 r^5 - 9a_1 a_2(a_1^2 + a_2^2)r^3 - 9a_1 a_2(a_1^4 + a_2^4)r + 58a_1^3 a_2^3 r}$$

(1)

and $L_2 = (U_2, U_1, a_2, a_1, r)$.

Similarly, if the velocities of the spheres are V_1 and V_2 perpendicular to their line of centres, the drag forces are perpendicular to the line of centres and to the same accuracy as above are $-6\pi\eta a_1 T_1$ and $-6\pi\eta a_2 T_2$, where

$$T_1 = T_1(V_1, V_2, a_1, a_2, r)$$

$$= \frac{V_1(16r^7 - 12a_1^3 a_2 r^3 - 17a_1^5 a_2 r) - V_2(12a_2 r^6 + 4a_2(a_1^2 + a_2^2)r^4 + 6a_1^3 a_2^4)}{16r^7 - 9a_1 a_2 r^5 - 18a_1 a_2(a_1^2 + a_2^2)r^3 - 18a_1 a_2(a_1^4 + a_2^4)r - 2a_1^3 a_2^3 r}$$

(2)

and $T_2 = T_1(V_2, V_1, a_2, a_1, r)$.

Before finding the equations of motion it is convenient to make the variables non-dimensional. The unit of length is a_1, the radius of the larger sphere, and the radius of the smaller sphere is denoted by $a = a_2/a_1$. The unit of velocity U, is the terminal velocity of the larger sphere falling by itself under gravity and is given by $U = 2\sigma g a_1^2/9\eta$, where σ is the density of the sphere and g is the gravitational acceleration. The hydro-static upthrust can be ignored for water drops in air. The terminal velocity of the smaller sphere is Ua^2. Taking the x-axis vertically downwards and the y-axis horizontal, the coordinates of the centre of the sphere of radius 1 in the non-dimensional system is (x_1, y_1) and its velocity components are (u_1, v_1); the corresponding quantities for the sphere of radius a have a suffix 2. As only the relative trajectory is required, the difference of the coordinates of the centres is all that is needed, i.e. $x_2 - x_1 = x$ and $y_2 - y_1 = y$, which determine the vertical and horizontal separations of the spheres. The distance between the centres r, is given by $r^2 = x^2 + y^2$. The vertical and horizontal components of the drag forces can be found in terms of these velocity components and positions and, with the weight included, can be equated to the mass-accelerations of the spheres, giving

$$I\frac{du_1}{dt} = 1 - \frac{l_1 x - t_1 y}{r},$$

$$I\frac{du_2}{dt} = 1 - \frac{l_2 x - t_2 y}{a^2 r},$$

(3)

$$I\frac{dv_1}{dt} = -\frac{l_1 y + t_1 x}{r},$$

$$I\frac{dv_2}{dt} = -\frac{l_2 y + t_2 x}{a^2 r}.$$

and the relations between the relative position and the velocities are

$$\frac{dx}{dt} = u_2 - u_1,$$

$$\frac{dy}{dt} = v_2 - v_1.$$

In these equations, I is a dimensionless parameter* defined by

$$I = \frac{4\sigma^2 g a_1^3}{81\eta^2} \tag{4}$$

and, with their values given by equations 1 and 2,

$$l_1 = L_1(a_1, a_2, 1, a, r)$$
$$l_2 = L_1(a_2, a_1, a, 1, r)$$
$$t_2 = T_1(\beta_1, \beta_2, 1, a, r)$$
$$t_2 = T_1(\beta_2, \beta_1, a, 1, r),$$

where

$$a_1 = \frac{u_1 x + v_1 y}{r}, \qquad a_2 = \frac{u_2 x + v_2 y}{r},$$

$$\beta_1 = \frac{v_1 x - u_1 y}{r}, \qquad \beta_2 = \frac{v_2 x - u_2 y}{r}.$$

It is supposed that initially the spheres are falling with their terminal velocities so that $u_1=1$, $u_2=a^2$, $v_1=v_2=0$. The initial vertical separation was taken as $x=50$. To test whether this was sufficiently large, one trajectory was calculated with $x=100$ initially and no significant difference was found. The initial value of the horizontal separation y was varied until the trajectory which made the smallest value of r, the distance between the centres, equal to $1+a$, the sum of the radii, was found. If this critical value of y is denoted by y_c, collision occurs if $y \leqslant y_c$ initially and the collision efficiency, E, is y_c^2. The method used for the solution of the equations of motions was a Runge-Kutta method of step-by-step integration and the calculations were performed on the DEUCE electronic computer at the London Computing Centre of the English Electric Company.

(3) DISCUSSION OF THE RESULTS

The values of E, shown in Fig. 1, were found for drop sizes up to 30μ radius and for all droplet sizes provided that $a \geqslant 0.2$, the reason for the exclusion of smaller values of a being explained above. The choice of 0.2 as the limiting value for a was suggested by calculations for smaller values of a and for drop sizes of 25μ and 30μ without including any extra terms in equations 1 and 2. If the results found were included in Fig. 1, the curves for these drop sizes would flatten out in the region $a < 0.2$ to give E a roughly constant value of 0.004. This predicted change in the shape of the curves is probably the result of the errors involved in using equations 1 and 2 for very small values of a; in reality one would expect the 25μ and 30μ curves to show a value for a below which collision cannot occur as with the curves for other drop radii. However,

* Related to the particle parameter; cf. Introduction and Appendix.

since even the approximate calculations predict a value of E which is only 0·004, this point is not of great practical importance.

No collisions occur if the drop radius is 18μ or less, and above that value for a_1, E is an increasing function of a_1 for fixed a. The effect of altering the drop size on the equations of motion (3) is solely to alter the parameter I which is a measure of the inertias of the drop and droplet. If the inertias are increased, the accelerations of the

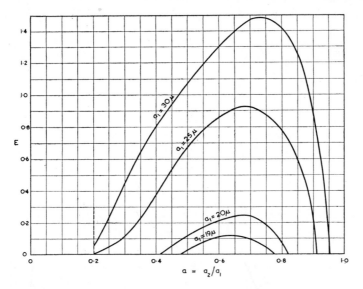

FIG. 1. The collision efficiency for drops of radius $a_1\mu$ colliding with droplet of radius $a_2\mu$.

drop and droplet are decreased so that their horizontal separation alters more slowly and they are more likely to collide so that E is increased. The inertias when the drop has a radius less than 18μ are small enough to make collisions impossible.

Collisions do not occur for sufficiently small droplets for each drop size (or, if the conjecture of the previous paragraph is not accepted, E becomes negligibly small). This can be partially explained by the low inertia of the droplet relative to that of the drop which allows it to be swept round the drop. But this would suggest that the drop roughly followed the streamlines of the flow past the drop which would give a non-zero value of E because of the size of the droplet. Some of the trajectories found indicated that the droplet sometimes moved round the drop keeping close to it but never colliding with it. This effect shows the importance of finding the flow patterns accurately when the spheres are close together. At the larger values for a, it is also found that there is a limiting droplet size above which no collisions can occur. When the drop and the droplet are of nearly equal size, the forces causing the horizontal separation to increase are small but the difference in the vertical velocities is also small, so that the forces have a long time in which to produce the horizontal displacement which is sufficient to ensure that collision does not occur. The general features of Fig. 1 have now been explained.

The results found by Pearcey and Hill[2] for the range up to 30μ radius differ greatly from those found here.

In the first place, they find collisions occurring for all drop sizes provided the droplet is large enough, whereas the present calculations give no collisions for drops of radius 18μ or less. In agreement with the present results, they find that there is a limiting droplet size for each drop size below which collision cannot occur, but they do not find the limiting upper value for the droplet size. On the contrary, they find that E increases as the ratio of the radii tends to 1, taking values as high as 100 or more, and these large values of E they attribute to the influence of the wake. Values of E taken from Pearcey and Hill's paper for drops of radius 19μ and 31μ are shown in Fig. 2

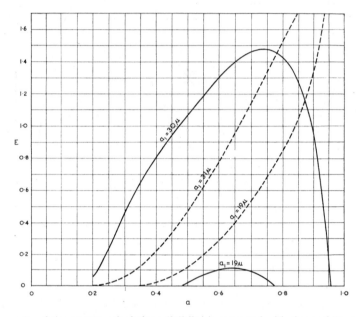

FIG. 2. The results of the present calculations (full lines) compared with those of Pearcey and Hill (broken lines).

with the present results for drops of radius 19μ and 30μ. The curve for drop radius 31μ would lie slightly above that for radius 30μ. The dissimilarity between the two pairs of curves emphasizes the importance of determining the forces on the spheres as accurately as possible, making full allowance for the mutual interference of the flows past the spheres.

In an attempt to find experimental values for E, some model experiments were conducted by Schotland and Kaplin.[4] By dropping steel spheres in a viscous sugar solution, it was possible to model all the physical quantities except the ratio of the density of the spheres to that of the surrounding medium, which is very large for water drops in air but was about six in the model experiments. The results found by Schotland and Kaplin gave values for E for various drop sizes up to $10\cdot5\mu$ radius. The results found in this paper make E zero over the whole range of these experiments. The reason for the discrepancy is the difference in the ratio of the densities in the actual problem and the model fluid motion.

In all calculations of the trajectories of particles which are small enough for their motion to be governed by the Stokes equations, it is assumed that the time derivative of the fluid velocity can be neglected. But as the particle accelerates, so does the fluid, causing the fluid motion to be unsteady. Suppose that the particle has a characteristic length l, velocity U and density σ and, for simplicity, that it is accelerating in fluid at rest. If p and $\mathbf{q}$ are pressure and fluid velocity and if the fluid has a density ρ and viscosity η, the Stokes equations are

$$\rho \frac{\partial \mathbf{q}}{\partial t} = -\nabla p + \eta \nabla^2 \mathbf{q}. \tag{5}$$

The force on the particle is of order $\eta U l$ and as this equals the mass-acceleration of the particle, its acceleration is of order $\eta U / \sigma l^2$. But this must be of the same order as the acceleration term $\partial \mathbf{q}/\partial t$ so that the left-hand side of equation 5 is of order $\rho \eta U / \sigma l^2$; the right-hand side is of order $\eta U / l^2$. The time derivative term in the equations of fluid motion can therefore be neglected if ρ/σ is small, which is certainly the case for water drops in air but was not so in the model experiments of Schotland and Kaplin. As the equations governing the motion are different in the two cases, it follows that the experimental results give no reliable quantitative information about E for water drops in air.

It has so far been assumed that the rotation of the spheres has no effect on their paths. When the spheres have velocity components perpendicular to their line of centres, there is a couple acting on each sphere, producing angular velocities which are of order $1/r^4$. The flow produced by two rotating spheres can be found in a similar way to that produced by their motion perpendicular to their line of centres. The effect of the rotation on the drag forces is of order $1/r^4$ times the angular velocity and is in a direction perpendicular to the line of centres. Thus the total effect of including the rotation is to add terms of order $1/r^8$ to the last two of equations 3, but terms of this order have been neglected in those equations so that it is permissible to neglect the rotation of the spheres in determining their collision efficiency.

(4) REFERENCES

1. MASON, B. J., *The Physics of Clouds*, Oxford University Press, Appendix A 1957.
2. PEARCEY, T. and HILL, G. W., *Quart. J. R. Met. Soc.*, **83**, 77–92 (1957).
3. KYNCH, G. J., *J. Fluid Mechs.*, **5**, 193–208 (1959).
4. SCHOTLAND, R. M. and KAPLIN, E. J., New York Univ. Met. Dept. Rep., No. AFCRC-TH-55-867 (1956).

COLLECTION EFFICIENCIES FOR WATER DROPS
IN AIR

by R. G. PICKNETT

Department of Meteorology, Imperial College, London

Summary—This paper describes an experiment to measure the collection efficiencies of free-falling water drops in air. The drop sizes used were 30μ and 40μ radius for the larger drops and 1–9μ radius for the smaller drops. The technique employed enables the sizes of coalescing drops to be determined directly, and collection efficiencies are obtained for a number of different size combinations.

The results show that there is a critical drop size below which coalescence does not occur, and the experimental efficiencies compare favourably with recently published theoretical collision efficiencies.

INTRODUCTION

ALTHOUGH there is now a considerable body of theoretical and practical work on the collision and collection efficiencies of water droplets in air, there was until recently nothing known concerning droplets of 0–40μ radius. Droplet coalescence in this range is of particular importance from the meteorological aspect as it governs the critical initial stages of rain formation in non-freezing clouds, and it is this range which is investigated in this paper.

Since this work was commenced, a paper has been published by Kinzer and Cobb[1] extending previous experimental measurements of collection efficiency to the range 6–60μ radius. This work had the drawback that the droplet size was not accurately known in the lower size range and, furthermore, the droplet concentration was great enough to cause considerable mutual interference between the trajectories of neighbouring non-colliding drops (clouds of volume fraction about 3×10^{-6} with a mean radius of 6μ were used).

In the experiment described in this paper, collection efficiencies are measured for water drops of 30μ and 40μ radius coalescing with droplets of 1–9μ radius falling in air. The technique is such that the size of coalescing drops is accurately defined. Also, the droplet concentration being of the same order as that occurring in natural clouds, the results should be applicable to meteorological phenomena and should be a fair approximation to the isolated two-sphere problem discussed by Hocking[2] and others.

OUTLINE OF EXPERIMENT

Uniform "collector" drops made from pure water were allowed to fall through a cloud of random-sized salt-water droplets, the salt content of each droplet being proportional to its volume. The number concentration of salt droplets in this cloud was sufficiently small that, on average, less than 5 per cent of the collector drops suffered coalescence with salt droplets. By treating the problem as a random process it may be shown that, under these circumstances, less than 0.1 per cent of the collector drops collide with more than one salt droplet; a proportion which is negligible. It follows that the amount of salt found in a collector drop after passing through the cloud is a measure of the size of the salt droplet with which it has coalesced. The proportion of collector drops ultimately containing salt is of course the proportion which has undergone coalescence.

Examination of a large number of collector drops therefore determines the fraction coalescing with each size of salt droplet. It will be shown in the following section that this information, together with the characteristics of the salt droplet cloud, is sufficient to evaluate collection efficiencies.

THEORY

The collection efficiency must be defined specifically in terms of the sizes of drops concerned. Consider a collector drop of radius R falling through a tranquil cloud of smaller droplets of radius r. Those droplets r whose centres lie inside a vertical cylinder of radius $(R+r)$ concentric with the collector drop are considered to be in its fall path. Only a fraction of these will ultimately coalesce with the collector drop, and this fraction is defined as the collection efficiency $E(R, r)$*.

In the case in question, the collector drop R falls right through a cloud of smaller droplets of a range of sizes. On the assumption that these droplets are distributed at random horizontally, Poisson's Law may be applied to give the probability of finding a given number of droplets in a vertical column of cross-sectional area A passing right through the cloud. For droplets in the size range r to $r+dr$, where $n(r)dr$ is the average number in this range in a vertical column of unit cross-sectional area, we have:

p_0, the probability of finding no droplets $\exp\left[-An(r)dr\right]$

p_1, the probability of finding 1 droplet $[An(r)dr]\exp\left[-An(r)dr\right]$

p_2, the probability of finding 2 droplets $\dfrac{[An(r)dr]^2\exp\left[-An(r)dr\right]}{2!}$

etc.

When A is put equal to $\pi(R+r)^2E(R, r)$, then $p_0, p_1, p_2\ldots$ become the probabilities that a collector drop R will collide with $0, 1, 2\ldots$ droplets in this size range.

As described in a previous section, the experiment measures the fraction $F(r)dr$ of a large number of uniform drops R which suffer coalescence with droplets in the size range r to $r+dr$. This can now be written as:

$$F(r)dr = 1 - \exp\left[-An(r)dr\right] = 1 - \exp\left[-\pi(R + r)^2E(R, r)n(r)dr\right] \qquad (1)$$

This equation expresses $E(R, r)$ in terms of experimentally determined parameters.

To fulfil the requirement that the number of multiple coalescences shall be negligible it is necessary to make p_1 very much greater than $p_2, p_3\ldots$ i.e.

$$\pi(R + r)^2E(R, r)n(r)dr \ll 1 \qquad (2)$$

DESCRIPTION OF EXPERIMENT

The apparatus used is shown diagrammatically in Fig. 1. Two tubes A and B mounted vertically end to end each 8 cm diameter by 1 m long were filled with a cloud of droplets

---

* It should be noted that this definition differs from that used by other workers[1,2,3,4] by the factor $R^2/(R+r)^2$. It is used here because it represents a true efficiency in that the value of unity has a distinct significance: for $E<1$ the smaller drops are swept out of the fall path, for $E>1$, the smaller drops are drawn into the fall path. The confusion has arisen because Langmuir's correct definition of E for $r\to0$ has been extended without modification to the case where r is finite. The term used by other workers is indeed useful, but I suggest it be given a more apt name, such as "capture cross-section".

produced by atomizing a 2N solution of sodium chloride (i.e. 117 g per l.). The spray-ing apparatus was sealed in the base of tube *B*. A stream of air at 85 per cent relative humidity was then passed upwards through the tubes at an average velocity of 1·7 cm/sec—just sufficient to support drops of 10–11 μ radius. This air flow served to attenuate the cloud while conserving the larger sized droplets, and also to bring the cloud to

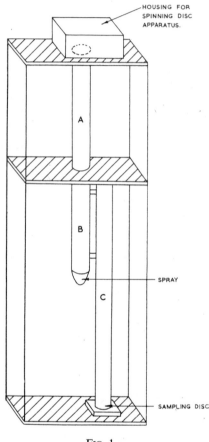

Fig. 1.

equilibrium with air of 85 per cent humidity at ambient temperature. After a standard time the air supply was cut off, the tubes sealed, and the cloud allowed to become tranquil. The salt droplet clouds produced in this way were satisfactorily reproducible in both size distribution and number concentration. The size range was from 1μ to 9μ radius.

   The next step was to replace tube *B* with tube *C*, 8 cm wide by 3 m long, so that *A* and *C* formed a continuous vertical column down which the salt droplets from *A* slowly moved. It was found necessary to enrich the air in *C* with carbon dioxide as otherwise the greater density of the droplet cloud caused it to move downwards in bulk, rapidly reaching the bottom of the tube. Approximately 10 per cent carbon dioxide at 85 per cent humidity satisfactorily prevented this.

   Meanwhile, a spinning disk apparatus[5] was producing uniform-sized pure water drops, a proportion of which was now directed down the tubes. These drops passed through the salt droplet cloud and, being larger, became well separated from them at the base of tube C. There they were collected on a Perspex disk whose surface had been treated as follows. Exactly one half of the disk surface was coated with a film of gelatine impregnated with naphthol green as described by Liddell and Wootten.[6] A water drop landing on such a coating leaves a clear disk-shaped mark of diameter proportional to that of the drop and which contrasts well with the green background of the dye. The other half of the disk was covered with a uniform film of hydrophobic grease (Apiezon "L"). Water drops landing on this assume a shape which was shown by calibration experiments to be almost exactly hemispherical under the conditions of the experiment.

After the experiment, the Perspex disk was transferred to a small humidity chamber set at 85 per cent relative humidity and mounted on a microscope. Pure water drops on the greased part of the disk were found to evaporate completely leaving no trace, but those drops which contained salt reached an equilibrium size in which the vapour pressure of the salt solution equalled that of the ambient air. Using vapour pressure/concentration curves for sodium chloride solutions, it was thus possible to determine the salt content of each drop from its equilibrium radius. Since the experimental conditions were such as to rule out the possibility of multiple coalescences, this salt content immediately gives the size of droplet which coalesced with the collector drop.

On attainment of equilibrium, the surface of the disk was examined microscopically, the drops on the grease and the marks on the gelatine being counted and sized. The number of marks on the gelatine gives the total number of collector drops landing on the disk; the number of drops on the grease gives the proportion of collector drops which have suffered coalescence. Thus the equilibrium sizes of these drops enable $F(r)dr$ to be determined. Naturally, a large number of experiments have to be made before the results become truly representative.

Two sets of experiments were carried out using pure water drops of 30μ and 40μ radius. Because of evaporation, slightly larger drops had to be introduced into the tubes by the spinning disk so that the average size while in the cloud was that required.

ANALYSIS OF SALT DROPLET CLOUD

The fact that the salt droplets are in equilibrium with air of known humidity greatly facilitates the determination of size distribution and number concentration, as measurements can be made without fear of change due to evaporation. A partition was placed part way down tube C, thus sealing off the lower section, and on this a grease-coated Perspex surface was exposed to the sedimenting salt cloud. After a time sufficient to ensure that all the droplets in the cloud had settled out, the disk was transferred to the humidity chamber. This procedure ensured that the effect of differential settling was minimized.

The droplet sample having come to equilibrium, the size distribution and number per unit area were determined visually. The whole procedure was repeated enough times to ensure that the results were representative.

It is a simple matter to convert the observed hemisphere radii to those for equivalent spheres. When this is done, the number of droplets in a given size range per unit area is in fact the term $n(r)dr$ required in equation 1.

All the experiments were carried out at room temperature, which was approximately $20°C$.

EXPERIMENTAL RESULTS

The salt droplet cloud radius distribution was determined at intervals of just under 0.5μ and is shown in Fig. 2. The probable error* in $n(r)dr$ was less than 5 per cent except for the biggest drops, where the largest probable error was 15 per cent. The droplet concentration on the sampling surface was, on average, 9.08×10^{-4} cm^{-2},

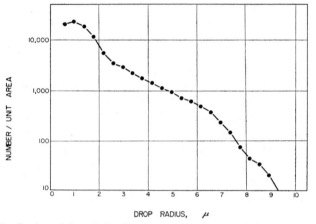

FIG. 2. The size distribution of the salt droplet cloud at 85 per cent relative humidity and 20°C. The total number of droplets in a column of unit cross-section through the cloud is 9.08×10^{4} cm^{-2}.

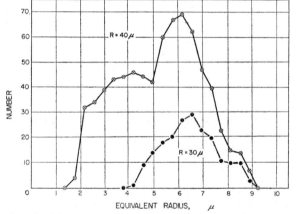

FIG. 3. The distribution of salt in those collector drops which have undergone coalescence. The salt content is expressed as the size of a drop containing that amount of salt in equilibrium with air at 85 per cent humidity and 20°C.

which corresponds to a volume ratio of approximately 5×10^{-8} in the salt droplet cloud at the time of the experiment. It should be noted that, with this cloud, the requirement that the number of multiple coalescences be negligible is fulfilled for all reasonable values of $E(R, r)$, as may be seen from equation 2.

The distribution of salt in the collector drops is shown in Fig. 3 for the two drop sizes used. With a drop radius of 30μ, 196 out of 24,083 collector drops were found

* The probable error used is such that there is a 50 per cent chance that the correct value lies within the range given.

to contain salt; with a radius of $40\,\mu$ the proportion was 732 out of 14,973. The amount of salt in a collector drop was expressed for convenience as the size of a drop containing that amount of salt in equilibrium with air at 85 per cent relative humidity. As only single collisions are likely, this is the size of salt droplet which has coalesced with the collector drop. The term $F(r)dr$ used in equation 1 is obtained by dividing the number of drops of equilibrium size in the range r to $r+dr$ by the total number of collector drops.

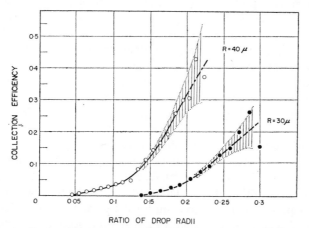

RATIO OF DROP RADII

FIG. 4. Experimental collection efficiencies. The shaded areas represent the probable errors in $E(R, r)$ due to variation in $n(r)dr$ and $F(r)dr$. The solid lines represent the smoothed values.

The values of $E(R, r)$ calculated from these results is shown in Fig. 4, where the shaded areas represent the probable errors in $E(R, r)$ due to the experimental variation in both $n(r)dr$ and $F(r)dr$. The smoothed values as represented by the solid lines are given in Table 1.

TABLE 1. SMOOTHED EXPERIMENTAL COLLECTION EFFICIENCIES $E(R, r)$ AND THE
CORRESPONDING EXPERIMENTAL CAPTURE CROSS-SECTIONS $E'(R, r)$
(Note: $(R+r)^2 E(R, r) = R^2 E'(R, r)$)

r/R	R = 30 μ		R = 40 μ	
	E(R, r)	E'(R, r)	E(R, r)	E'(R, r)
0·02	—	—	10^{-4}	10^{-4}
0·04	10^{-4}	10^{-4}	10^{-4}	10^{-4}
0·06	10^{-4}	10^{-4}	0·008 ± 0·005	0·009
0·08	10^{-3}	10^{-3}	0·021 ± 0·003	0·024
0·10	10^{-3}	10^{-3}	0·033 ± 0·004	0·040
0·12	10^{-3}	10^{-3}	0·054 ± 0·005	0·068
0·14	0·001 ± 0·001	0·001	0·097 ± 0·009	0·126
0·16	0·013 ± 0·003	0·018	0·151 ± 0·016	0·203
0·18	0·026 ± 0·004	0·036	0·24 ± 0·03	0·32
0·20	0·046 ± 0·006	0·066	0·33 ± 0·06	0·47
0·22	0·079 ± 0·010	0·118	0·41 ± 0·12	0·61
0·24	0·120 ± 0·015	0·184	—	—
0·26	0·161 ± 0·026	0·256	—	—
0·28	0·20 ± 0·06	0·33	—	—
0·30	0·24 ± 0·15	0·44	—	—

DISCUSSION

The collector drops are appreciably affected by evaporation during their passage through the salt droplet cloud, the estimated change in radius being 4μ for 30μ drops and 2μ for 40μ drops. Because of this, the values of R quoted above are averages and there is consequently an uncertainty in $E(R, r)$ additional to that shown in Fig. 4 and Table 1. Another factor is that the drops produced by the spinning disc were not perfectly uniform, the spread being about 6 per cent of the mean radius. It has not been possible to estimate accurately the effect of these factors on $E(R, r)$, but it is felt that the probable error introduced should not be greater than 5 per cent.

A striking fact brought out by these experiments is that, for a given size of collector drop, there is a size of droplet below which the collection efficiency is negligibly small. For R equals 40μ this critical value of r is about 2μ: below this no coalescences were detected although the technique was extremely sensitive in this region, and in fact $E(R, r)$ must be less than 10^{-4} when r is less than 2μ. For R equals 30μ the critical value of r is about 4μ: below this, $E(R, r)$ is smaller than 10^{-3}.

Comparison of these experimental collection efficiencies with the theoretical collision efficiencies of Hocking[2] is of some interest. Hocking's values are for spheres of unit density falling through air at $0°C$, but can readily be modified as described in the paper to allow for the effect of the different temperature and the presence of carbon dioxide in the present experiment. The correction for the greater density of the droplet (due to the presence of salt) is not so straightfoward and this accounts for the uncertainty in the collision efficiency values shown in Fig. 5. The net effect of these corrections is an increase of some 10 per cent in Hocking's values.

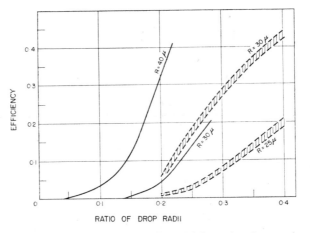

Fig. 5. Comparison of experiment with theory. The solid lines give the experimental results. The shaded areas represent the values of Hocking[5] corrected to conform to the experimental conditions.

Unfortunately, it is only for R equals 30μ that both the collision and the collection efficiency is known, but Fig. 5 shows that for this case the latter is smaller by a factor of about $0·8$. This difference is only a little greater than the estimated error in $E(R, r)$, so it is difficult to say whether it is significant or not.

It has often been suggested that the collection efficiency could be lower than the collision efficiency because of the possibility that coalescence need not always follow collision. However, it would seem more likely in the present case that the difference, if real, is due to some other effect, such as a slight flattening of the drops on close approach, or perhaps the interaction of electrostatic charges on the drops. This last point is certainly worthy of investigation, but has not been studied in this present work.

The collection efficiencies given in this paper may be applied to conditions other than those under which the experiment was done by correcting the values of R, the collector drop radius, as mentioned above. Some corrected values are listed below:

Experimental conditions:	$R = 30\,\mu$	$R = 40\,\mu$
Pure water drops in air at 0°C:	$R = 29{\cdot}7\,\mu$	$R = 39{\cdot}6\,\mu$
Pure water drops in air at 20°C:	$R = 28{\cdot}5\,\mu$	$R = 38{\cdot}0\,\mu$

As an example of the use of these corrections, under experimental conditions $E(R, r)$ for drops of radii $30\,\mu$ and $6\,\mu$ is 0·046. In the case of pure water drops in air at 20°C, $E(R, r)$ for drops of radii $28{\cdot}5\,\mu$ and $5{\cdot}7\,\mu$ will also be 0·046.

REFERENCES

1. KINZER, G. and COBB, W., *J. Met.*, **15**, 138 and 374 (1958).
2. HOCKING, L., *Q.J. Roy. Met. Soc.*, **85**, 44 (1959).
3. TELFORD, J., THORNDYKE, N. and BOWEN, E., *Q.J. Roy. Met. Soc.*, **81**, 241 (1955).
4. GUNN, K. and HITSCHFELD, W., *J. Met.*, **8**, 7 (1951).
5. MAY, K. R., *J. Appl. Phys.*, **20**, 932 (1949).
6. LIDDELL, H. and WOOTTEN, N., *Q.J. Roy. Met. Soc.*, **83**, 263 (1957).

SCAVENGING ACTION OF RAIN ON NON-WETTABLE PARTICULATE MATTER SUSPENDED IN THE ATMOSPHERE*

by C. S. Pemberton
Atomic Weapons Research Establishment, Aldermaston, Berks.

Summary—A mechanism of capture of a non-wettable particle by a liquid drop, in which capture is opposed by the surface tension of the drop, is investigated and a non-dimensional number called the penetration factor is derived, together with a condition for the retention of the particle by the drop. The equations of motion of a particle moving under Stokes' law of resistance in the velocity field due to potential flow around a sphere are integrated numerically. The collection efficiencies so obtained are shown to depend not only on the inertia parameter, as demonstrated by previous work on wettable particles and droplets[1,2] but upon the penetration factor, and a non-dimensional form of the retention condition.

Together with experimentally determined drop size distributions[3] and the application of a statistical procedure,[4] the new results are used to determine the fraction of particles of a given size removed by rainfalls of several intensities and durations, and a nomograph is constructed.

Finally, an application is made to determine the total amount of material rained-out from a particulate cloud having an empirical particle-size distribution. The effectiveness of the scavenging action of rain is shown to be considerably reduced for non-wettable particles.

(1) DETERMINATION OF VELOCITY OF PENETRATION AND PENETRATION FACTOR

A WETTABLE particle or droplet has only to touch a rain-drop to be captured. However, experimental work[5] has shown that, if the interfacial tension between drop and particle is high, the capability of the drop to capture the particle is reduced. In this case the entry of the particle into the drop is resisted by surface tension forces.

The penetration of a liquid drop by a spherical, non-wettable particle is considered. Defining the degree of wettability of a solid surface by a liquid with which it is in contact in terms of the static advancing angle of contact, this is assumed to be 180°. The surface tension force at the contact perimeter is then always tangential to the surface. Neglecting any induced mass effects associated with the impact, the deformed surface of the drop is assumed to conform exactly to the shape of the embedded surface of the particle.

As penetration proceeds, work is done against the surface tension force, at the expense of the kinetic energy of the particle. The particle can thus enter the drop, only if its incident kinetic energy is sufficient to allow it to penetrate to such a depth that the drop is able to close behind it.

1.1 *Energy Required to Penetrate Surface Tension Barrier*
Consider first the case of normal impact between the drop and the particle (cf. Fig. 1).

---

* The work contained in this paper is published by kind permission of The Director, Atomic Weapons Research Establishment, Aldermaston, Berks.

The total amount of work done by the particle against surface tension during complete penetration of the drop is found to be:

$$W = \tfrac{8}{3}\pi r^2 T \tag{1}$$

In order that penetration can occur, the particle must have an incident kinetic energy at least equal to W.

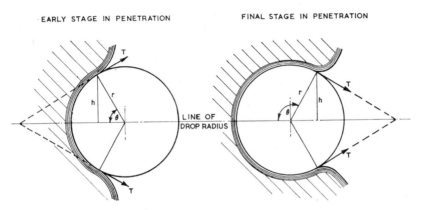

EARLY STAGE IN PENETRATION   FINAL STAGE IN PENETRATION

FIG. 1. Particle radius r entering drop assumed to have infinite radius motion opposed by surface tension forces T.

1.2 Dynamics of Capture

The capture of a particle of mass m and radius r, which strikes a drop of mass M and radius R, with an impact velocity v at an angle of incidence a, is now considered.

In this case of oblique impact, the simplifying assumptions are made that the net force acting on the particle still lies along the direction of the drop radius at the point of impact, there being no net force tangential to the drop. Then, since during penetration the particle will communicate a part of its momentum to the drop, the drop will move along its diameter at the point of impact as shown (cf. Fig. 2).

Let u and V be the velocities of the particle and drop respectively along the common diameter, measured relative to an absolute frame of reference outside the drop, at time t. Then an application of Newton's third law of motion leads to the momentum conservation equation

$$MV + mu = mv \cos a \tag{2}$$

Relative to a coordinate system with origin at the centre of the drop, the component of the particle velocity along the common diameter at time t becomes $u^* = u - V$. Let the depth of penetration then be x (cf. Fig. 2 (a)). If r/R is small, then $u^* = dx/dt$ approximately, so that $du^*/dt \sim u^* du^*/dx$. The equation of motion of the particle as it penetrates into the drop takes the form:

$$mu^* \frac{du^*}{dx} = -2\pi T \left(1 + \frac{m}{M}\right)\left(2x - \frac{x^2}{r}\right) \tag{3}$$

which integrates, using the initial condition $x=0$, $u^*=v \cos a$, to:

$$\tfrac{1}{2}mu^{*2} = \tfrac{1}{2}mv^2 \cos^2 a - 2\pi T \left(1 + \frac{m}{M}\right)\left(x^2 - \frac{x^3}{3r}\right) \tag{4}$$

M

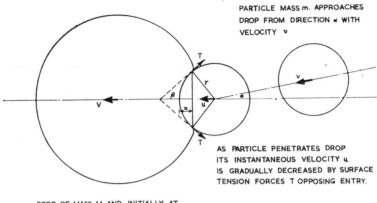

PARTICLE MASS m. APPROACHES
DROP FROM DIRECTION α WITH
VELOCITY v

AS PARTICLE PENETRATES DROP
ITS INSTANTANEOUS VELOCITY u
IS GRADUALLY DECREASED BY SURFACE
TENSION FORCES T OPPOSING ENTRY.

DROP OF MASS M AND INITIALLY AT
REST STARTS TO MOVE WITH VELOCITY
V AS SHOWN WHEN STRUCK BY PARTICLE.

(a)

AFTER PENETRATION IS COMPLETED, DROP RADIUS R, IS MOVING WITH
VELOCITY V₁ ; PARTICLE HAS VELOCITY (v_R^*, v_T^*) AS SHOWN. PARTICLE NOW
STARTS TO MOVE THROUGH DROP UNDER STOKES' LAW OF VISCOUS DRAG.

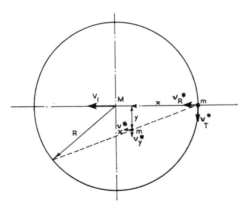

(b)

FIG. 2. Dynamics of capture.

When penetration is completed, $x=2r$. Let the components of the relative particle velocity immediately after penetration be v_R^*, v_T^*, along the radius of the drop and tangential to its surface respectively (cf. Fig. 2 (b)). Let the final velocity of the drop be V_1. Then from (4) it follows that:

$$\tfrac{1}{2}mv_R^{*\,2} = \tfrac{1}{2}mv^2 \cos^2 \alpha - \left(1 + \frac{m}{M}\right)W \tag{5}$$

where W is given by 1 and is the energy expended during penetration.

Since there is no net force in a direction normal to the common radius at the point of impact:

$$v_T^* = v \sin \alpha \tag{6}$$

Furthermore, equation 2 becomes:

$$(m + M)V_1 + mv_R^* = mv \cos \alpha \tag{7}$$

The motion of the particle inside the drop, after penetration, will now be considered. The resistance offered to the motion of the particle through the body of the drop is assumed to obey Stokes' Law and the effect of gravity and circulation within the drop will be neglected. Relative to a coordinate system moving with the drop, origin at the point of impact and axes parallel and normal to the direction of motion of the drop, the equations of motion take the form:

$$mv_x^* \frac{dv_x^*}{dx} = -C\left(1 + \frac{m}{M}\right)v_x^* \tag{8}$$

and,

$$mv_y^* \frac{dv_y^*}{dy} = -Cv_y^* \tag{9}$$

where $C = 6\pi\mu_w r$ and μ_w is the viscosity of the liquid.

These are now integrated using the condition that the particle must come to rest, relative to the drop, before it reaches the surface; the following inequality is obtained:

$$v_R^{*2} + \left(1 + \frac{m}{M}\right)^2 v_T^{*2} - \frac{2RC}{m}\left(1 + \frac{m}{M}\right)v_R^* \leqslant 0. \tag{10}$$

Elimination of V_1, v_R^* and v_T^* between the four equations 5, 6, 7 and 10 (taken with equality sign), leads to an equation for v. Since the general expression so found for v does not lend itself readily to interpretation, several special solutions to the problem will be obtained, with the object of determining the minimum velocity required for penetration.

The first approximation is to assume that, on penetrating the surface tension barrier, the particle immediately comes to rest relative to the drop. This leads to the equation:

$$\tfrac{1}{2}mv^2 \cos^2 \alpha = \left(1 + \frac{m}{M}\right)W$$

Thus, the velocity required for penetration increases with the angle of incidence and with the approach to equality of the masses of particle and drop. Clearly then, the minimum velocity of penetration occurs when $\cos \alpha \rightarrow 1$ and $m/M \ll 1$, and then the required minimum velocity of impact becomes:

$$V_{PN} = \left(\frac{2W}{m}\right)^{\frac{1}{2}} \tag{11}$$

If the impact is oblique, then the condition for penetration is that the component of particle velocity normal to the drop surface should be not less than V_{PN}. However, a non-wettable particle has only to touch the side of the drop to escape, and it has been assumed that the tangential component of impact velocity is conserved during penetration. What is required in this case is that the particle should have a normal impact energy sufficient to carry it so far into the drop that the tangential component of velocity is destroyed before the particle reaches the surface again.

Retaining the condition $\dfrac{m}{M} \ll 1$, it may be shown, using equation 10, that this further condition leads to the inequality:

$$\frac{(v^2 - V_{PN}^2)^2}{(v^2 \cos^2 a - V^2_{PN})} \leqslant \frac{4R^2C^2}{m^2} \tag{12}$$

To sum up then, the particle will be assumed to be captured and retained by the drop, when the velocity of impact is such that its component normal to the surface of the drop is greater than V_{PN}, while its total value, v, satisfies the inequality (equation 12). Replacing W by its value from equation 1, the velocity required for penetration is given by:

$$V_{PN} = \left(\frac{8T}{\rho_s d}\right)^{\frac{1}{2}} \tag{13}$$

where d is the diameter of the particle and ρ_s is its density.

In Fig. 3, the values of V_{PN} for different particle sizes are compared with experimentally determined values of the terminal velocities of raindrops.[6] It is inferred from

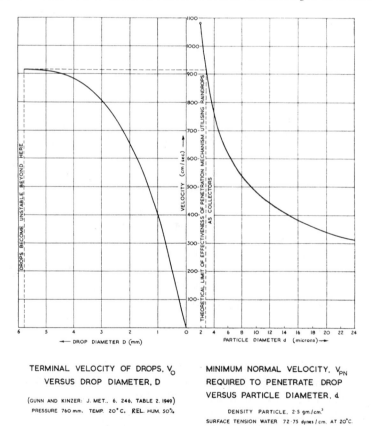

TERMINAL VELOCITY OF DROPS, V_O
VERSUS DROP DIAMETER, D

(GUNN AND KINZER: J. MET., 6, 246, TABLE 2, 1949)
PRESSURE 760 mm, TEMP. 20°C, REL. HUM. 50%

MINIMUM NORMAL VELOCITY, V_{PN}
REQUIRED TO PENETRATE DROP
VERSUS PARTICLE DIAMETER, d

DENSITY PARTICLE, 2·5 gm./cm.³
SURFACE TENSION WATER 72·75 dynes/cm. AT 20°C.

Fig. 3.

these curves that non-wettable particles with diameters less than $2 \cdot 8 \mu$ are not collected by collision with raindrops.

Finally, a new non-dimensional parameter, which will be called the penetration factor, is introduced, and defined by:

$$\chi = \frac{V_{PN}}{V_0} \tag{14}$$

where V_0 is the terminal velocity of a drop. When $\chi = 0$, i.e., the particle requires no impact velocity to enter the drop, the case of completely wettable particles dealt with by previous authors[1,2] is obtained.

(2) DYNAMICS OF COLLISION PROCESS AND CALCULATION OF COLLECTION EFFICIENCIES OF DROPS

The collision process considered here, by which a raindrop falling through a cloud of particles may collect several of them, will be called the modified Langmuir capture process. As the drop approaches the particle the inertia of the latter carries it across the streamlines, so that, provided it lay initially within a certain "capture cross-section" about the axis of the drop, it will strike the leading surface of the drop. Experiments on the collection of cloud droplets by raindrops[7] have suggested that, provided there is a large disparity in size between droplet and collector, it is reasonable to assume potential flow around the drop.

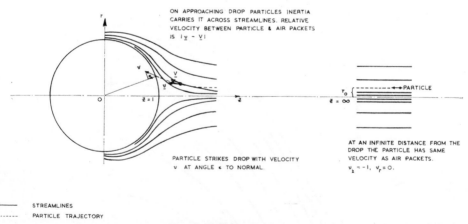

FIG. 4. Collision process.

The collection efficiencies of raindrops for non-wettable particles will be obtained by integrating the equations of motion of a particle moving in the potential flow around a sphere, and imposing the condition of a minimum velocity of impact as derived in the previous section.

A system of cylindrical coordinates in which the drop is stationary, the particle moving towards it with a velocity at infinity equal to the terminal velocity of the drop, is adopted, Fig. 4.

Assuming the drag experienced by the particle to be of Stokesian form, and neglecting the velocity field of the particle, the equations of motion take the non-dimensional form:

$$P \frac{dv_z}{dt} = (V_z - v_z) \qquad (15)$$

and

$$P \frac{dv_r}{dt} = (V_r - v_r) \qquad (16)$$

where $v = v(v_r, v_z)$ is the velocity of the particle, and P is the dimensionless particle parameter:

$$P = \frac{2}{9} \frac{\rho_s r^2 V_0}{\mu_a R},$$

μ_a representing the viscosity of air.

In cylindrical coordinates, the components of the fluid velocity for potential flow around a sphere are given by:

$$V_z = -1 + \frac{(2z^2 - r^2)}{2(z^2 + r^2)^{5/2}} \qquad (17)$$

and

$$V_r = \frac{3}{2} \frac{rz}{(z^2 + r^2)^{5/2}} \qquad (18)$$

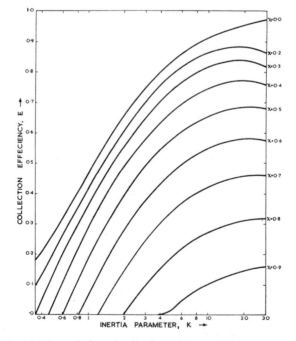

Fig. 5. The variation of collection efficiency of liquid drops for solid particles with particle parameter, P, and penetration factor, X. The case when X is zero corresponds to completely wettable particles.

The boundary conditions appropriate to the collision mechanism, and subsequent capture of the particle by the drop are that:

$$v = (0, -1) \text{ at } (r_0, \infty) \tag{19}$$

$$\left.\begin{array}{l} v \cos a > \chi \\ \dfrac{2(v^2 \cos^2 a - \chi^2)^{\frac{1}{2}}}{(v^2 - \chi^2)} \geqslant \left(\dfrac{\mu_a}{\mu_w}\right) P \end{array}\right\} \quad \text{when } z^2 + r^2 = 1 \tag{20}$$

Here, equation 20 insists that the particle strike the drop with a velocity such as to ensure capture and retention; the second of the conditions (equation 20), is the non-dimensional form of the inequality (equation 12) and will be referred to as the Retention Condition.

The integration of the equations of motion was effected numerically on the I.B.M. 704 electronic digital computer. The minimum value of r_0 which gave a particle trajectory for which the conditions (equation 20) were *not* satisfied, was taken to be the radius of the capture cross-section. Thus

$$\text{Collection efficiency of drop} = r_0^2$$

Critical values of r_0 were obtained for values of $0 \cdot 0 \leqslant \chi \leqslant 0 \cdot 9$ and $0 \cdot 35 \leqslant K \leqslant 30$. The resulting collection efficiency curves are shown in Fig. 5. The values of collection efficiency for zero penetration factor, agree well with values obtained previously for completely wettable particles.[1,2]

(3) INTERACTION OF RAIN WITH AN AIRBORNE CLOUD OF PARTICULATE MATERIAL

Using the results of the preceding sections, it is now possible to determine quantitatively the effectiveness of rain as an agent for removing suspended particles from the atmosphere. It is assumed that, as a raindrop falls through a cloud of particles, it gradually sweeps them up by the collection mechanism considered in Section 2. In this way, the particles are brought to the ground.

In order to determine the net effect of many raindrops of varying sizes, such as would be produced by a rain storm, on the particle cloud, it is necessary to have recourse to a statistical formulation of the problem. In the present paper, a statistical model of rain scavenging[4] will be utilized.

3.1 *Statistical Model of Rain Scavenging*

We now proceed to determine the fraction of particles of size d removed from a cloud, by a rainfall of intensity R mm/hr lasting for a time t hr. Reference should be made to Greenfield's paper[4] for the details. Let $E(D, d)$ represent the collection efficiency of a drop with diameter D, for a particle of diameter d. By definition, $E(D, d) = d_0^2/D^2$, where d_0 is the diameter of the capture cross-section. In the same way, let $E'(D, d) = d_0^2/D_L^2$ be the collection efficiency of the drop relative to the vertical cylinder, diameter D_L, through which it passes. D_L is taken to be equal to the diameter of the largest raindrop considered. Then:

$$E'(D, d) = \left(\frac{D}{D_L}\right)^2 E(D, d). \tag{21}$$

If $P_i(D)$ is the probability that a raindrop has a diameter lying in a size interval i, it may be shown that the number of drops passing through the cylinder in time t, is given by

$$n(R) = \frac{3}{2} \frac{D_L^2 R t}{\sum_i [P_i(D) D_i^3]} \tag{22}$$

where D_i is the diameter of a drop at the centre of the size interval i.

Finally, the total expected fraction of particles of diameter d that is removed from the cylinder in time t, by a rainfall having intensity R mm/h, is obtained from:

$$\bar{T}_d = 1 - [1 - \overline{\{E'(D)\}}_d]^n \tag{23}$$

where,

$$\overline{\{E'(D)\}}_d = \sum_i [P_i(D) E'(D, d)] \tag{24}$$

and D is taken to be that of the leading drop in the size interval i. In order to obtain values of $P_i(D)$, actual observations of drop size distributions for rainfall intensities of 0·5, 1, 2·5, 5 and 10 mm/h were utilized.[3] With this information, and the help of equations 21–24, a nomograph for T_d was constructed, as shown in Fig. 6.

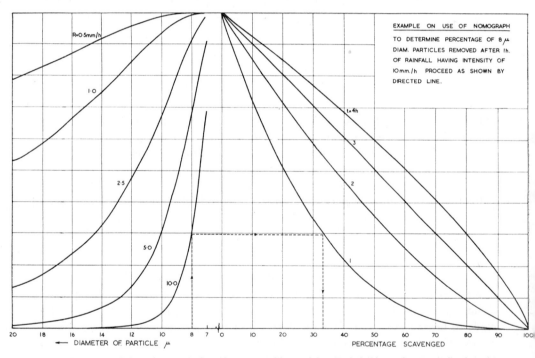

FIG. 6. Nomograph for rain-scavenging of non-wettable particles. (Rainfall intensity, R mm/hr duration of rainfall, t hr).

The most significant immediate conclusion to be drawn from Fig. 6 is that the assumed model of scavenging by raindrops is completely ineffective with non-wettable particles of diameter $<6\mu$. In the corresponding theory for wettable particles there is a similar, but smaller, limiting particle size. However, it was shown[4] that the model could be extended to account for the effective removal of particles below 1μ diameter by the introduction of a "sweeping-up" process prior to the onset of rain. The particles are allowed to mix with the water-droplets of the rain cloud which sweep them up by a process of coagulation brought about by Brownian and turbulent motions within the rain cloud. The main scavenging model is then applied to the droplets.

In contrast, when the particles are non-wettable it would appear no longer possible for the coagulation of particles and water-droplets to take place; a minimum value of impact velocity is required which is greatly above the relative velocities provided by Brownian and turbulent motions obtainable under the physical conditions existing in rain clouds.

3.2 *Application to Determine Fraction of Total Mass of an Airborne Particulate Cloud Removed by Rain*

This investigation is concluded by a calculation of the accumulated fraction of the total mass of an airborne cloud of non-wettable particles, rained-out over several

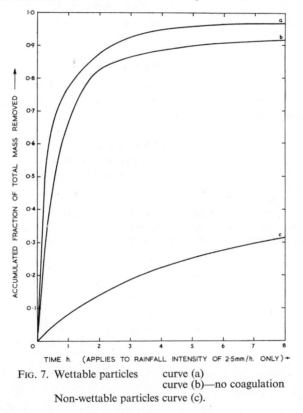

Fig. 7. Wettable particles   curve (a)
curve (b)—no coagulation
Non-wettable particles curve (c).

durations of rainfall. The results obtained will then be compared with previous results for completely wettable particles.[4]

To facilitate comparison with the earlier paper, an exponential distribution of particle sizes within the cloud will be assumed, of the form:

$$N_d = N_0 \exp\left(-\frac{d}{b}\right) \qquad (25)$$

where N_d represents the number of particles of diameter d, and b is a weighting function which equals the median particle diameter. For the same reason, a value for b of 2μ will be used in the sequel. From equation 25, it follows that the fraction of the total mass of the cloud contributed by those particles whose diameters are below d^* is given by:

$$f_m = 1 - \left\{ \frac{1}{6}\left(\frac{d^*}{b}\right)^3 + \tfrac{1}{2}\left(\frac{d^*}{b}\right)^2 + \left(\frac{d^*}{b}\right) + 1 \right\} \exp\left(-\frac{d^*}{b}\right) \qquad (26)$$

Combining the results of Section 3.1 with equation 26 the accumulated fraction of the total mass removed from a cloud of non-wettable particles can be derived. The values for a rainfall of intensity 2·5 mm/hr are shown in Fig. 7 (curve (c)), where they are compared with corresponding results for completely wettable particles obtained from Greenfield's paper. Since the percentage of non-wettable particles of a given size scavenged from the cloud *is not independent of rainfall intensity* (cf. Fig. 6), *curve (c) in Fig. 7 is true for a rainfall of intensity* 2·5 mm/hr *only.*

It will be seen that the assumption of particle non-wettability has led to a considerable reduction in the effectiveness of rain as a means of scavenging airborne particulate material.

(4) ACKNOWLEDGEMENTS

The author would like to express his gratitude to Dr. I. C. Cheeseman for suggesting this study and for his help and encouragement, and to Dr. D. J. Mather for many stimulating discussions.

(5) REFERENCES

1. Langmuir, I. and Blodgett, K. B., AAF Tech. Report 5418 (1946).
2. Fonda, A. and Herne, H., N.C.B. Mining Research Establishment Report No. 2068 (1957).
3. Best, A. C., Q. J.Roy. Met. Soc., **76,** 16 (1950).
4. Greenfield, S. M., J. Met., **14,** 115 (1957).
5. Mc. Cully, C. R., et al., Industr. Engng. Chem., **48,** 9, 1512 (1956).
6. Gunn, R. and Kinzer, G. D., J. Met., **6,** 246 (1949).
7. Gunn, K. L. S. and Hitschfeld, W., J. Met., **8,** 7 (1951).

LABORATORY EXPERIMENTS RELATING TO THE WASH-OUT OF PARTICLES BY RAIN

by B. Oakes

King's College, Newcastle upon Tyne

(1) INTRODUCTION

THE object of the experimental work described in this paper is to investigate the effect of rain on wettable and non-wettable clouds of smoke and to see if the results can be related to the theory of non-wettability described in the previous paper. The theory predicts that non-wettable particles must strike the raindrops with a certain minimum velocity before they can be captured, and by virtue of this resistance to capture, the clearance of smoke clouds with rain falling should be dependent upon the particle wettability. The experiments are carried out initially in a small chamber and then later in a much larger smoke chamber. The particle sizes used range from 0·5 to 3·7 μ, with rain intensities ranging from 6 to 87 mm/hr. The wettable smoke clouds investigated are ammonium chloride and ammonium salicylate, and the non-wettables, oil, paraffin wax, and stearic acid.

(2) THEORY

2.1 The Collision of Particles With Raindrops

In the collision process between raindrops and small smoke particles, a spherical drop is considered to be at rest with air streamlines flowing around it and the particles move with the velocity of the air stream towards the drop. Near the drop the stream-lines are more curved and the inertia of the particles enables them to cross the stream-lines. Those particles lying initially within a circular area called the "capture cross-section" whose plane is at right angles to the axis of the drop, are able to strike the drop. Particles lying outside of the "capture cross-section" are carried around the drop without collisions taking place. Langmuir[1] defined the collision efficiency E as the ratio of the capture cross-section to the cross-sectional area of the diametral plane of the drop

$$E = \frac{\pi x^2}{\pi R^2} = \frac{x}{R} \tag{1}$$

where x is radius of capture cross-section and R is the radius of the raindrop. E is also defined as the ratio of the number of particles striking the drop to the number striking if the streamlines were not deflected around the drop. If allowance is made for the finite radius of the particles then

$$E = \frac{(x + r)^2}{R^2} \tag{2}$$

where r is the radius of the particles.

2.2 The Capture of Wettable and Non-wettable Particles

A raindrop has only to touch a wettable particle and the permanent capture of the particle is assured. McCulley[2] observed that when the interfacial tension between a

179

drop and a particle is high the chances of the particle being captured are reduced. In the case of a non-wettable particle, the surface tension forces oppose the entry of the particle into the raindrop and the particle must do work at the expense of its kinetic energy to overcome this resistance before it can be captured. It must possess sufficient kinetic energy to enable it to penetrate far enough into the drop for the latter to close behind the particle. The retention of the non-wettable particle by the raindrop may not be permanent since the particle can escape by touching the surface of the drop from inside. Although many non-wettable particles will be captured on colliding with raindrops, many will avoid capture either by bouncing off the drops or by passing straight through them. In this research the term "washout coefficient" is defined as the rate of decrease of mass concentration in a given cloud when rain is falling. Because the non-wettable particles are thought to have a resistance to capture by the raindrops the washout coefficients in their case should be less than those for wettable particles.

2.3 *Light Extinction*

When a beam of light is passed through a fluid containing particles in suspension only part of the incident light energy is transmitted. The emergent intensity is given by the Lambert and Beer law.[3]

$$I = I_0 \exp\left(-\sigma c l\right) \tag{3}$$

where I_0 is the incident intensity of the light beam, I the emergent intensity of the beam after passing through a path length l of the absorbing medium. σ is the extinction coefficient and c the concentration of the suspended particles.

$$I/I_0 = \exp\left(-\sigma c l\right) \tag{4}$$

$$\log_e I_0/I = \sigma c l \tag{5}$$

The quantity $\log_e I_0/I$ is usually referred to as the light extinction and $\log_{10} I_0/I$ as the optical density.

It has been shown by Richardson[4] that with particles which are large compared with the wavelength of the light used, the light cut off is proportional to the total projected area of the particles i.e. $\Sigma n r^2$, where n is the number of particles having radius r. Providing the concentration of the particles is not large, this shadow effect holds good for particle diameters down to 2μ. When white light is used the extinction coefficient, σ, varies with the wavelength of the light and in particular, as the particle diameters approach the wavelengths of the light, σ increases. For any given wavelength, the parameter $x = 2\pi r/\lambda$ is the important criterion. When the value of x is less than 10, the amount of light cut off by the particles is greater than would be expected if a simple shadow effect were assumed. The predominant particle sizes in the smoke clouds used lie between 0·6 and 0·95 μ (with the exception of ammonium salicylate) and these diameters are comparable with the wavelengths of the white light which are approximately 0·4 to 0·7μ. It can be seen that we are working in the critical region mentioned above. If precise determinations of the extinction coefficient are required the uncertainty which exists in the region where $r \to \lambda$, can be removed by using a short wavelength monochromatic beam of light, e.g. mercury vapour lamp and filter with a suitable photo-cell. White light is used in this research to compare the clearance of different smoke clouds with time, as exact values of σ are not required.

The light extinction used in this research is not that quantity as defined in equation 5 but a related form. Light extinction is defined as the fraction of the light intensity cut off by the suspended particles and is given by

$$\frac{I_0 - I}{I_0} = 1 - \frac{I}{I_0} \tag{6}$$

therefore light extinction $= \left(1 - \frac{1}{\exp \sigma cl}\right)$

This is the quantity which is plotted in all subsequent graphs.

(3) DESCRIPTION OF THE EXPERIMENTAL WORK CARRIED OUT IN A SMALL CHAMBER

3.1 *Description of the Apparatus*

The preliminary work was carried out in a small chamber, shown in Figs. 1.1 and 1.2, which had a volume of 0·134 m³. Raindrops were produced by the hollow lead spiral

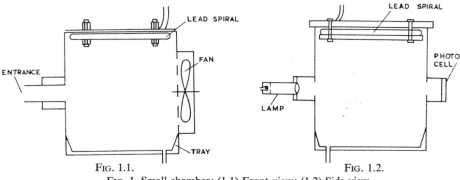

FIG. 1.1.   FIG. 1.2.
FIG. 1. Small chamber: (1.1) Front view; (1.2) Side view.

fitted into the lid of the chamber. The raindrops which issued from small holes pierced in the lower surface of the spiral had a mean diameter of 0·5 mm. The intensity of the rain was varied by adjusting the rate at which water was supplied to the spiral. The water was collected in the tray and drained away. The optical system consisted of a photo-cell which was connected to a spot galvanometer and a parallel beam of white light was passed across the chamber and directed on to the photocell. From the galvanometer deflection, values of the light extinction at any instant, i.e. fraction of light cut off by the particles, could be calculated.

In the small chamber work ammonium chloride and oil smokes were used. The ammonium chloride was generated by mixing two streams of air, one laden with ammonia and the other with hydrogen chloride. The ammonium chloride formed was blown into the chamber where it was thoroughly mixed by the fan. Oil smoke was generated by heating some oil and the oil vapour was blown into the chamber where it was again mixed by the fan.

3.2 *Experimental Procedure for the Wash-out of Ammonium Chloride and Oil Smokes*

The smoke being used was passed into the chamber from the generator, and the fan was operated for 10 min. The smoke was then allowed to age under still conditions and also under various intensities of rain. In this series of experiments, values of the light extinction were taken at 5-min intervals and graphs plotted of light extinction against time for the wettable ammonium chloride smoke and the non-wettable oil smoke are given in Figs. 2 and 3.

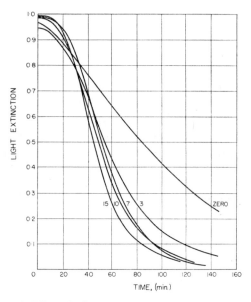

FIG. 2. Effect of rain upon ammonium chloride cloud.

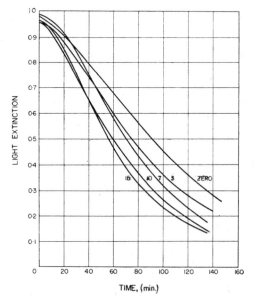

FIG. 3. Effect of rain upon oil cloud.

3.3 *Discussion of the Results*

With rain of 16 mm/hr intensity a marked deviation from the graph for zero intensity is observed in the case of ammonium chloride. When the rain intensity is increased small increases in the deviation are produced. The initial introduction of the rain is more effective in clearing the smoke than any subsequent increases in rain intensity. In the case of the oil smoke, the introduction of rain produces a less marked effect upon the clearance than was observed with ammonium chloride. Increased

TABLE 1

Rain intensity mm/hr	Rate of change of light extinction (min^{-1})			
	Ammonium chloride		Paraffin wax	
	A	B	C	D
0	0·0063	1·0	0·0058	1·0
16	0·0136	2·16	0·007	1·2
33	0·016	2·54	0·0081	1·5
69	0·0165	2·62	0·0087	1·5
87	0·02	3·17	0·01	1·72

rain intensity produces a further increase in the deviation from the zero intensity graph. The gradients of the linear portions of the graphs, which are the rates of change of light extinction, are proportional to the maximum rates at which the smoke clouds clear under the differing conditions. The figures given in columns B and D in Table 1 are the gradients of the graphs compared with the gradients for still conditions.

It can be seen from Table 1 that the minimum intensity of rain attainable with this apparatus produces a marked increase in the rate of clearance of the ammonium chloride smoke but a much smaller increase with the oil smoke. In general it would appear that raindrops are approximately twice as effective in clearing the wettable smoke as compared with the non-wettable smoke, and this is consistent with the theory that non-wettable particles possess a resistance to capture by raindrops.

(4) DESCRIPTION OF THE EXPERIMENTAL WORK CARRIED OUT IN A LARGE CHAMBER

4.1 *Description of the Apparatus*

A large room having the dimensions shown in Fig. 4 was converted into a smoke chamber. The apparatus for producing the raindrops was a steel tank with 288 ¾ in. diameter holes drilled in the bottom 4 in. apart. Rubber bungs carrying fine bore capillary tubing were fitted into the holes. To obtain small uniform drops, the ends of the capillary tubes were ground to points and smeared with petroleum jelly. The raindrops produced in this way had a mean diameter of 3·6 mm. The intensity of the rain could be changed by adjusting the head of water in the tank. Four large collection tanks collected the water which could be drained off. Three parallel beams of white light were directed across the chamber on to three photo-cells adjusted so that the currents produced by the photo-cells were proportional to the light intensities falling upon them. The smoke generator consisted of an electrical heater over which a controlled stream of air was blown. The material to be dispersed was contained in a Vitreosil basin and heated to the required temperature. The concentrated smoke was carried into the chamber by the stream of air where it was diluted and fanned to obtain

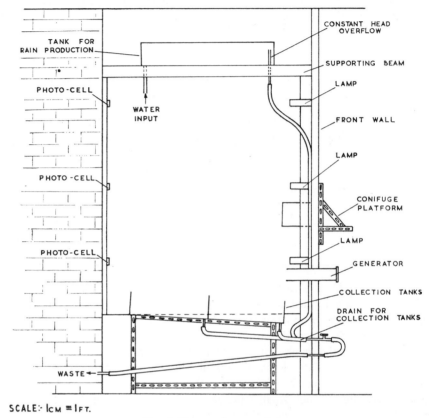

FIG. 4. Large scale apparatus.

a uniform composition. The wettable smokes ammonium chloride and ammonium salicylate and the non-wettable smokes of oil, paraffin wax, and stearic acid were all produced in this generator. It was possible to disperse 10 g of smoke material in about 3 min.

4.2 *The Conifuge*

The conifuge[5] is an instrument for sampling airborne particles and operates on the principle of the conical centrifuge. It consists essentially of a solid inner cone, which rotates about a vertical axis, and an outer cone which rotates about the same vertical axis. The air containing the suspended particles is drawn through the annular space between the cones, and the particles are deposited on the inner surface of the outer cone in positions which are determined by their settling velocities. Two glass slides are accommodated in the outer cone and the particles deposited on these collecting surfaces can be examined by means of a powerful microscope. From the position on the collecting surface and the number of particles deposited in a small area at this position, the total number of particles deposited on the outer cone can be calculated graphically. Since a sampling rate of 25 cm³/min is used in the conifuge, the number concentration in a smoke cloud can be determined. The mass concentration can also be found if the density of the smoke material is known.

4.3 *Measurement of Particle Sizes*

Particle sizes were measured by a high power optical microscope having a 4 mm objective, numerical aperture 0·85, and a ×25 eyepiece giving an overall magnification of approximately ×1000. A comparator eyepiece graticule modified by May[6] was calibrated by means of a stage micrometer. Particle diameters were measured by comparison with graded circles and vertical lines on the eyepiece graticule and the number of particles deposited on unit area of the conifuge slides could be found. Using sodium light illumination and an achromatic condenser N.A. 1·0, particles as small as 0·4 μ in diameter could be resolved.

4.4 *Experimental Procedure*

A fixed amount of smoke material was dispersed and the smoke was fanned for 10 min in the chamber. The smoke was then allowed to age under still conditions and also with rain falling at various intensities. Samples were taken with the conifuge at 20-min intervals and analysed. Graphs of particulate volume ($1/n$) and mass concentration (m) were plotted against time. Both wettable and non-wettable smokes were treated in the manner described and Figs. 5 to 9 show the variation of the mass concentration (g/m³) with time.

4.5 *Results Obtained with Wettable Smokes*

4.5.1 *Ammonium chloride smoke* (a) *Still conditions.* The particles in this smoke have diameters ranging from 0·55 to 2·7 μ and the predominant size initially has a diameter of 0·6 μ. As time proceeds the number of particles present with diameters greater than 1·7 μ remains constant while the number of smaller particles decreases, and the predominant size changes from 0·6 to 0·7 μ diameter. This suggests that the larger particles are continuously replenished by aggregates of small particles. When the graph of $(1/n)/t$ is plotted, a straight line is obtained as anticipated by the Schmolukowski law

$$\frac{1}{n} - \frac{1}{n_0} = kt$$

The gradient gives a value of $0·57 \times 10^{-9}$ cm³/sec⁻¹ for the coagulation constant as compared with values of $0·72 \times 10^{-9}$ and $0·6 \times 10^{-9}$ cm³/sec⁻¹ quoted by Nonhebel[7] and Green and Lane[8] respectively. The size ranges in these references are not given but Langstroth and Gillespie[9] obtained a value of $0·8 \times 10^{-9}$ cm³/sec⁻¹ for ammonium chloride with particle sizes ranging from 0·3 to 2·2 μ diameter and a predominant size of 0·6 μ. Electronmicrographs show that the majority of the ammonium chloride particles under these conditions tend to be spherical, but some irregular aggregates are also present. It can be seen from Fig. 5 that the mass concentration (m) in the smoke decreases linearly under still conditions and the rate of decrease, (dm/dt) is $8·75 \times 10^{-6}$ g/m³ sec.

N

(b) *Rain falling at various intensities*. In this series of experiments the particle diameters again range from 0·55 to 2·7 μ but the predominant diameter remains constant at 0·75 μ. With the rain falling the numbers of both large and small particles decrease with time and this suggests that the larger particles are removed from the smoke at a greater rate than they can be replenished by aggregates formed from small particles.

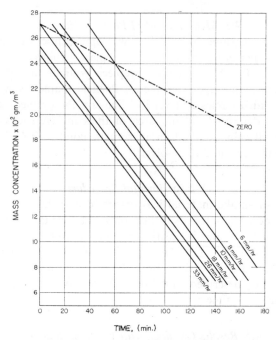

FIG. 5. Variation of mass concentration with time in ammonium chloride smoke.

The results in Fig. 5 show that the mass concentration (m) decreases markedly with rain falling. Values of the decrease in mass concentration (dm/dt) with rain falling, i.e. washout coefficients, are given in Table 2. It can be seen that (dm/dt) changes from 8·75 to 22×10^{-6} g/m³ sec when rain of the smallest intensity is used, but no further

TABLE 2

Rain intensity mm/hr	Rate of decrease of (m) $\times$ 10^6 or washout coefficients (g/m³ sec)	
	NH$_4$Cl	Paraffin wax
0	8·75	18·3
6	22·0	
8	22·2	
10	22·5	
18	22·5	18·3
26	21·9	17·5
33	22·0	19·8

significant change is observed when the rain intensity is increased. Electron micrographs show that the particles are more spherical in moist conditions and large aggregates are also present which are deposited on the collecting surfaces as circular disks.

4.5.2. *Ammonium Salicylate Smoke.* Ammonium salicylate smoke differs from the others used in so far that the particle diameters range from 1·5 to 3 μ and it is obvious from microscopic examinations that the particles are mainly spherical aggregates.

Fig. 6 shows that the amount of ammonium salicylate dispersed is much less than for ammonium chloride, and consequently the number of particles available for counting is reduced in this case. Under still conditions the value of (dm/dt) is

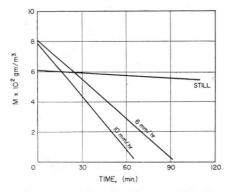

FIG 6. Variation of mass concentration with time in ammonium salicylate smoke.

$1·1 \times 10^{-6}$ g/m³ sec and this increases to $14·3 \times 10^{-6}$ g/m³ sec with rain of 6 mm/hr intensity falling. Increased rain intensity produces a further increase in the value of dm/dt and with rain of intensity 10 mm/hr falling the rate of decrease of (m) has a value of $19·3 \times 10^{-6}$ g/m³ sec. It can be seen that as in the case of the wettable ammonium chloride, the introduction of rain produces a marked effect upon the mass concentration but a small variation of (dm/dt) with rain intensity is also observed in this case.

4.6 Results Obtained with Non-wettable Smokes

4.6.1. *Paraffin wax smoke.* Under still conditions the paraffin wax particle sizes range from 0·69 to 3·7 μ in diameter and the predominant size changes from 0·76 to 0·95 μ as the experiment proceeds. When rain is falling the same size range is observed but the predominant size changes from 0·85 to 0·95 μ. In all conditions there is a decrease, as time proceeds, in the number of particles with diameters greater than 1·25 μ as well as a decrease in the number of smaller particles. Fig. 7 shows a linear decrease of mass concentration (m) with time under conditions of different rain intensities. Table 2 gives values of the washout coefficients which show that the amount of paraffin wax removed from the smoke per second is unchanged with rain falling. This result is unsatisfactory because the decrease in (m) for still conditions is more rapid than would be expected, and may be due to electric charges residing on the particles and producing increased coagulation, or to turbulence generated when the smoke was formed.

4.6.2. *Oil smoke.* The oil particle diameters lie between 0·68 and 3·5 μ with a predominant diameter of 0·74 μ which changes as coagulation proceeds under still conditions to 0·82 μ. This is due to the formation of aggregates from small particles and the evaporation of the small particles. Fig. 8 gives the graphs of mass concentration (m) plotted against time and straight lines are obtained. For still conditions (dm/dt) is 9.54×10^{-6} g/m³ sec.

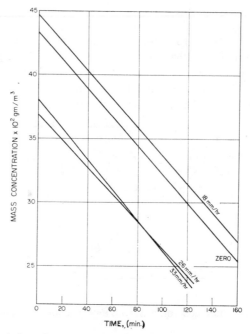

FIG. 7. Variation of mass concentration with time in paraffin wax smoke.

TABLE 3

Rain intensity mm/hr	Rate of decrease of $(m) \times 10^6$ (g/m³ sec)
0	9·54
6	10·14
10	10·4
18	13·6
26	14·7

Table 3 gives values of the washout coefficient, (dm/dt), calculated from the gradients of the graphs in Fig. 8. It can be seen that (dm/dt) increases slightly when rain is introduced and thereafter further increases are observed with increasing rain intensity. Under moist conditions the particle diameters again range from 0·68 to 3·5 μ but the predominant diameter remains constant at 0·82 μ. The initial mass concentrations lie between 0·28 and 0·3 g/m³ which are comparable with the concentrations observed in the NH₄Cl experiments. In all conditions the number of the larger particles with diameters greater than 1·5 μ remain more or less constant but the number of smaller particles gradually decreases with time.

4.6.3. *Stearic acid smoke*. The results for stearic acid are very similar to those obtained with the oil smoke. In still conditions the particle sizes range from 0·68 to 3·5 μ in diameter with an initial predominant size of 0·74 μ which increases to 0·82 μ as the coagulation proceeds. The deposits examined show that both large and small particles are removed from the smoke although the latter appear to be most affected. In Fig. 9 mass concentrations (m) are plotted against time and straight lines are

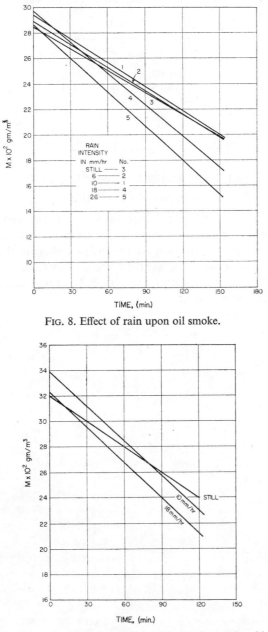

FIG. 8. Effect of rain upon oil smoke.

FIG. 9. Variation of mass concentration with time in stearic acid smoke.

obtained. For still conditions the rate of decrease of mass concentration is $11 \cdot 2 \times 10^{-6}$ g/m³ sec.

When rain is falling the same size range as for still conditions is observed with a constant predominant diameter of $0 \cdot 82 \, \mu$. The particles with diameters less than $1 \cdot 8 \, \mu$ are removed from the smoke to a greater extent than the larger ones. The gradients of the lines in Fig. 9 yield washout coefficients for rain falling at 10 and 18 mm/hr, which are both greater than the rate of decrease of (m) for still conditions.

TABLE 4

Rain intensity (mm/hr)	Rate of decrease of $(m) \times 10^6$ (g/m³ sec)
0	11·2
10	15·0
18	15·4

(5) ADDITIONAL EXPERIMENTAL WORK CARRIED OUT IN A PERSPEX CHAMBER

Further experiments were carried out in view of the results obtained with ammonium chloride in the large chamber where it appears that the amount of material washed out is independent of the rain intensity. The objects of the experiments were (a) to see if increased drop rates increase the amount of material washed out of a given smoke cloud, and (b) to detect the presence of turbulence produced by the drops when they fall through the smoke cloud.

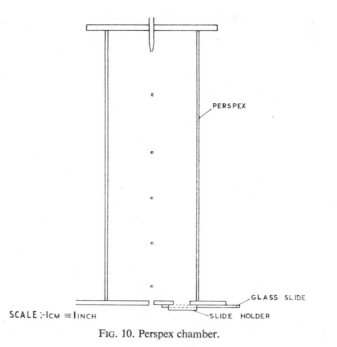

FIG. 10. Perspex chamber.

5.1 *Description of the Single Drop Apparatus*

A small Perspex chamber was constructed having the dimensions shown in Fig. 10. Single drops 3·5 mm in diameter, were produced in a capillary tube in the top of the chamber and they could pass through a hole in the bottom after falling through the chamber. The drops were then collected in a suitable collection vessel. A $\frac{3}{4}$ in. square hole was cut in the floor and provision was made for a removable glass slide to cover the hole. When the chamber was filled with smoke, particles settled on to the slide under gravity and the deposit could be examined by means of the microscope. A parallel beam of white light was directed through the chamber on to a photo-cell.

5.2 *Experimental Procedure and the Results Obtained for Collection of Ammonium Chloride by Single Raindrops*

Ammonium chloride smoke was passed into the chamber until the light beam was completely extinguished. Raindrops were passed through the smoke at different drop rates for 10 min and they were collected. The amount of chloride in the water was then estimated gravimetrically.

TABLE 5

No. of drops in 10 sec	Mass of AgCl (g) collected in 10 min
6	0·0065
9	0·0085
15	0·0137
20	0·0178

The results given in Table 5 show that when the drop rate is increased the amount of chloride brought out of the smoke by the drops in a given time is also increased. These results contradict those obtained with ammonium chloride in the large chamber, 4.5.1 (b), if it is assumed that the clearance is due entirely to the capture of the smoke particles by the raindrops. This suggests that clearance is brought about by a combination of factors.

5.3 *Tests for Turbulence Produced by Falling Drops*

When the chamber was illuminated from behind, the falling drops were observed to drag the smoke down behind them and "smoke rings" were also detected. Large swirls were observed which moved from the bottom to the top of the chamber keeping mainly to the sides.

The presence of this turbulent motion produced by the drops was confirmed by taking counts of the particles deposited in a given time on unit area of the glass slides attached to the bottom of the chamber under still conditions and also with drops falling at different rates. The three smokes tested were ammonium chloride, oil and paraffin wax.

The results given in Table 6, show that when the drop rate is increased the number of particles collected in a given time decreases in all of the three smoke clouds. This is due to the turbulence produced by the falling drops mixing the smoke cloud and preventing normal settling.

TABLE 6

No. of drops in 10 sec	No. of particles deposited in 0·004 mm² in 2 min		
	NH₄Cl	Oil	Paraffin wax
0	56	33	31
13	56	27	31
25	43	23	25
44	42	20	22

(6) CONCLUSIONS

The results of 5.2, which show that the ammonium chloride washed out increases as the drop rate increases, are a direct contradiction of the results obtained in the large chamber, 4.5.1 (b), where the rate of clearance is independent of the rain intensity. In the large chamber, the relative humidity is high since the falling drops are collected inside the chamber, whereas in the Perspex chamber the smoke is separated from the collection vessel and the relative humidity is low. A marked change in the relative humidity due to the introduction of rain is evident in the large chamber since the light extinction measurements are observed to increase when rain begins to fall, although the light beam is unaffected with rain falling in the pure fluid. This behaviour of the hygroscopic ammonium chloride and water vapour is also reported by Dalla Valle[10] and others, and it is suggested that the presence of water vapour increases the aggregation of the particles and also the rate of clearance. The increased aggregation is confirmed by electronmicrographs.

TABLE 7

Intensity	Wettable		Non-wettable		
	NH₄Cl	Ammonium Salicylate	Oil	Paraffin wax	Stearic acid
0	8·75 (1·0)	1·1 (1·0)	9·54 (1·0)	18·3 (1·0)	11·2 (1·0)
6	22·0 (2·5)	14·3 (13)	10·14 (1·06)	—	—
8	22·2 (2.54)	—	—	—	—
10	22·5 (2·57)	19·3 (17·5)	10·4 (1·09)	—	15·0 (1·34)
18	22·5 (2·59)		13·6 (1·43)	18·3 (1·0)	15·4 (+1·37)
26	21·9 (2·5)		14·7 (1·54)	17·5 (0·96)	
33	22·0 (2·51)			19·8 (1·08)	

The figures in brackets are relative values, the rates of clearance for still conditions taken as unity.

In general it can be seen from Table 7, which summarizes the results obtained, that there is a difference in the behaviour of the wettable and non-wettable smoke clouds with rain falling. There is a pronounced increase in the rates of clearance with rain falling in the case of the wettable smokes although it is obvious that this may not be due entirely to a simple capture process. The properties of the smoke clouds used are important, e.g. the hygroscopic nature of ammonium chloride as well as the turbulence produced by the falling raindrops.

All the non-wettable smokes, except paraffin wax, clear more rapidly with rain falling, although the magnitude of the effect is much smaller than observed with the wettable smoke clouds. The rain falling with intensities greater than 10 mm/hr probably produces considerable turbulence.

(7) REFERENCES

1. LANGMUIR, I., *J. Met.*, **5**, 175 (1948).
2. McCULLEY, C. R., *Industr. Engng. Chem.*, **48**, 9, 1512.
3. GILLAM A. E. and others, *Analyst*, **67**, 164 (1942).
4. RICHARDSON, E. G., *Proc. Phys. Soc.*, **55**, 48 (1943).
5. SAWYER, K. F. and WALTON, W. H., *J. Sci. Instrum.*, **27**, 272 (1950).
6. MAY, K. E., *J. Sci. Instrum.*, **22**, 187 (1945).
7. NONHEBEL, G., and others, *Proc. Roy. Soc.*, **A116**, 547 (1927).
8. GREEN, H. and LANE, W. R., *Particulate Clouds, Dusts, Smokes and Mists*, Spon, 1958.
9. LANGSTROTH, G. O. and GILLESPIE, T., *Canad. J. Res.*, **325**, 455 (1947).
10. DALLA VALLE, J. M., and others, *Brit. J. Appl. Phys.*, Sup. No. 3, S198 (1954).

Collection of Small Particles by Drop

HERNE: If one assumes that the drag on the particle is linearly related to the relative velocity of the particle and fluid the particle parameter P must enter the problem whatever flow pattern one assumes round the sphere.

The method Langmuir used for interpolating between the viscous flow and the potential flow solutions for collision efficiency seems to have been a matter of personal inspiration; I think it would be unwise to use this interpolation in detail for further action without a more precise check on it.

WALTON: The parameters Re, P and d/D should cover every case.

GREEN: Why such a large drop-holder?

WALTON: This was a hollow tube down which water was passed to replenish loss by evaporation.

EISENKLAM: Drops issuing from pressure nozzles travel at their ejection velocity but because of air entrainment this velocity is not the relative velocity. The equations given on page 10 (i, ii, iii) and the results of "Range" in Table 6 and subsequent calculations should therefore take air entrainment into account. Since such calculations are difficult because of lack of experimental data on entrainment, suitable approximations might be made based on available results of gas entrainment of jets.

The same comment applies to the treatment of evaporation of water sprays based on that of drops travelling through quiescent air, in Appendix I.

In practice, the range will be smaller than that given and the time of evaporation will in general be longer because of entrainment.

Collisions of Comparable Particles

KYNCH: I wish to make two comments on Dr. Hocking's paper. The first is relevant to the subject of dimensionless parameters. In the collision between two particles the obvious time scale is the $a_1 \div$ (difference of relative velocities), which suggests that a suitable parameter is not I (Hocking) but $I(1-a^2)$. In fact a rough calculation from his Fig. 1 gives the following values of $\alpha = a_1^3(1-a^2)$ at the larger of the two values of a for each value of E

a_1	$E=0$	0·1	0·2
19	278	357	
20	262	301	361
25	268	282	297
30	264	263	290

The constancy of the values α for $E=0$ is striking.

My other comment concerns the accuracy of the values using a few terms of a series expansion of a_1/r. My own calculations show, as might be expected, that a very large number of terms are needed to obtain a good approximation when the spheres are close together. The use of only a few terms as in Hocking's paper suggests collisions under circumstances where they do not in fact occur, so that the efficiency is over-estimated. Some idea of the magnitude can be obtained by a simple calculation neglect-ing the inertia terms, i.e. for very small spheres where I believe E to be zero.

The velocity of a droplet of radius a_2 with Stokes velocity V_2 relative to a drop of radius a_1 with Stokes velocity V_1 is the sum of a vertical velocity u and a velocity $v \sin \theta$ along the line of centres which is assumed to make an angle θ downward with the horizontal. The equations of the relative motion (neglecting inertia) are, therefore,

$$dr/dt = (u + v) \sin \theta, \qquad r(d\theta/dt) = u \cos \theta.$$

Using an approximation nearly, but not quite, as good as that of Hocking

$$
\begin{aligned}
u/(V_2 - V_1) &= 1 - (\lambda/4r^3)(3r^2 + a_1^2 + a_2^2) \\
v/(V_2 - V_1) &= -(3\lambda/4r^3)(r^2 - a_1^2 - a_2^2)
\end{aligned}
\left.\right\} \lambda = \frac{a_1 V_1 - a_1 V_2}{V_2 - V_1}
$$

and these equations easily integrate to

$$x^2 \{1 - (\lambda/2r^3)(3r^2 - a^2 - a_2^2)\} = x_0^2$$

where $x = r \cos \theta$, and $x \to x_0$ as $r \to \infty$.

Now given correct expressions for u and v, the particle paths of a_2 should not inter-sect the sphere a_1. In my view, the path for $x_0 = 0$ should consist of a vertical line and a sphere of radius $r = a_1 + a_2$. This value of r should make $dr/dt = 0$, i.e. $u + v = 0$. In fact, this does not happen with the approximate expressions for u and v, and we are led to spurious collisions and a spurious efficiency for collisions. It may be noted that $(u+v)$ steadily decreases with r, so that the grazing path which just leads to collisions is that for which $x = a_1 + a_2$, i.e. $\theta = 0$ when $r = a_1 + a_2$. The corresponding value of x_0 yields the efficiency as defined by Hocking, for particles of equal density

$$E' = \frac{x_0^2}{(a_1 + a_2)^2} = \frac{a_1^2 a_2^2}{(a_1 + a_2)^4} = \frac{a^2}{(1 + a)^4},$$

where $a = a_2/a_1$. Thus the spurious efficiency E' increases steadily with a to a maximum of 7 per cent approximately when $a = 1$.

We could try to correct for this by saying that the "effective" radius of a_1 for this approximation is that for which $u + v = 0$, or

$$\lambda(3r^2 - a_1 - a_2^2) = 2r^3.$$

However, I prefer to argue that, although the errors are not the same when inertia terms are included, the values of E' give the order of magnitude of the error in excess of Hocking's results.

HOCKING: Professor Kynch's argument seems to be as follows: For very small spheres, the acceleration term can be neglected and $E = 0$ (by intuition). A rough calculation gives E between 0 and 7 per cent. Therefore, *my* results may be up to 7 per cent too large. But my results, in the range considered, are exactly correct as they make $E = 0$ for $a_1 \leqslant 18 \mu$. This accuracy as against his inaccurate results cannot be explained by my inclusion of the acceleration term as this tends to increase E. The other difference between our calculations is that I take a better approximation for the forces on the spheres and the conclusion to be drawn from his calculations is that my approximation is sufficiently better than his to give accurate values of E for very small spheres.

RICHARDSON: Is discrepancy between Hocking's and Pearcey and Hill's results due to different assumptions with regard to behaviour in the wake?

HOCKING: Pearcey and Hill explained the very high values of E which they obtained by extrainment in the wake but this is not likely to occur at very low Reynolds numbers.

WALTON: A recent paper by Eveson, Hall and Ward[1] describes an experimental study of the fall of two equal spheres through a viscous liquid. In all cases the spheres maintained their positions relative to one another throughout the whole of their fall and there was no rotation of the spheres. The paths were deflected from the vertical by a small angle except when the line of centres was horizontal or vertical. This appears to confirm Dr. Hocking's result for $a=1$ against that of Pearcey and Hill.

1. Eveson, G. F., Hall, E. W., and Ward, S. G. *Brit. J. Appl. Phys.*, **10**, 43 (1959).

RICHARDSON, SCORER: Wake of a sphere ceases to be laminar at a Reynolds number about 1 thereafter it assumes a complex spiral eddy formation, as shown in Goldstein: *Recent Developments in Fluid Dynamics*, Chapter XI.

HOCKING: The vortex behind a sphere appears at Reynolds number 1, but the shedding of this vortex to form the spiral eddy only takes place at higher Reynolds numbers.

Wettable Particles

WALTON: Mr. Pemberton neglects induced mass effects on impact of particle and drop and considers only work done against surface tension. It would seem, however, that an impacting particle would have to share its momentum with a comparable volume of water, with consequent loss of energy, before penetration effectively commenced. No doubt some of the kinetic energy imparted to the water would also do work against surface tension. Nevertheless, the assumption that all the energy is expended against surface tension appears to require some justification.

RICHARDSON: Negligible at low Reynolds number of particle, as Bond showed dropping large spheres into glycerine.

PICKNETT: I would like to ask Mr. Oakes if he has considered the effect of humidity on his experiments with wettable smokes? I ask because the marked effect on introducing the water spray, together with the lack of effect on altering the intensity, is just what would be expected if the humidity of the chamber were low at the start of the experiment and rose to near saturation value on introducing the spray. Gillespie and Langstroth (*Canad. J. Chem.*, **29**, 133 (1951)) working with ammonium chloride smoke, attributed this effect to increased effective particle size and more rapid deposition on the walls. In the present case, air circulation produced by the spray would certainly aid wall deposition.

OAKES: The effect of humidity on the wettable smokes has been considered and is discussed in the conclusion of my paper, with special reference to ammonium chloride. Measurements show that the relative humidity changes from 50 per cent to a constant value of approximately 75 per cent in 30 min, with the raindrops falling. It should be mentioned that the relative humidity appears to affect only the ammonium chloride and not the ammonium salicylate.

WALTON: It is of interest to compare Mr. Oakes' results with collection efficiencies calculated from Fonda and Herne's theory. In both his small chamber and large chamber experiments using ammonium chloride smoke, the particle parameter is estimated to be less than 10^{-2} for the "predominant size" of particle. This is far below the critical value (1/12) for potential flow at which the collection efficiency becomes zero when a/R is negligible. If allowance is made for a/R according to Fonda and Herne's data the collection efficiency becomes about 0·0005. At this value 10 mm of rainfall of the drop size employed would reduce the concentration by only 0·2 per cent. If the calculation is made for the maximum particle size observed in the cloud, $2 \cdot 7 \mu$ diameter, the particle parameter becomes 0·2 and the collection efficiency 0·05, 10 mm of rain would then reduce the concentration by about 20 per cent. From these results and from the observation that the rate of decay of the cloud varied little with the rain intensity it would appear that the rate determining process is coagulation to a capturable size.

APPENDIX

THE PARTICLE RESISTANCE/INERTIA PARAMETER

by C. N. Davies

The dimensionless group, which has variously been termed Stokes criterion or number, basic parameter, impaction parameter, inertial parameter, impact number, etc., comes from the equation of motion of a spherical particle, subject to Stokes' law of resistance, in an independently moving fluid.

$$m\dot{u} = 6\pi a\eta(U - u) \qquad \text{etc.,}$$

where m is the mass of the particle, a its radius, u its velocity, U the stream velocity and η the viscosity of the fluid.

Reducing these equations to dimensionless form gives

$$\frac{mU_0}{6\pi a\eta L}\left(\frac{\dot{u}L}{U_0{}^2}\right) = \frac{U - u}{U_0} \qquad \text{etc.,}$$

in which L is a characteristic length of the boundaries of flow and U_0 is a reference velocity. If units of U_0 and L are used for measurement the quantity

$$P = \frac{mU_0}{6\pi a\eta L}$$

is the velocity difference producing unit acceleration in the particle and when the equations are integrated for a particular set of initial conditions the resulting particle trajectory is fully determined by P for all dynamically similar flow fields.

If the resistance is not viscous but is equal to

$$\psi . \pi a^2 \tfrac{1}{2}\sigma(U - u)^2,$$

ψ being the drag coefficient of the particle and σ the density of the fluid, the velocity difference per unit acceleration becomes

$$P . \frac{24}{\psi Re}$$

where Re is the Reynolds number of the particle.

ψ is a unique function of Re for steady motion but ψRe is not constant, depending on the difference between the velocities of particle and fluid. The concept of a characterizing resistance/inertia parameter therefore fails when the resistance law is non-linear. Dynamical similarity between particle trajectories is not established for particles having the same value of P when they are launched at corresponding points in dynamically similar, but not identical, flow fields.

The particle resistance/inertia parameter is strictly applicable only for viscous flow of the fluid relative to the particle at low Reynolds numbers.

The authors of several papers on the motion of particles have computed trajectories for which the Reynolds number of the particle takes values too high to permit the use of Stokes' law; they have used for the drag coefficient values appropriate to the steady motion of spheres. This is incorrect, since the relationship between ψ and Re is unique only so long as the velocity difference is constant. For accelerated motion the steady flow curve of ψ versus Re is not traversed; the precise curve which is followed depends on the velocity history of the particle. The instantaneous drag may be greater or less than the steady flow value.

The error resulting from the use of steady motion drag coefficients only becomes large at velocities well outside the limit of Stokes' law so this approximation is useful over a certain range of Reynolds numbers, the upper limit of which is not easily defined; it is lowered by the fluid density being comparable with that of the particle.

The validity of assuming dynamical similarity for constant P breaks down at the limit of Stokes' law, however, and must not be pressed too far beyond. The error is related to the amount by which ψ differs from $24/Re$, its Stokes' law value.

The definition of P can be transformed in several ways but it is considered that each expression should contain a numerical factor to make it equal to the form coming directly from the equation of motion. Hence,

$$P = \frac{mU_0}{6\pi a\eta L} = \frac{2}{9} \cdot \frac{a^2\rho}{\eta} \cdot \frac{U_0}{L} = \frac{v_s}{g} \cdot \frac{\rho}{\rho - \sigma} \cdot \frac{U_0}{L}$$

where ρ is the density of the particle and v_s its terminal velocity under gravity.

The last form is particularly useful for particles in gases since v_s is easily determined experimentally and $\rho/(\rho - \sigma) \approx 1$.

The values to be assigned to U_0 and L depend on the nature of the problem under consideration; the particle parameter has significance only in this context. A quantity with meaning peculiar to the particle itself is the stop-distance, PL which is the distance in which it comes to rest when projected into fluid at rest with velocity U_0; this, of course, has the dimension length.

Irregular particles introduce difficulties about the meanings of a, ρ and v_s. Since the particle may experience not only drag but also lift and rotation, even in viscous flow, the definitive nature of P is spoiled. It will often be true that the fluctuations of viscous force on the particle will average out to a mean which is derivable experimentally as v_s.

The expression of P in terms of v_s was obtained by cancelling a^3 in the numerator (volume) with a in the denominator (Stokes resistance). The resultant a^2 is thus the square of the Stokes radius (radius of a sphere of the same density as the particle and having the same terminal velocity under gravity) but the concept, in common with many associated with irregular shapes, is inexact on account of the different meanings of the radii.